Genetics and human behaviour: the ethical context

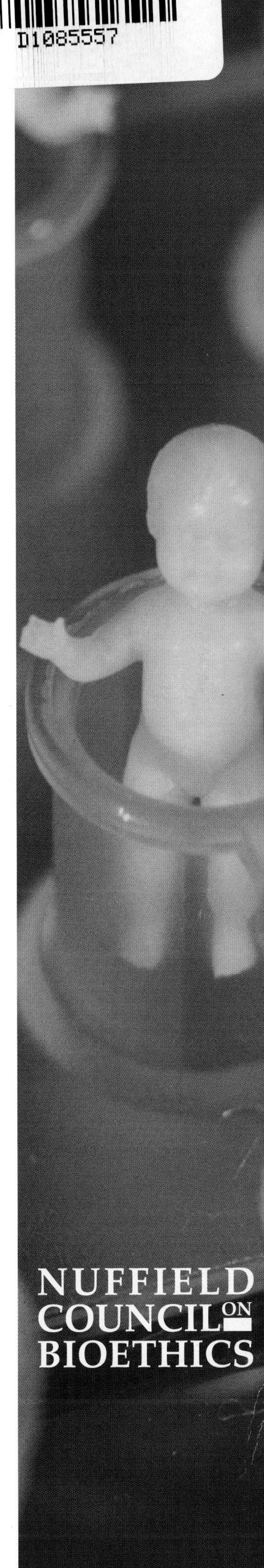

Nuffield Council on Bioethics

The terms of reference are as follows:

1 to identify and define ethical questions raised by recent advances in biological and medical research in order to respond to, and to anticipate, public concern;

2 to make arrangements for examining and reporting on such questions with a view to promoting public understanding and discussion; this may lead, where needed, to the formulation of new guidelines by the appropriate regulatory or other body;

3 in the light of the outcome of its work, to publish reports; and to make representations, as the Council may judge appropriate.

The Nuffield Council on Bioethics is funded jointly by the Medical Research Council, the Nuffield Foundation and the Wellcome Trust

Preface

I was apprehensive when asked by the Nuffield Council on Bioethics to chair the Working Party which has produced this Report. First, because the subject has an ugly history: within living memory perverted science was put at the service of ideologies that led to the subjugation and even extermination of people judged to be genetically 'inferior'. Secondly, because modern behavioural genetics is rich in promise but, as yet, poor in hard verifiable evidence. Thirdly, because it seemed unlikely that one would be able to reach any agreed recommendations in this highly complex and controversial field.

All these fears have been dispelled over the past two years in which the Working Party has met eleven times, held six fact-finding sessions with more than twenty experts, commissioned reviews of the scientific evidence, and undertaken a public consultation. It became clear that this investigation, believed to be the first of its kind, is necessary if we want to avoid the mistakes of the past, make an impartial assessment of the emerging scientific evidence, and reach valid moral and legal conclusions about the potential applications of the research. The agreed recommendations are important, but perhaps even more significant are the careful explanation that we have attempted to give of the methods of research in this area, the assessment of the current evidence for genetic influences on behaviour, and the balanced discussion of the ethical and legal choices that lie ahead. Our expectation is that this Report will help non-specialists to understand what behavioural genetics aspires to achieve, what has thus far been achieved and equally importantly, how much has not yet been achieved. We hope that it will promote an informed debate between scientists, policy makers, and the lay public about the ethical and legal implications.

I should like to thank the members of the Working Party for their hard work and dedication; working with them was an enjoyable and stimulating experience. We are all grateful to Dr Sandy Thomas, Director of the Nuffield Council on Bioethics, for her guidance and sound judgment. Tor Lezemore made a truly outstanding contribution as our inventive scribe, editor and secretary; her sparkling humour and enthusiasm kept us going. Thanks are also due to Julia Fox, Yvonne Melia, Susan Bull, Natalie Bartle and Nicola Perrin for their support. Finally, since this is the last Report which will be published under Sir Ian Kennedy's chairmanship of the Nuffield Council on Bioethics, I should like to pay tribute to his enormous contribution to bioethics in general, and to his role as mentor of this Working Party in particular.

Bob Hepple

Bob Hepple QC

Acknowledgements

The Working Party wishes to thank the many organisations and individuals who have assisted its work, particularly those who attended fact-finding meetings or submitted responses to the public consultation. The Working Party is very grateful to Professor Sir Robert Hinde, Professor Erik Parens, Professor Nikolas Rose, Tim Radford and Professor Sir Michael Rutter, who all reviewed an earlier draft of the Report. Their comments contained constructive criticisms and suggestions for further discussion, which were extremely helpful. The Working Party would like to thank the following individuals from whom it commissioned papers reviewing the scientific evidence in research in behavioural genetics: Professor John Crabbe, Professor Jeffery Gray, Professor Nicholas Mackintosh and Professor Terrie Moffitt. The Working Party is also grateful to individuals who responded to requests for advice on specific parts of the Report, including Dr Jonathan Flint, Mrs Nicola Padfield and Professor Mark Rothstein.

Genetics and human behaviour: the ethical context

Table of Contents

Genetics and human behaviour: the ethical context

Members of the Working Party

Professor Bob Hepple QC (Chairman)
Master, Clare College, Cambridge

Professor Martin Bobrow CBE
Head of Department of Medical Genetics, University of Cambridge
Deputy Chairman of the Nuffield Council on Bioethics

Professor Tom Baldwin
Head of Department of Philosophy, University of York
Member of the Nuffield Council on Bioethics

Professor Annette Karmiloff-Smith
Head of Neurocognitive Development Unit
Institute of Child Health, University College London

Professor Sandy McCall-Smith
Professor of Medical Law, University of Edinburgh

Professor Terrie Moffitt
Social, Genetic and Developmental Psychiatry Research Centre
Institute of Psychiatry, King's College London

Dr Paul Pharoah
CRC Senior Clinical Research Fellow
Strangeways Research Laboratories, Cambridge

Professor Nicholas Rawlins
Professor of Behavioural Neuroscience, University of Oxford

Professor Martin Richards
Centre for Family Research, University of Cambridge

Mr Pushpinder Saini
Blackstone Chambers, Temple

Dr Tom Shakespeare
Policy, Ethics and Life Sciences Research Institute, International Centre for Life, Newcastle

Professor Anita Thapar
Professor of Child and Adolescent Psychiatry, University of Wales College of Medicine

Professor Andrew Wilkie
Wellcome Senior Clinical Fellow, Honorary Consultant in Medical Genetics, Institute of Molecular Medicine, University of Oxford

Genetics and human behaviour: the ethical context

Terms of reference

1 To define and consider ethical, social and legal issues arising from the study of the genetics of variation within the normal range of behavioural characteristics.[1]

2 To survey the current field of research, in particular, to review:

- **a** the evidence for the relative importance of genetic influences;
- **b** the basis for characterisation and measurement of behaviour;
- **c** the relationship between normal variation in behaviour and disease processes.

3 To consider potential applications of the research.

4 To consider:

- **a** the ethics of undertaking research on the genetics of normal variation in behavioural characteristics[2] on human participants;[3]
- **b** the implications of applying the findings of such research through the development of genetic tests to establish particular characteristics in practical contexts including education, employment, insurance, legal proceedings;
- **c** the particular impact of the findings of a genetic test on the individual, including an individual child or fetus, on family members, and on various social groups;
- **d** the broader impact of genetic knowledge on the perception of those with relevant behavioural characteristics, including questions about stigma.

---

[1] And to identify the issues which are additional or complementary to those dealt with in the Council's Report: *Mental disorders and genetics: the ethical context.*

[2] Including, for example, research on intelligence, antisocial behaviour, sexual orientation and addiction.

[3] Including ethnic groupings, criminal offenders and children.

Summary and recommendations

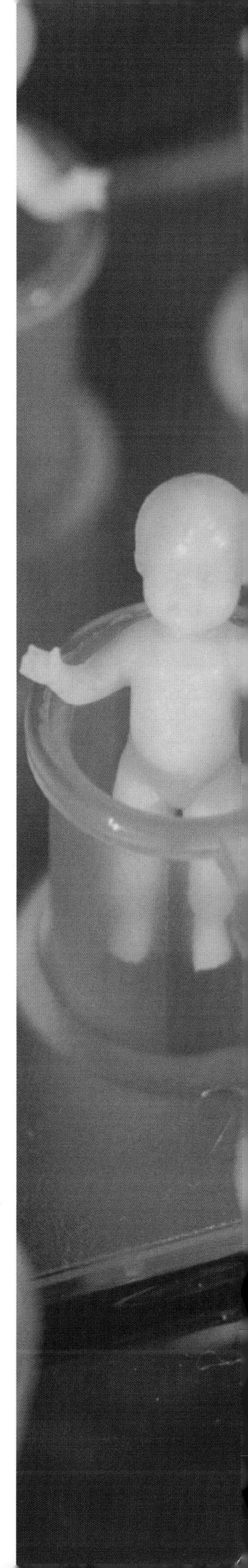

Summary and recommendations

Human behaviour is influenced both by the genes that we inherit and the environment in which we live. With the significant advances in our knowledge of genetics and publication of the draft sequence of the human genome, the focus of research has moved once again towards understanding the biological contribution to behaviour.[1] Some researchers are attempting to locate specific genes, or groups of genes, associated with behavioural traits and to understand the complex relationship between genes and the environment. This is called research in behavioural genetics. In contrast to research into the genetic basis of diseases and disorders, researchers in behavioural genetics investigate aspects of our personalities such as intelligence, sexual orientation, susceptibility to aggression and other antisocial conduct, and tendencies towards extraversion and novelty-seeking.

If genes that influence particular behavioural traits are identified, it could become possible to test for the presence of variations in these genes in individual people. No such tests currently exist. Moreover, there is disagreement about whether tests that predict human behaviour accurately could ever be developed. But even if genetic tests could not yield predictions of a *definite* outcome, it may nonetheless be possible that tests that suggest an individual will have an *increased chance* of possessing a particular trait to a greater or lesser degree might be developed. Such hypothetical tests might be undertaken for a variety of purposes. One purpose would be simply to gain more knowledge about the influence of genes on behaviour. Another purpose might be that of intervention or treatment, for example to prevent aggressive behaviour by using medicines, or by attempts to change relevant aspects of the environment. A further purpose might be that of selection. This encompasses, for instance, prenatal testing, the streaming of children in schools on the basis of intelligence and aptitude, the screening of employees and jobseekers to exclude those with traits that employers consider undesirable, and the use by insurers of genetic information about behaviour and personality traits in order to estimate risk. Yet another purpose might be to claim diminished legal responsibility for one's actions or to mitigate punishment for criminal behaviour.

In 1999, the Nuffield Council on Bioethics agreed that it was important to anticipate the ethical, legal and social implications raised by research in behavioural genetics. Previous work by the Council and other groups has focused on inherited disease and susceptibility to clinical disorders. This Report is intended to fill that gap and to draw attention to the implications of research in genetics which falls outside the medical sphere. The objectives of the Working Party established by the Council in 2000 were to define and consider the ethical, legal and social issues arising from the study of the genetics of variation within the normal range of behaviour characteristics.

The subject of this Report is human behaviour within the normal range, as opposed to traits that are defined as illnesses or diseases. An important preliminary question is whether it is actually feasible to talk about a 'normal range' of behavioural traits. There is a danger that, in speaking of the 'normal' range, this Report may be misunderstood as stigmatising certain kinds of behaviour, namely those that are at the extremes of variation. It therefore needs to be emphasised that when we use the phrases 'normal variation' or 'behaviour in the normal range', no moral evaluation or judgement is implied. In these phrases, 'normal' has a statistical meaning – it refers to the range of variation, usually that which includes about 95% of the population, and

[1] See for example Duster, T. (1990). *Backdoor to Eugenics.* New York: Routledge. This account reports a substantial rise, during the 1980s, in the publication of scientific articles that attempt to explain the genetic basis of behavioural traits.

which is thought not to contain any individuals with clinical disorders or diseases. There are other approaches to defining normal behaviour. They include the theory that abnormal behaviour is that which results in impaired function in society for the individual, either from the individual's own perspective, or from an objective standpoint, regardless of whether the behaviour is statistically rare or not. We take the statistical approach merely as our starting point, using it to limit the field of inquiry. We have focused on traits, such as intelligence, that are continuously distributed measures, displayed by each individual in the population to a greater or lesser extent, and which are not commonly viewed as disorders.

The Report is divided into three parts. The first part of the Report explains the historical and scientific background to research in the field of behavioural genetics. Chapter 2 outlines the history of the eugenics movement and its profound effect on the development of clinical genetics and developmental psychology since the Second World War. Chapter 3 attempts to explain what is meant by the suggestion that genes influence or affect human behaviour. There are different ways in which one can study the contribution that genetic factors make to human behaviour. Chapters 4-6 explain the different methods used by researchers in behavioural genetics.

The second part of the Report, Chapters 7–11, contains reviews of the findings that have been obtained to date in each of these methods of research, with respect to the following behavioural traits: intelligence, personality, antisocial behaviour and sexual orientation. The principal themes that emerge from the reviews of the evidence are summarised in Chapter 11. The Report has been written so that readers not wishing to digest the scientific information contained in the reviews of the evidence can refer to Chapter 11 instead, without compromising their understanding of the Report.

The third part of the Report examines the ethical, legal and policy issues and offers a series of conclusions and recommendations. Chapter 12 begins by discussing whether there is an inherent conflict between understanding the genetic influences on behaviour and human dignity, as it is expressed in the concepts of free will and moral responsibility. Chapter 13 then addresses some of the potential applications of the research including genetic, medical and environmental interventions aimed at changing behavioural traits, as well as prenatal selection. Chapter 14 is concerned with the implications of research in behavioural genetics for the criminal justice system, in relation to attributions of legal responsibility and sentencing, and in predicting antisocial behaviour. Chapter 15 considers genetic testing and selection with regard to education, employment and insurance. The conclusions and recommendations from the Report are summarised in the remainder of this section.

Behavioural genetics and eugenics

Eugenics has been a major social and political force in the twentieth century. Aspects of eugenic policies and practices, in particular, the violation of reproductive freedoms through the segregation and sterilisation of tens of thousands of people in the US, Europe and elsewhere, and the horrors of the 'euthanasia' programmes in Nazi Germany, have been widely, and correctly, condemned.

Behavioural genetics formed a major part of the scientific foundations on which eugenic policies were claimed to be based and the development of behavioural genetics was itself shaped by eugenic concerns. However, this does not necessarily imply that contemporary research on the genetics of behaviour is in any sense eugenic or is driven by considerations that could be considered eugenic. In fact, as we have pointed out, part of the reason for the decline in the support of eugenic policies in many countries from the 1930s onward was scientific research which demonstrated that the policies of segregation and sterilisation of those deemed to be unfit would not achieve their stated goals. However, as a number of respondents to our consultation have suggested, there remains a view that research on the genetics of human behaviour, particularly in the area of intelligence, is necessarily eugenic or will lead to the re-establishment of eugenic policies. It is possible that contemporary understanding of the heritability of IQ and other behavioural characteristics, and increasing knowledge of the processes of inheritance of other traits, could provide a scientific foundation for a programme of positive or negative eugenics, were there to be the political will or power to construct and implement such a policy (paragraph 2.19).

We conclude that historical and philosophical studies of eugenic practices and policies should be encouraged so that it may be clearly understood what was, and was not, unacceptable about the past and the ways in which this may, or may not, be distinguished from contemporary genetic policies and practices (paragraph 2.20).

The science of behavioural genetics

There are different ways in which researchers can study the contribution that genetic factors make to human behaviour. First, there are observational studies, which involve assessing and comparing relatives such as twins or siblings, families and adopted children. This type of research is called quantitative genetics because it aims to examine the extent to which variation in a trait is influenced by genetic factors in a population. It uses statistical methods to examine and compare groups of people, without focusing on particular genes (Chapter 4). Secondly, researchers can try to identify differences in genes that contribute to trait variation in characteristics or traits between individuals. This type of research is called molecular genetics (Chapter 5). Thirdly, researchers can use animals to try and examine the effects of particular genes on behaviour (Chapter 6).

It is common to hear of research that claims to identify a 'gene for aggression' or a 'gene for homosexuality'. But how could our genes *cause* us to act in a particular way? What is really meant by saying 'a gene for X'? The connection between genes and diseases is far from straightforward, and the relationship between genes and behaviour is even more complicated. It is often difficult to establish which genes contribute to a trait and how they do so because:

- More than one genetic factor usually contributes to a particular trait.
- These multiple genetic factors may interact with each other and have different effects depending on which other factors are present in the individual's genotype.
- As well as genetic factors, many non-genetic (environmental) factors may contribute to the manifestation of a trait.
- These environmental factors may also interact with each other.
- The genetic factors may affect which environmental factors have an effect. (This is called gene–environment interaction.)
- Conversely, environmental factors may affect which genetic factors have an effect.
- Certain genetic and environmental factors may go hand in hand. (This is called gene–environment correlation.)
- A protein may be modified after it has been produced from a gene, and this can alter its function.
- Genes do not have a continuous effect in our bodies. They may be turned on and off, both during our overall development and within the lifetime of an individual cell.

So, while it might be correct to say that a particular genetic variant is part of the cause of a particular trait, or that it is one causal factor, it will seldom be the only cause, nor is it likely to be either a necessary or sufficient condition for the trait to be manifested. Furthermore, even if particular genes that contribute to a trait can be identified, this is only a small part of the story. There is still a need to understand the very indirect pathway between a gene, a particular protein and an individual scoring highly on an IQ test or having an aggressive personality. Our understanding of these causal pathways is at an even earlier stage than our understanding of which genes influence behavioural traits, which is itself extremely limited (paragraphs 3.9 – 3.14).[2]

The complexity of human behaviour and the difficulties in understanding how genes are involved may seem overwhelming. There is wide agreement that genes do have an indirect effect on behaviour. However, some commentators have suggested that any attempt to understand the processes by which genes influence behaviour will certainly fail. We disagree. We consider that it is neither a theoretical nor a practical impossibility to identify genes that contribute to behavioural traits and to understand some of the mechanisms by which they do so. However, we note that terminology such as 'a gene for X' or 'a set of genes for X' is very misleading because it fails to convey the complexity of the role of genetic factors in causal explanations of human behaviour. Genes determine which proteins are made. They do not determine which behavioural or personality traits an individual possesses. Furthermore, the product of an individual gene will only very rarely be directly related to a complex behavioural characteristic. It will normally interact with many other genes and with many non-genetic factors, which means that the predictive capability of tests for any single or small number of genes will in general probably be quite limited. Nonetheless, the proteins that genes make and the way these affect our bodies and brains will be one part of an explanation of human behaviour (paragraph 3.20).

Reporting research in behavioural genetics

Research which claims to show an association between particular genetic variants and particular traits tends to receive considerable attention in the scientific and lay media. The various methods of research in this field are not infallible, and the reviews of the evidence in Chapters 7–10 show that few findings have been replicated successfully to date. Thus, reports of such things as 'gay genes' or 'smart mice' convey a highly inaccurate impression of the state of the research. The lack of reporting of negative or contradictory findings exacerbates this problem. These difficulties are not unique to research in behavioural genetics. However, it does seem that such research is, at present, particularly susceptible to reporting which, whether strictly accurate or not, is misleading in the impression it gives to the reader. The potential for the abuse of findings in this area means that the reporting of this research ought to be conducted with particular care.

We consider that researchers and those who report research have a duty to communicate findings in a responsible manner. We welcome the *Guidelines on Science and Health Communication* published by the Social Issues Research Centre, the Royal Society and the Royal Institution of Great Britain and recommend that further initiatives in this area should be encouraged (paragraph 11.14).[3] In the context of research in behavioural genetics, we recommend that the following points, concerning the various types of research, are borne in mind by those who report on, comment on and evaluate such research:

[2] Rutter, M. & Silberg, J. (2002). Gene-environment interplay in relation to emotional and behavioural disturbance. *An. Rev. Psychol.* **53**, 463-490.

[3] Social Issues Research Centre, the Royal Society and the Royal Institution. Guidelines on Science and Health Communication. November 2001. http://www.sirc.org/publik/revised_guidelines.pdf (9 Aug 2002).

Quantitative genetics

- Quantitative genetics involves statistical methods that attempt to distinguish the effects of genetic and environmental factors on variation in certain behavioural traits, which can be quantitatively measured, between groups of individuals.
- The subjects of the research are usually twins, siblings, adopted children, and families.
- The statistics such as estimates of heritability generated by the research refer to groups of people, not to individuals. Nor do they refer to particular genes or regions of DNA or to specific environmental factors. This requires further research and additional measurement.
- Estimates of heritability and other statistical techniques are useful in understanding the relative contribution of different types of influence and their relation to each other. They are also useful for understanding why some types of behaviour often occur together. They do not, however, lead directly to predictive information regarding individuals, nor do they give reliable estimates of how strongly predictive a genetic test might be if it were developed (Box 4.1).

Molecular genetics

- Research in molecular genetics tries to identify variation in particular genes that influences behaviour, by examining the DNA of individuals.
- This is difficult because there are usually many genes involved, each of which may only have a small effect. Many associations between a genetic variant and a behavioural trait have been reported but have not been successfully repeated by other researchers.
- In most cases, the research does not explain how the gene influences the behaviour. However, some researchers predict that they will overcome these difficulties and that genes that influence behaviour will be reliably identified.
- When associations are reported by researchers, it is important to consider the following questions:
  - How convincing is the evidence, in terms of both statistical analysis and the supposed pathway of causation, that the claim is correct? Much more credibility can be attached to findings that have been independently replicated by a different research group, and first reports of gene–behaviour associations should be treated with caution until they are replicated.
  - Over what range of populations and environmental conditions has the effect been tested?
  - If claims are made about the practical application of the findings to influence human behaviour, what is the size of the effect of the genetic variant? Is it large enough to have any relevance for the testing of individuals?
  - What are the implications for the pathway of causation of the behaviour? (Box 5.1)

Research involving animals

- Animal models have greatly advanced our understanding of how genes have an effect in the organism and of how the brain develops.
- Animal models can be created by various techniques including selective breeding and the direct manipulation of specific genes.
- Although there are many similarities with regard to genetics between human and non-human animals, there are also considerable differences in the expression of their genes both within the organism and over time.

- It is difficult to equate directly the richness of complex human traits such as intelligence, personality and sexual orientation with the behaviour of animals. This may limit the potential value of the research.
- For these reasons, caution should be exerted when hypothesising that genes studied in research involving animals will have the same effect in humans (Box 6.2).

The evidence for genetic influences on human behaviour

In Chapters 7–10 we set out some recent findings in research in behavioural genetics into antisocial behaviour, intelligence, personality and sexual orientation. As these chapters demonstrate, research is at different stages in different areas. For some traits, areas of the genome have been identified that might contain genes which have an effect on behaviour. For most traits, the route from such genetic factors to a particular behaviour is unclear. The bulk of research in behavioural genetics to date has relied on quantitative methods to assess the relative contributions of different types of factor. However, the use of molecular genetics is increasing, a trend which is expected to continue. In Chapter 11, we draw some general conclusions about the research in all the areas described and highlighted some central themes that emerge. These inform our consideration of the ethical, legal, social and policy issues to which the research gives rise. The central themes that emerge are:

- the difficulty of defining and measuring behavioural traits;
- the dangers of the misinterpretation and misapplication of heritability estimates;
- the lack of replicated findings relating to specific genes that might influence behaviour.

Ethical issues arising from research in behavioural genetics

Free will and human dignity

We conclude there is no inherent conflict between a greater understanding of genetic contributions to behaviour and due regard for human dignity. A non-reductive, rationalist, understanding of human freedom can coexist with recognition of the genetic influences on our human abilities, capacities and motivations, even though a reductive, functionalist, account fits more readily alongside the scientific perspective employed by behaviour geneticists. It is not necessary here to take a stand on this debate. But any sensible understanding of human freedom and dignity must allow for some starting-point in the development of the abilities which are central to this freedom and dignity. Behavioural genetics promises to elucidate this starting-point, and thereby contribute to the understanding of humanity. But it no more offers a complete theory of human behaviour than does any other single scientific discipline. Thus, there is no reason for adherents of behavioural genetics, or critics, to regard it as offering a radically new way of understanding human life which threatens to undermine the dignity of humanity. It complements, and does not displace, the familiar social sciences, the humanities and indeed our ordinary understanding of behaviour (paragraph 12.38).

Will there be any practical applications of research in behavioural genetics?

While everyone accepts that genes have an impact on behaviour, genetic tests will have a low predictive capacity because of the myriad other factors that influence our behaviour and the vastly complex interactions between genetic factors themselves. Hence, it has been argued that it will be impossible to make any robust predictions based on genetic tests, or to design any effective interventions as a result of them, and therefore, that there is no point in discussing the ethics of their application. We take the view that these considerations do not exempt us from considering anxieties aroused by popular beliefs in this area, even if these beliefs turn out to be misconceptions. For in the past, social policies, for example eugenic policies, have been built on minimal or erroneous scientific foundations. More recently misunderstandings about genetics have led to unwarranted discrimination. Moreover, we consider that, in the future it may become possible to make predictions, albeit limited ones, about behaviour based on genetic information and to design useful applications of this knowledge. Therefore, while it is certainly too early to discuss detailed applications of behavioural genetics, we need to confront anxieties based on current beliefs about this subject (paragraphs 13.2-13.6).

Medicalisation and other concerns

Traits such as sexuality, aggression and intelligence have in the past been thought of as outcomes of inheritance, family background, socio-economic environment, individual choice and even divine intervention. If research in behavioural genetics identifies the influence of genes on such traits, these traits may mistakenly come to be thought of as being fundamentally determined by genetic factors and even as aspects of life which belong to one's 'fate'.

As the reviews of the evidence in chapters 7-11 indicate, fatalism about genetics is a misconception. Even when behavioural traits are influenced by genes, there are always other influences, and the existence of genetic influences does not show that we are powerless to change or modify our character. Nonetheless, this misconception is pervasive and gives rise to the anxiety that behavioural genetics will lead to the 'medicalisation' of those who are found to be genetically predisposed to certain behavioural traits. At the root of such concerns is the idea that behavioural traits that have previously been regarded as 'normal' will come to be viewed as 'abnormal' or pathological.

Medicalisation is an issue that affects many areas of life, not just behavioural genetics. In the case of behavioural traits, since research into genetic influences is at an early stage, it is not possible to say whether medicalisation will be likely, or whether it will have, on balance, positive or negative implications. However, examples of the deleterious effects of medicalisation in other areas suggest the need for awareness of potential problems. **We conclude that research in behavioural genetics has the potential to contribute to the existing phenomenon of medicalisation. Deleterious effects that should be borne in mind include shifting the boundary between normal variation and disorder further away from the extremes of variation; reducing social tolerance of previously 'normal' behavioural traits; and the routine selection of genetic or medical interventions without adequate consideration being given to environmental interventions and other options** (paragraph 13.23).

Any discovery of biological mechanisms that influence behaviour, including genes, may aid in the development of drugs which modify behaviour. We consider that there is potential for the unhelpful widening of diagnostic categories, to encourage the use of medication by people who would not necessarily be thought of as exhibiting behavioural traits outside the normal range. In addition to the potentially harmful effects already listed, this could lead to unnecessary increased expenditure by the health service. **We recommend that health service providers, and in particular the Department of Health, specifically charge a named agency with monitoring and, if necessary, controlling, this means of the deliberate medicalising of normal populations** (paragraph 13.24).

Despite concerns about medicalisation and stigma, we consider that there is, *prima facie*, no reason for preferring one type of intervention over another as a matter of principle. For any given trait and any given individual, the factors influencing the development and expression of that trait are likely to be many and varied. In different cases, there may be reasons for thinking that different forms of intervention are appropriate. We identify five features of any intervention that may provide moral reasons for accepting or rejecting their use, namely the effectiveness, safety and reversibility of the intervention, the extent to which one can make choices about its use, and its implications for individuality (paragraph 13.26).

Gene therapy

The United Nations Educational, Scientific and Cultural Organization (UNESCO) Universal Declaration on the Human Genome and Human Rights states in Article 5 that 'Research, treatment or diagnosis affecting an individual's genome shall be undertaken only after rigorous and prior assessment of the potential risks and benefits pertaining thereto and in accordance with any other requirement of national law'.[4] The Clothier Report on the ethics of gene therapy identified a number of ways in which gene therapy might pose a risk to safety.[5] These included mistakes in inserting the correcting gene, the possibility that the gene would be expressed in the wrong place or at the wrong time, the possibility that insertion of the gene might cause a new mutation or genetic disease, and the possibility that the correcting gene might move from its target location in the body and affect other cells. As a result, all applications to carry out trials of gene therapy in humans in the UK are monitored by the Gene Therapy Advisory Committee (GTAC). **We consider that in view of the risks inherent in gene therapy, considerable caution should be exercised before contemplating its application to traits that do not have serious implications for health. We note that if somatic gene therapy for traits in the normal range were to become a possibility, any research would fall under the remit of the Gene Therapy Advisory Committee (GTAC).**[6] **We recommend, therefore, that the GTAC and other relevant bodies should develop guidelines for research into gene therapy for normal behavioural traits before such research takes place** (paragraph 13.31).

Germline gene therapy raises particular issues concerning safety because the effects of the therapy reach far into the future and cannot be easily predicted. The Clothier Report concluded that 'there is insufficient knowledge to evaluate the risks [of germline gene therapy] to future generations' and that therefore 'gene modification of the germ line should not yet be attempted'. In the context of behavioural variation within the normal range, which by definition is not life-threatening, we cannot envisage any circumstances in which the modification of the human germline would be justifiable (paragraph 13.32).

Access to interventions

Therapy versus enhancement

The way to distinguish between those interventions which count as 'therapies' and those which count as 'enhancements' is by reference to the condition that is to be altered: therapies aim to treat, cure or prevent diseases and to alleviate pathological conditions which place someone outside the normal range, whereas enhancements aim to improve already healthy systems and to advance capacities which already fall within the normal range. This distinction is often used to justify a distinction between interventions which merit public support and those which do not.

---

[4] United Nations Educational, Scientific and Cultural Organisation. (November 1997). *Universal Declaration on the Human Genome and Human Rights.*

[5] Committee on the Ethics of Gene Therapy (Chairman: Clothier, C.). (1992). *Report of the Committee on the Ethics of Gene Therapy*. London: HMSO; Cm 1788.

[6] GTAC's remit is 'the deliberate introduction of genetic material into human somatic cells for therapeutic, prophylactic or diagnostic purposes'. An analogous role is performed in the US by the Food and Drug Administration (FDA). In July 2002, it was reported that the FDA is to create a new department to oversee gene therapy, within the Center for Biologics Evaluation and Research (New FDA Office for Gene Therapy. (2002). *Nat. Med.* **8**, 646).

The suggestion is that there is a duty to ensure that our fellow citizens receive therapies, but no duty to ensure that they receive enhancements. The distinction between therapy and enhancement is not straightforward and requires qualification, but the principle which associates it with that between public and private provision is a useful starting-point in this area.

Although therapy is usually thought of as the treatment of diseases with an identifiable biochemical basis, there can be cases in which someone suffers from a pathological condition which places them outside the normal range in some respect, without there being any such identified basis for it. In such cases, interventions to overcome the resulting impairment are also to be regarded as therapies; hence, such interventions merit public support to make them available to all. The important issue is the severity of the handicap, not its cause. We take the view that this conclusion should be applied to interventions which become available in the field of behavioural genetics. Any decision to provide public support through the National Health Service (NHS) for interventions to enable individuals to overcome disabilities which obstruct their capacity for behaviour in the normal range should not be dependent on the underlying cause of the disability (paragraphs 13.41-13.43).

Providing tests and interventions

Who should be able to make use of genetic tests and interventions if they are developed? And who should bear the cost of the tests and interventions? A standard view is that since the state does not have an obligation to provide techniques for improving intelligence or athleticism or changing behaviours, these interventions should not normally be provided as part of a public healthcare system. Nonetheless, it may also be argued, that within a free society and a free market, these techniques should be available for purchase.

The anxiety, however is that if such tests and interventions were available for private purchase, the result could be that only the more affluent members of society would have access to them. Because these techniques would enhance capabilities, this could lead to even greater inequalities and increase social and economic polarisation. Public provision of new tests and interventions, especially when accompanied by further efforts to prevent the formation of an underclass, would, of course, require considerable resources. From an egalitarian perspective, if these resources are not available, then the tests and interventions should not be introduced at all. However, libertarians argue that there is no moral basis for a distinction between interventions based on genetic variants and the familiar use of extra resources in the fields of education and sport. In particular, if a trait is desirable and there is an intervention that will increase the likelihood of it occurring, the correct response is to ensure that it is available as widely as possible. While this may entail that, for at least a limited period of time, there will be some who do not have access, the overall goal should be to raise everyone to the highest level.

It is difficult to adjudicate in the abstract between these egalitarian and libertarian positions. It is only once some effective intervention is under consideration that the costs and benefits of full public availability versus limited private availability for a privileged few can be assessed seriously. **We believe that equality of opportunity is a fundamental social value which is especially damaged where a society is divided into groups that are likely to perpetuate inequalities across generations. We recommend, therefore, that any genetic interventions to enhance traits in the normal range should be evaluated with this consideration in mind** (paragraph 13.48).

Monitoring the provision of genetic tests and interventions

If genetic tests and corresponding genetic, medical or environmental interventions relevant to traits in the normal range are developed, it is important to consider how such tests and interventions may be made available. Genetic tests for variants that influence behaviour in the normal range might be thought of as comparable to personality or IQ tests, rather than genetic tests that are used to diagnose or predict the onset of a serious disease such as cancer. Similarly, interventions might be seen as comparable to vitamin supplements or cosmetic surgery. In both cases, therefore, if the comparisons are a guide, it may turn out that individuals are left to make decisions about whether to make use of tests or interventions without the involvement of health professionals.

This has important implications for the regulation and monitoring of tests and interventions. Without appropriate safeguards, consumers may be at risk of exploitation through misleading marketing practices. This is particularly likely in novel areas of science, where most people will not be well placed to make informed judgements. In the case of genetic tests, there is currently no specific legislation in place that would provide a regulatory mechanism for assessing the efficacy or reliability of a test. This applies even to genetic tests for diseases, as well as to the hypothetical tests for genetic influences on behavioural traits that are the focus of this Report.

We consider that the issues raised by tests for behavioural traits and other traits that exhibit normal variation, rather than tests for diseases, require specific attention. The questions addressed by these tests include very sensitive areas of personal and family vulnerability, and there is considerable potential for exploitation of the anxieties and aspirations of members of the public in an area where the science is not well understood. This danger is particularly important since both tests and interventions might be applied to children without their consent. Thus, we take the view that it is not adequate in this area to rely on the same mechanisms that apply to non-genetic or non-medical enhancements, such as recourse to the Advertising Standard Authority or the Office of Fair Trading, to prevent misleading claims being made and ineffective tests from being sold.

In 1997, the Advisory Committee on Genetic Testing (ACGT), a non-statutory committee that reported to the Department of Health, produced a *Code of Practice and Guidance on Human Genetic Testing Services Supplied Direct to the Public.*[7] The ACGT was subsumed in 2001 by the Human Genetics Commission (HGC), which currently has responsibility for administering the Code of Practice. The HGC issued a public consultation document on the supply of genetic tests direct to the public in July 2002.[8] This summarises the current situation and poses a number of specific questions covering issues such as consent to testing, storage and use of samples, and confidentiality of data. It notes that tests in the field of behavioural genetics are likely to be particularly controversial.

On the presumption that tests for genetic influences on behavioural traits in the normal range, of varying quality and predictive power, will become available, we welcome the consideration by the Human Genetics Commission (HGC) of genetic tests supplied directly to the public. We encourage the HGC to give thorough consideration to the issues raised by genetic tests for behavioural and personality traits. We recommend that both the public and private provision of such tests, if they are developed, should be stringently monitored and regulated as necessary (paragraph 13.53).

[7] Advisory Committee on Genetic Testing. (September 1997). *Code of Practice and Guidance on Human Genetic Testing Services Supplied Direct to the Public.* London: Health Departments of the United Kingdom.

[8] Human Genetics Commission. (July 2002). Consultation on Genetic Testing Services supplied Direct to the Public. http://www.hgc.gov.uk/testingconsultation/index.htm (16 Jul 2002).

In addition to genetic tests, interventions may be developed, whether medical, genetic or environmental, on the basis of information about genetic variants. The HGC consultation document recognises that some genetic tests may be accompanied by a corresponding intervention that is recommended, depending on the test results. How should such interventions be regulated?

In the case of genetic interventions the use of gene therapy will be regulated by the Gene Therapy Advisory Committee (GTAC). Medical interventions such as pharmacological substances will not necessarily be classified as medicines. While some would be subject to the existing regulation in place for medicines, others might be classified as foodstuffs or herbal remedies. Those which are not classified as medicines are unlikely to be harmful, but there is a risk that they will be promoted on the basis of unreliable, or even non-existent scientific evidence, and that consumers will be misled. Similarly, environmental interventions, such as changes in lifestyle or surroundings, may be promoted on the basis of genetic information about an individual. As noted above, we do not consider that there are currently any public bodies constituted in such a way as to monitor the provision of such interventions effectively and ensure that they are appropriate and of sufficiently high quality. **We recommend, therefore, that those charged with the monitoring and regulation of genetic tests for behavioural traits in the normal range should also be responsible for ensuring appropriate monitoring of the provision of interventions based on such genetic information, which fall outside the scope of other regulatory bodies** (paragraph 13.55).

We note the difficulties for monitoring and regulation raised by the sale of existing tests and interventions on the internet, and encourage the efforts of the Office of Fair Trading and consumer protection agencies such as the National Consumer Council and the Consumers' Association in developing codes of practice and strategies, such as kite-marks, for assisting consumers.

Prenatal selection

There are various ways in which we can affect the characteristics of our children. Most fundamentally, our children are influenced by our choice of mate. However, in recent decades, other techniques have been developed which extend our capacity in this area. The first is prenatal diagnosis (PND) which is in widespread use in the UK to detect pregnancies affected by diseases such as Down's syndrome and spina bifida. Many couples opt for termination of pregnancy if abnormalities are detected. Secondly, in the past 15–20 years, the technique of preimplantation genetic diagnosis (PGD) has been developed, which enables embryos created by *in vitro* fertilisation (IVF) programmes to be tested for genetic disorders before they are implanted. A third, largely theoretical, approach is to move selection further back in time, by allowing choice between different gametes. Experimental techniques now allow sperm to be sorted, enabling parents to choose the sex of their embryo. This technique remains somewhat unreliable: there are reports of an 8% error rate for females and 28% in males. It is not clear that this type of technique will ever be applicable to traits other than sex, and it is particularly difficult to envisage its applications to the complex traits considered in this Report.

The use of these techniques, particularly PGD and gamete selection, has often been referred to in the press and in popular debate as a question of 'designer babies'. 'Designer baby' is one of those terms, like 'Frankenstein foods' and 'slippery slope', which is central to public discourse on genetics, but which can be misleading. The selection of gametes before fertilisation, of embryos before implantation, or selective termination of pregnancy are all examples of the selection or choice of alternative options rather than the manipulation or design of babies. The possibility of truly designing a child, by choosing characteristics from a menu of possibilities to create a child, for example using gene therapy, is still in the realms of science fiction (Box 13.2).

The forms of selection outlined above are currently only practised on clinical grounds in the UK. However, a trend towards selection on other grounds can be identified. The recent decision by the Human Fertilisation and Embryology Authority (HFEA) to allow the selection of embryos that are free from genetic diseases and that can act as donors to existing siblings is an important move in this direction. Moreover, recently, the Government has requested that the HFEA examines the advances in techniques of gamete selection on the basis of sex, something which is already possible and unregulated in the private sector. The HFEA intends to launch a public consultation on sex selection in late 2002.

Law and clinical practice support the use of genetic information to provide informed choice for prospective parents. But professional and public opposition has been voiced, for a variety of reasons, to the use of non-clinical attributes such as the traits considered in this Report in testing and selection. There seems to be a consensus in clinical genetics and in public opinion against use of PGD or PND in order to select babies on the basis of non-clinical characteristics. **In the case of prenatal diagnosis (PND), we share this view. Setting aside the contested issue of the ethics of abortion on social grounds, which is outside the scope of this Report, we take the view that the use of selective termination following PND to abort a fetus merely on the basis of information about behavioural traits in the normal range is morally unacceptable** (paragraph 13.65).

But the issues raised by the use of PGD are different. Whereas selective termination following PND is applied to a fetus that has already implanted and is developing in the womb, PGD is used to select which embryos to implant. Thus, PGD does not precede the termination of a potential human life, but precedes instead the choice as to which embryo, among those created by IVF, is to be given a chance of developing into a human being. And in this context, it is not so clear that it is morally unacceptable to make this choice on the basis of genetic information about the traits that are the focus of this Report. Whereas PND would be used to end a life, PGD is, in effect, used to choose which life to start. Hence, the moral prohibitions which apply in the case of PND, do not apply in the same way in the use of PGD. Nonetheless, the potential use of PGD to select embryos that are more or less likely to exhibit particular behavioural traits is widely thought unacceptable.

One line of argument in favour of the use of PGD is described in terms of a 'right to procreative autonomy' which would include a right to employ safe and reliable methods for the selection of children with a genetic predisposition for enhanced abilities within the normal range.[9] However, we identify a number of arguments against the use of PGD for traits in the normal range. In particular, we address the question of 'natural humility'.

At present, parents accept their children as they find them in an attitude of 'natural humility' to the unchosen results of procreation. This attitude is an important feature of parental love, the love that parents owe to their children as individuals in their own right; for this is a love that does not have to be earned and is not dependent on a child having characteristics that the parents hoped for. Parental love which includes this element of natural humility is, therefore, incompatible with the will to control. It is not compatible with attempts to interfere in the life of a child except where the interference is in the child's own interest. Equally, it is not compatible

[9] Dworkin, R. (1993). *Life's Dominion*. London: Harper Collins.

with the practice of prenatal selection which seeks to identify, as a basis for choice, genetic predispositions for enhanced abilities or special character traits. For this is an attempt to determine the kind of child one will have – which is precisely not the unconditional, loving acceptance of whatever child one turns out to have.

Given that we are dealing here with only speculative possibilities, and since the likely small effects of individual genes may make accurate predictions of future behaviour very difficult, it is hard to evaluate the disagreement between the contrasting positions. In particular, it may be that the contrast between the affirmation of a right to procreative autonomy and the defence of natural humility is too simple. It might turn out that there are possibilities for modest applications of PGD in relation to the traits considered in this Report which would not seriously undermine the present relationship between parents and their children. **While not entirely persuaded by this conservative line of argument, we do accept that, at present, the case for permitting prenatal selection based on the identification of genetic predispositions for enhanced abilities remains to be made. We recommend, therefore, that the technique of preimplantation genetic diagnosis, which is currently restricted to serious diseases and disorders, should not be extended to include behavioural traits in the normal range such as intelligence, sexual orientation and personality traits** (paragraph 13.78).

Legal issues: criminal responsibility

Attributing responsibility

We conclude that research in behavioural genetics does not pose a fundamental challenge to our notions of responsibility as they are applied in the legal context. We consider that genetic variants in the normal range are unlikely to be considered an excuse for legal purposes, at least for the foreseeable future. They fall outside the scope of the defences of insanity and diminished responsibility and cannot be said to absolve individuals from responsibility for their actions (paragraph 14.24). If progress in behavioural genetics were to be such that close and clearly identifiable associations between particular genetic variants and particular forms of antisocial acts were to be demonstrated, there would be a case for a re-examination of the legal implications. It might be that the concept of diminished responsibility, for example, could be expanded to embrace such conditions, perhaps by redefining views of illness. If this possibility were to be considered, thought would have to be given to the potential dangers of unwarranted over-reliance on genetic information and the consequences of reducing responsibility for our actions (paragraph 14.25).

Sentencing

We conclude that, with regard to the sentencing of convicted offenders, the criminal law should be receptive to whatever valid psychiatric and behavioural evidence is available. The taking into account of genetic factors would depend on the degree to which such evidence is convincing and relevant. Credible evidence of influence and a robust test for the genetic factor in question would be essential: the weight to be accorded to such information would be determined by the judge (paragraph 14.32). Currently, environmental, social and psychiatric assessments may be taken into account by judges in determining appropriate sentences. These must also be supported by valid, accurate and reliable evidence. It would be unwise to assume that genetics will not be able to assist in determining degrees of blame, even if the 'all-or-nothing' question of responsibility is not affected by genetic factors themselves. Such a role would not compromise basic assumptions as to responsibility.

Exchanges between genetics and the criminal law are at present not very productive given the uncertain nature of the evidence. This is likely to change. **We recommend that the criminal**

justice system should be open to new insights from disciplines that it has not necessarily considered in the past. The regular exchange of ideas in this area between researchers in behavioural genetics, criminologists and lawyers could be an effective means of ensuring that legal concepts of responsibility are assessed against current evidence from the behavioural and medical sciences (paragraph 14.33).

Predictive use of genetic information

We take the view that while the reduction of antisocial behaviour and crime are important goals, any attempt to predict the behaviour of an individual who has not exhibited antisocial behaviour, and to intervene accordingly, poses a significant threat to civil liberties and should be treated with great caution. The use of predictive genetic tests to anticipate antisocial behaviour for the purposes of preventive action in the case of individuals who have not already exhibited such behaviour raises ethical questions about balancing the interests of individuals against those of society. **We consider that the predictive use of genetic information about behaviour in the normal range, used in isolation in the case of individuals who have not exhibited antisocial behaviour, is unlikely to be warranted because of the predictive power of such information is likely to be weak and there is a risk of false predictions. However, we take the view that the use of such information in conjunction with information about other, non-genetic influences on behaviour may be justified if the aim is to benefit the individual, and in doing so, to benefit society also. We recommend that the prediction of behaviour with a view to detaining an individual who has not committed a crime is not justified, whether such predictions are based on information about genetic or non-genetic influences on behaviour** (paragraph 14.44).

Policy issues: employment, education and insurance

Employment

Various bodies have made recommendations concerning the occupational health and safety of employees and jobseekers in the context of genetics. These have tended to apply a model of the autonomy of the individual patient in the medical sphere to the employment relationship. In the case of behavioural traits within the normal range, which are the subject of this Report, we are not concerned with patients. Moreover, the employment relationship is less receptive to the application of the medical model. The inherent inequality of bargaining position and power between the employer and the individual employee means that the employer is likely to initiate the tests and to decide how they are to be administered and used. A 'right to refuse' to take a test to disclose genetic information or a 'right to know' the outcome, is likely to be of little practical value where the employee has to choose between exercising the right or waiving it in order to secure a livelihood. The public interest or paternalistic justifications for overriding the individual's wishes where there is a serious danger to the health or safety of the employee or third parties do not exist in the case of non-clinical behavioural traits (paragraph 15.20). This leads us to make the following conclusions and recommendations in the context of the use by employers of genetic testing for behavioural traits:

- **The primary duty of employers is to provide a safe environment for their employees and others. The aim should be to remove hazards from the workplace, not to remove employees on the basis of inherited characteristics or susceptibility to particular forms of behaviour within the normal range.**
- **Employees should be selected and promoted on the basis of their ability to meet the requirements of the job, and they should be monitored to ensure that their performance meets those requirements.**

- **Employers should not demand that an individual take a genetic test for a behavioural trait as a condition of employment. The proper approach would be to monitor employees for early warning signs of behaviour (such as violence) that would make them incapable of performing the job satisfactorily.**
- **Any inquiry into the potential use of genetic testing of behavioural traits in the workplace should include an investigation of the use of other purportedly predictive scientific methods, such as psychometric tests, for similar purposes** (paragraph 15.21).

Education

We note, with some concern, that the implications for education of research in behavioural genetics have not yet received significant critical attention. **In the light of the issues that may arise if genetic information about behavioural traits is applied in the context of education, we recommend that further investigation of the ways in which such research might be applied, and the resulting ethical and social issues, be undertaken. We recommend that dialogue between those involved in education and researchers in behavioural genetics be promoted. We recommend, further, that until such dialogue and research is undertaken, genetic information about behavioural traits in the normal range should not be used in the context of the provision of education** (paragraph 15.26).

Insurance

We recommend that the use of genetic information about behavioural traits in the normal range should be interpreted as falling under the scope of the five-year moratorium agreed in the UK in 2001, and should therefore not be used by insurance companies in setting premiums. Future discussion of possible legislation should include specific consideration of genetic information regarding behavioural traits. If the use of such information were considered, a thorough examination of the accuracy and reliability of any genetic tests and their likely predictive power would be essential (paragraph 15.37).

Funding research in behavioural genetics

It has proved difficult to gauge the precise extent of UK funding in this area. Our public consultation showed that many people consider that, compared to research on disease, research into genetic influences on behavioural traits in the normal range ought to receive low priority for funding. This was partly due to doubts about the likely success of the research, and partly due to concerns about the potential applications. **We take the view that research in behavioural genetics has the potential to advance our understanding of human behaviour and that the research can therefore be justified. However, we note that it is important that those who fund research in this area should continue to fund research of a high calibre, should be transparent about their funding practices and should be aware of the potential for the abuse and misinterpretation of results. In addition, we recommend that research sponsors who intend to focus strategic funding in this area should pay careful attention to public concerns about the research and its applications** (paragraph 11.17).

Section 1

Introduction and context

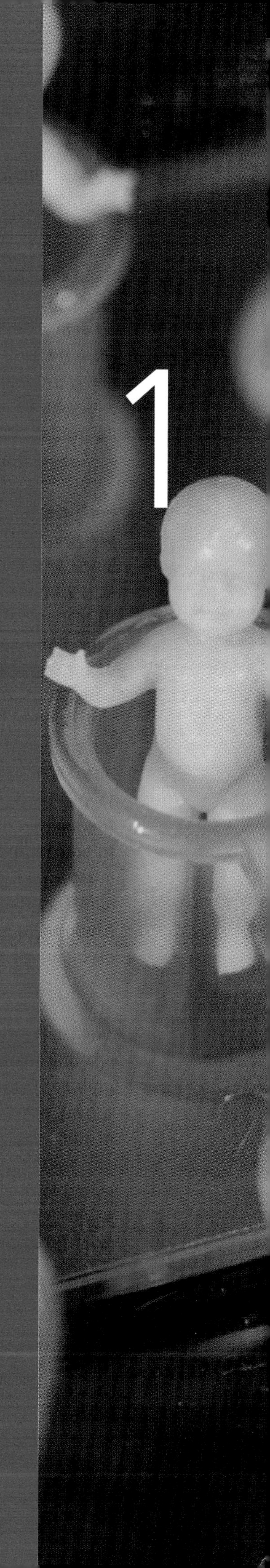

Chapter 1

Introduction

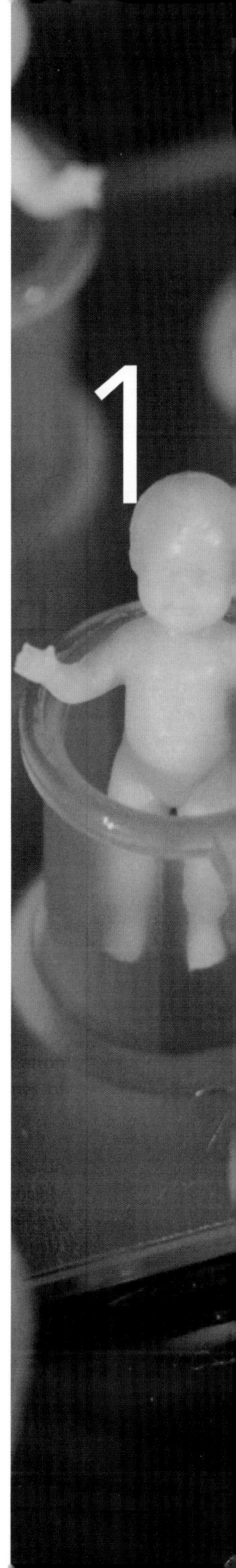

Introduction

Why this Working Party is important

1.1 Human behaviour is influenced both by the genes that we inherit and the environment in which we live. With the significant advances in our knowledge of genetics and publication of the draft sequence of the human genome, the focus of research has moved once again towards understanding the biological contribution to behaviour.[1] Some researchers are attempting to locate specific genes, or groups of genes, associated with behavioural traits and to understand the complex relationship between genes and the environment. This is called research in behavioural genetics. In contrast to research into the genetic basis of diseases and disorders, researchers in behavioural genetics investigate aspects of our personalities such as intelligence, sexual orientation, susceptibility to aggression and other antisocial conduct, and tendencies towards extraversion and novelty-seeking.

1.2 This is a complicated area of research in genetics, often controversial, occasionally explosive and with the capacity to ignite dangerous passions. There are concerns about the validity of some of the scientific methodologies involved. It is difficult to identify and interpret the influence of genetic factors, and it can be just as hard to define and measure the behavioural traits themselves. There is no evidence that research in behavioural genetics can expect to uncover simple correlations between one gene and one behavioural trait. Rather, complex interactions between a number of genes may be involved in an individual's susceptibility to possessing a particular trait. There will also be environmental influences on behaviour and genes, and genetic influences on both the environments we seek out and the activity of other genes. Moreover, the effects of our genes change over time as we develop – they do not have a continuous and unchanging influence on our brains and bodies. A further complication is that one gene, or group of genes, is likely to affect more than one trait. For example, in 1999, researchers in the US produced a strain of mice that had been genetically modified and that appeared to have an improved memory.[2] But in 2001, another group of researchers discovered that mice whose genes had been altered in this way also had the capacity to suffer more from long-term pain.[3]

1.3 A useful analogy that has been used to convey this complexity is that of an orchestra playing a difficult score, whereby a particular group of genes (or the notes of the music) can generate a large number of different outcomes (or interpretations of the music).[4] This complexity means that, even if some genes are found to be associated with certain types of behaviour, the contribution they each make may be very small, and the precise effect they have on any particular person may be extremely difficult to predict. This weak contribution of individual genes, or groups of genes, to overall susceptibility, is compounded by the subtle interaction of genes amongst themselves and with the environment, and the relative unpredictability of human development. If, notwithstanding all these difficulties, genes that influence particular behavioural traits are identified, it could become possible to test

---

[1] See for example Duster, T. (1990). *Backdoor to Eugenics*. New York: Routledge. This account reports a substantial rise, during the 1980s, in the publication of scientific articles that attempt to explain the genetic basis of behavioural traits.

[2] Tang, Y. P. *et al*. (1999). Genetic enhancement of learning and memory in mice. *Nature* **401**, 63–9.

[3] Wei, F. *et al*. (2001). Genetic enhancement of inflammatory pain by forebrain NR2B overexpression. *Nat. Neurosci*. **4**, 164–9. This effect is called *pleiotropy*.

[4] Schmikle, S. (2002). Intelligence genes prove hard to map. *Minneapolis-St Paul Star Tribune* 18 February. Reporting Professor Jonathan Beckwith (Harvard University).

for the presence of variations in these genes in individual people. No such tests currently exist. Moreover, there is disagreement about whether tests that predict human behaviour accurately could ever be developed.

1.4 Even if genetic tests could not yield predictions of a *definite* outcome, it may nonetheless be possible that tests that suggest an individual will have an *increased chance* of possessing a particular trait to a greater or lesser degree might be developed. Such hypothetical tests might be undertaken for a variety of purposes. One purpose would be simply to gain more knowledge about the influence of genes on behaviour. For example, studying traits within the normal range of behaviour, such as anxiety, might help in the search for treatments for disorders, such as clinical depression. Another purpose might be that of intervention or treatment, for example to prevent aggressive behaviour by using medicines, or by attempts to change relevant aspects of the environment. A further purpose might be that of selection. This encompasses, for instance, prenatal testing, the streaming of children in schools on the basis of intelligence and aptitude, the screening of employees and jobseekers to exclude those with traits that employers consider undesirable, and the use by insurers of genetic information about behaviour and personality traits in order to estimate risk. Yet another purpose might be to claim diminished legal responsibility for one's actions or to mitigate punishment for criminal behaviour.

1.5 These possibilities raise important ethical, legal and practical issues. If genetic tests for behaviour in the normal range are developed, parents who want children with certain traits might be encouraged to select particular embryos or fetuses, or to seek to enhance the traits of their existing children using genetic manipulation. Those with the most desirable genetic endowments could be streamed into the best schools, universities, jobs, while those without the benefit of enhancement would be relegated to a pool of the less educated and less skilled. Although this may be the stuff of science fiction,[5] there can be no doubt that the idea that qualities of the human race could be improved by selective breeding was to some extent taken as justification for acts of genocide by the regime in Nazi Germany. This idea also encouraged the compulsory sterilisation of mentally handicapped people in Europe and North America. While modern behavioural genetics is not in any sense driven by eugenic policies, there is a need to understand why past ideas and practices were unacceptable and to be aware of the potential dangers of genetic discrimination in our open society, where decisions tend to be made by individuals and based on freedom of choice. Other important issues include the protection of the privacy and confidentiality of personal genetic information, and the role of education and the media in influencing mistaken beliefs about the factors that affect particular behavioural traits and the stigmatisation of individuals who display such traits.

1.6 In view of considerations such as these, the Nuffield Council on Bioethics agreed that it was important to anticipate the ethical, legal and social implications raised by research in behavioural genetics. The scope of the Council's 1993 Report on *Genetic Screening: The Ethical Issues*, was limited to serious diseases. In focusing on the major psychiatric disorders, the scope of the 1998 Report on *Mental Disorders and Genetics: The Ethical Context* was similarly restricted. The work of the Human Genetics Advisory Council (HGAC) in the UK,

---

[5] An extreme form of such a society is imagined in the film *Gattaca* (1997) where the "InValids" who have not been genetically engineered are condemned to the lower ranks of society. While the society envisaged in *Gattaca* is based on parental choice, Aldous Huxley's *Brave New World* (1932) presents a vision of an authoritarian society in which the state is responsible for producing and conditioning the requisite supply of intelligent and less intelligent individuals.

and the Human Genetics Commission (HGC) which replaced it, has also focused on inherited disease and susceptibility to clinical disorders. This Report is intended to fill that gap and to draw attention to the implications of research in genetics which falls outside the medical sphere. The objectives of the Working Party established by the Council were to define and consider the ethical, legal and social issues arising from the study of the genetics of variation within the normal range of behaviour characteristics. In order to provide a factual and contextual background to the issues, this Report first sets out the historical and scientific background and examines the evidence for the relative importance of genetic influences on selected behavioural traits. It then considers the potential applications of this research and the ethical, legal and social implications.

Defining the normal range of behavioural characteristics

1.7 The subject of this Report is human behaviour within the normal range, as opposed to traits that are defined as illnesses or diseases. An important preliminary question is whether it is actually feasible to talk about a 'normal range' of behavioural traits. According to one view, there is no such state as 'normality', and nor is there a 'normal genome', as each individual is subject to different genetic and environmental influences.

1.8 There is a danger that, in speaking of the 'normal' range, this Report may be misunderstood as stigmatising certain kinds of behaviour, namely those that are at the extremes of variation. It therefore needs to be emphasised that when we use the phrases 'normal variation' or 'behaviour in the normal range', no moral evaluation or judgement is implied. In these phrases, 'normal' has a statistical meaning – it refers to the range of variation, usually that which includes about 95% of the population, and which is thought not to contain any individuals with clinical disorders or diseases. There are other approaches to defining normal behaviour. They include the theory that abnormal behaviour is that which results in impaired function in society for the individual, either from the individual's own perspective, or from an objective standpoint, regardless of whether the behaviour is statistically rare or not.

1.9 We take the statistical approach merely as our starting point, using it to limit the field of inquiry. We have focused on traits, such as intelligence, that are continuously distributed measures, displayed by each individual in the population to a greater or lesser extent, and which are not commonly viewed as disorders. In Chapter 13, we consider further the question of defining normal behaviour with reference to issues such as medicalisation and the distinction between therapy and enhancement. For now, we observe that not only are the boundaries between disorders and variation in the normal range difficult to draw, but also that they can be disputed at any time and can alter as society changes. Homosexuality has, at times, been regarded as a disorder, but today is usually regarded as a variation within the normal range of sexual preferences. We also note the further question, whether patterns of behaviour can properly be seen as lying on a continuum, with disorders as extremes of normal variation, or whether disorders are qualitatively different from behaviour in the normal range. For example, is depression an extreme manifestation of neuroticism, a trait which is present in everyone to some degree, or is it a distinct disorder? At present, it is not known whether there will prove to be any evidence from research in genetics for making a qualitative distinction between normal and abnormal behaviour, or for viewing behaviour as lying on a continuous spectrum. This is one reason why researchers in behavioural genetics and other disciplines consider it important to examine the genes of people considered to be within the normal range as well as those who display extremes of behaviour.

The scope of research in behavioural genetics

1.10 We focus on four areas of research in behavioural genetics: research into intelligence, personality traits, antisocial behaviour and sexual orientation. These were selected to illustrate the range of topics that are being investigated, and because of the important issues they raise.

- *Intelligence* is a complex phenomenon and there is considerable debate about whether it can be measured effectively. There is substantial disagreement regarding the extent to which genetic and environmental factors influence intelligence.

- *Personality traits* have been studied by psychologists for many years. Five core traits have been the focus of research in both psychology and behavioural genetics: neuroticism, introversion/extraversion, openness, agreeableness and conscientiousness.

- *Antisocial behaviour* is classified differently by mental health clinicians, criminologists and psychologists, but a common factor is that it is behaviour which violates the rights and safety of others. It includes traits such as aggression and violent behaviour.

- *Sexual orientation* is regarded by some as a matter of choice and by others as a matter of biology. What role, if any, do genetic factors play in sexual orientation? The answer to this question is bound to influence the way in which people react to homosexuality.

1.11 We acknowledge that terms such as 'antisocial behaviour' and 'extraversion' arise from particular disciplines, for example psychology, and that there is often dispute about what they refer to. However, since certain behavioural traits, thus defined and labelled, are the focus of research into behavioural genetics, we use these terms. In discussing these characteristics we have found it useful to compare them to certain other quantitatively varying human characteristics, such as height, which are more amenable to definition and measurement than behavioural traits.

The structure of the Report

1.12 The first two parts of the Report explain the historical and scientific background to research in the field of behavioural genetics. Chapter 2 outlines the history of the eugenics movement and its profound effect on the development of clinical genetics and developmental psychology since the Second World War. There is a brief account of evolutionary psychology as a reaction to the behaviourism of the 1950s and 1960s.[6] Chapter 3 attempts to explain what is meant by the suggestion that genes influence or affect human behaviour. It does so by examining what genes are and how they work, what is meant by genetic variation, what we mean by human behaviour within the normal range, and how genes might influence such behaviour. There are different ways in which one can study the contribution that genetic factors make to human behaviour. Chapter 4 examines one of these approaches, namely quantitative genetics. This field of research aims to determine the extent to which variation in a trait is genetically influenced in a population. It uses statistical methods to examine and compare groups of people without focusing on

[6] The Report has been confined to behavioural genetics. Evolutionary psychology, which attempts to provide explanations for similarities in human behaviour rather than variation between individuals, raises different scientific and ethical issues and is not discussed in the Report.

particular genes. Chapter 5 explains another approach, that of molecular genetics. This attempts to identify differences in particular genes that contribute to variation between particular individuals. A third approach is the use of animals to try to examine the effects of particular genes on behaviour. Chapter 6 examines this type of research.

1.13 The third part of the Report, Chapters 7–11, contains reviews of the findings that have been obtained to date in each of these methods of research, with respect to the behavioural traits already listed: intelligence, personality, antisocial behaviour and sexual orientation. The principal themes that emerge from the reviews of the evidence are summarised in Chapter 11. The Report has been written so that readers not wishing to digest the scientific information contained in the reviews of the evidence can refer to this summary chapter instead, without compromising their understanding of the overall Report.

1.14 The fourth part of the Report examines the ethical, legal and policy issues and offers a series of conclusions and recommendations. A starting point is the recent United Nations Educational, Scientific and Cultural Organization (UNESCO) *Universal Declaration on the Human Genome and Human Rights* which states that the 'human genome underlies the fundamental unity of all members of the human family, as well as the recognition of their inherent dignity and diversity'.[7] Chapter 12 begins by discussing whether there is an inherent conflict between understanding the genetic influences on behaviour and human dignity, as it is expressed in the concepts of free will and moral responsibility. Chapter 13 then addresses some of the potential applications of the research including genetic, medical and environmental interventions aimed at changing behavioural traits, as well as prenatal selection. Chapter 14 is concerned with the implications of research in behavioural genetics for the criminal justice system, in relation to attributions of legal responsibility and sentencing, and in predicting antisocial behaviour. Chapter 15 considers genetic testing and selection with regard to education, employment and insurance.

[7] United Nations Educational, Scientific and Cultural Organisation. (November 1997). *Universal Declaration on the Human Genome and Human Rights.*

Chapter 2

The historical context

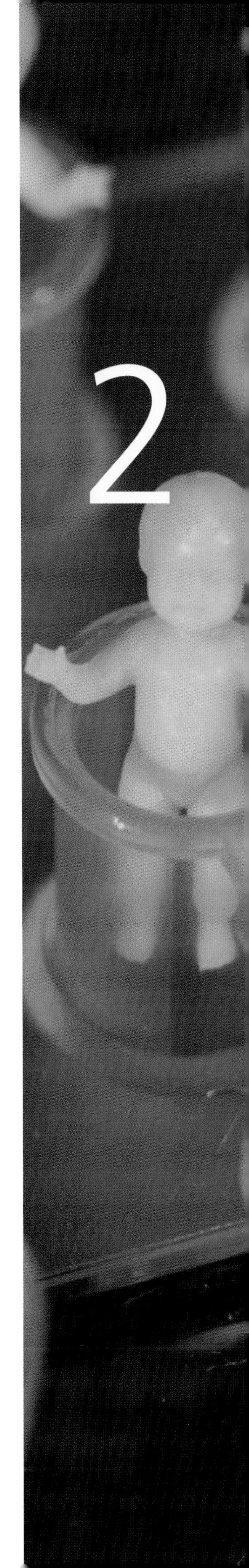

The historical context

2.1 The literal meaning of the term eugenics is 'well born'. It refers to the doctrine that humanity can be improved by selective breeding, that is, by encouraging those with desirable traits to reproduce or discouraging those with undesirable traits from doing so. The eugenic movement is relevant to the present considerations of genetics and behaviour because intellectual abilities and behaviour of various kinds were central to most eugenic policies and practices, and the study of behavioural genetics was established by scientists working within the context of the eugenics movement. This history remains part of what underlies many of the anxieties expressed today among professionals and members of the public towards work on genetics and intellectual abilities and other behavioural traits. Current work in behavioural genetics has been described as 'the second of two eras in which the science of heredity has promised to offer great benefits for mankind', making it 'inevitable that today's genetics proceeds in the shadow of eugenics.'[1] Many of the respondents to the Working Party's public consultation made links of various kinds between research in behavioural genetics and eugenics (see Box 2.1).[2]

Box 2.1: Concerns about eugenics expressed by respondents to the public consultation

'The notion that behavioural traits are passed from one generation to another, "in the blood", has been common currency for a very long time. It has been used to justify racism, persecution and genocide, it has been used to stereotype individuals, and it has been used to proclaim the superiority of an individual or group over others.'

British Psychological Society

'Public health policy in the context of genetics is frequently described as eugenic ... behavioural genetics will, on balance, be contrary to the public interest, precisely because it may lead to reduced acceptance and respect for diversity and people with handicap.'

Public Health Genetics Network

'there is a possible scenario of a genetic master race being created, something between Hitler and Brave New World with unpredictable consequences. Even if the techniques are new, the lessons of the Third Reich should not be forgotten.'

Mr Chris Barchard

'The research would seem to be unnecessary since it is concerned with normal people. The main justification of this research would seem to be some form of eugenics which is morally repugnant to most people and so the research should not take place.'

Mrs Gaynor Mitchell

'intelligence, aggression, antisocial behaviour ... The very choice of this list links modern behavioural genetics to its eugenic past, as these were exactly the issues that concerned the early twentieth century eugenicists.'

Professor Steven Rose

---

1 Buchanan, A., Brock, D., Daniels, N. & Wikler, D. (2000). *From Chance to Choice: Genetics and Justice*. Cambridge: Cambridge University Press.

2 Nuffield Council on Bioethics. (19 March 2001). *Genetics and human behaviour: the ethical context. Public consultation document.* http://www.nuffieldbioethics.org/filelibrary/doc/consultation_document_final.doc (13 Aug 2002).

2.2 While selective breeding in plants and animals is as old as agriculture, it became increasingly effective in the nineteenth century. This populated farms in Western Europe, and 'Neoeurope' (temperate North and South America and Australasia) with improved breeds and strains which came to dominate the world food trade, as they still do today. The success of the selective breeding of plants and animals is evidence that both physical and behavioural characteristics can be changed over generations by selection so that the relevant characteristics are, at least to some degree, inherited. Not surprisingly, in a climate in which the breeding of animals was much discussed and visibly effective, debates also included the possibility of the selective breeding of humans, and, consequently, the improvement of the gene pool. This latter is what Francis Galton, in 1883, termed eugenics. His cousin, Charles Darwin, put the argument clearly:

> 'With savages, the weak in body or mind are soon eliminated, and those that survive commonly exhibit a vigorous state of health. We civilised men, on the other hand, do our utmost to check the process of elimination, we build asylums for the imbecile, the maimed and sick, we institute poor-laws; and our medical men exert their utmost skill to save the life of everyone to the last moment. There is reason to believe that vaccination has preserved those who from a weak constitution would have formerly succumbed to smallpox. No-one who has attended to the breeding of domestic animals will doubt that this must be highly injurious to the race of man. It is surprising how soon a want of care, or care wrongly directed, leads to the degeneration of a domestic race; but excepting in the case of man himself, hardly anyone is so ignorant as to allow his worst animals to breed'.[3]

2.3 The first recorded experiment in the selective breeding of humans took place in John Humphrey Noyes' Perfectionist Community at Oneida in New York State.[4] Between 1869 and 1879 fifty-eight 'stirpicults'[5] were born to members of the Community selected on grounds of intelligence, physique and other characteristics. The children were carefully studied and judged to be superior in their physique and intellect.[6] However, whether this can be attributed to the Community's attention to 'the laws of breeding', or its material prosperity, education and social policies, is another matter.

2.4 By the early decades of the twentieth century, eugenic policies and practices were in place in almost all industrialised countries, and some version of eugenic thought was common ground across the political spectrum. Policies and practices varied widely from country to country. Most included positive eugenics, designed to increase fertility among those deemed to be fit, and negative eugenics, designed to reduce or prevent reproduction by those held to be unfit. In Britain the demographic transition, with falling birth rates especially among the middle and upper classes, provided a strong incentive for eugenic policies which included the incarceration of the 'feeble minded' and 'morally incompetent' to segregate them, as well as attempts to increase the birth rate of the middle classes. Following a Royal Commission on the Causes and Control of the Feeble Minded, the 1914 Mental Deficiency Act allowed the compulsory detention of individuals in state institutions to control fertility. The First World War was generally regarded as a eugenic disaster

---

3 Darwin, C. (1871). *The Descent of Man, and Selection in Relation to Sex.* 2nd ed. London: John Murray. pp. 133–4.

4 Carden, M. L. (1998). *Oneida: Utopian Community to Modern Corporation.* Syracuse: Syracuse University Press.

5 Stirpiculture is defined as the production of pure races or stocks by careful breeding.

6 McGee, A. N. (1891). An experiment in human stirpiculture. *Am. Anthropol.* **4**, 319–29.

because of the particularly high death rate among officers. This aided the promotion of eugenic policies in the 1920s. In Britain and elsewhere, there was a wide consensus that behavioural and personality traits and moral qualities were largely determined by inheritance. This was repeatedly emphasised by eugenic educational programmes, which claimed, particularly in the early years of the movement, that these characteristics were transmitted as Mendelian traits ('like the coat colours of guinea pigs').[7]

2.5 In many countries, although not in Britain, programmes of the compulsory sterilisation of the 'unfit' were instituted in the 1920s and 1930s to combat 'racial degeneration' and crime. It is estimated that in the US about 30,000 people were sterilised. In Germany the figure was probably 400,000.[8] In Nazi Germany there was selective breeding of the 'racially pure', the 'euthanasia' of thousands of children living in institutions, and the killing of adults from families that carried Mendelian conditions such as Huntington's disease. Eugenics had its critics, who argued on moral, political, social and scientific grounds. In Britain, by the 1930s, there was increasing opposition for both social and political reasons and because of the lack of any evidence demonstrating that the characteristics central to the eugenic programmes were inherited to any significant degree.

2.6 It is often believed that knowledge of what had occurred in Nazi Germany before and during the Second World War was sufficient to end eugenic policies elsewhere. This is not so. Some countries, including Canada, Sweden and Switzerland, continued sterilisation on eugenic grounds until at least the 1960s.[9] In many countries, the traditions of political thought, which in a general sense might be regarded as eugenic, have continued in minority politics. Amongst scientists, eugenic ideas continued to have their supporters. For instance, in 1962 an international group of distinguished biologists met at the Ciba Foundation to consider 'Man and his Future'.[10] The meeting was much preoccupied by eugenics:

> 'The improvement of human genetic quality by eugenic methods would take a great load of suffering and frustration off the shoulders of evolving humanity, and would much increase both enjoyment and efficiency. Let me give one example. The general level of genetic intelligence could theoretically be raised by eugenic selection; and even a slight rise in its average level would give a marked increase in the number of the outstandingly intelligent and capable people needed to run our increasingly complex societies.
>
> How to implement eugenic policy in practice is another matter. The effects of merely encouraging well-endowed individuals to have more children, and vice versa, would be much too slow for modern psychosocial evolution. Eugenics will eventually have to have recourse to methods like multiple artificial insemination by preferred donors of high genetic quality.'[11]

---

[7] A poster published by the American Eugenics Society, 1927.

[8] Paul, D. B. (1998). *Controlling Human Heredity 1865 to the Present.* Amhurst, NY: Humanity Press.

[9] It has recently been reported that since 1996, as many as 200,000 indigenous people in Peru have been pressured into being sterilised, as part of a family planning programme run by the government, which offered incentives to those who agreed to be sterilised and threatened to impose fines for reproducing. (Mass sterilisation scandal shocks Peru. *BBC News Online*. 24 July 2002. http://news.bbc.co.uk/1/hi/world/americas/2148793.stm).

[10] Wolstanholme, G., editor. (1963). *Man and His Future.* London: Churchill.

[11] Wolstanholme, G., editor. (1963). *Man and His Future.* London: Churchill. p. 17 Julian Huxley.

Similarly, geneticist and Nobel Prize winner, Hermann Muller argued that:

> 'modern civilization has instituted a negative feedback from cultural progress to genetic progress ... The social devices and the individual persuasion regarding family size advocated by old-style eugenics are inadequate to meet the situation, except in extreme cases of specific defects. For the major problems concerned with qualitative characters, the more effective method and the one that is ultimately more acceptable psychologically, is germinal choice.'[12]

2.7 The usual method advocated for 'germinal choice' was artificial insemination by selected donors (AID). Others at the meeting doubted whether these methods would be acceptable or would achieve their desired results. Some questioned whether human populations were deteriorating in genetic terms. They pointed out that IQ levels were rising and wondered whether human beings could be trusted to formulate long-term eugenic objectives.[13] Twenty years later, at the Eugenics Society's 75th anniversary meeting, which focused on eugenic and ethical aspects of new reproductive and genetic techniques, there was discussion of Robert Graham's Californian sperm bank of samples taken from Nobel Prize winners. It was suggested that 'there is a case on eugenic grounds for choosing donors who are above, but not greatly above, the parental level of intelligence.'[14] While the British Eugenics Society lost some support after the Second World War, it continued to attract prominent scientists, including geneticists, to its meetings into the 1980s. Throughout this post-war period the Society advocated voluntary policies using such techniques as contraception, AID, carrier detection of Mendelian diseases and prenatal diagnosis.

2.8 The eugenic movement has had a profound effect on the development of clinical genetics in the post-war era, with increasing attempts to separate genetic counselling from eugenic policies. This may be seen, for example, in the emphasis on non-directive counselling in contrast to the provision of advice (and treatment) which characterises other clinical medicine. The educational activities of the eugenics movement may be, in part, responsible for the continuing beliefs that some behavioural characteristics are largely determined by genetic factors.[15]

2.9 In order to learn from the history of eugenics, there is a need for clarity about exactly what was wrong about past eugenic programmes:

> 'For the history of eugenics to be instructive in ensuring social justice with greater knowledge about genes, and perhaps some ability to alter them, the key question is whether ... eugenics was wrong in its very inception. If so, any eugenics programme will be wrong. On the other hand, if the abuses done in the name of eugenics do not necessarily reflect badly on eugenic ideas themselves, then our task will be to ensure that any eugenic interventions of the future avoids these abuses.'[16]

---

[12] Wolstanholme, G., editor. (1963). *Man and His Future*. London: Churchill. p. 261. Muller went on to be associated with the Repository for Germinal Choice, a non-profit sperm bank that solicited donations from Nobel Prize winners and other eminent scientists.

[13] Wolstanholme, G., editor. (1963). *Man and His Future*. London: Churchill.

[14] Carter, C. O., editor. (1983). *Developments in Human Reproduction and their Eugenic and Ethical Implications. Proceedings of the Nineteenth Annual Symposium of the Eugenics Society*. London: Academic Press.

[15] Paul, D. B. (1998). *Controlling Human Heredity 1865 to the Present*. Amhurst, NY: Humanity Press.

[16] Buchanan, A., Brock, D., Daniels, N. & Wikler, D. (2000). *From Chance to Choice: Genetics and Justice*. Cambridge: Cambridge University Press.

In what they term an 'ethical autopsy' of eugenics, Buchanan *et al* have identified five possible answers to the question: what is wrong with eugenics? We describe these in the paragraphs that follow, drawing largely on the account offered by these authors.

- *Replacement rather than therapy.* Eugenics sought to improve society by causing 'better' people to be conceived, rather than improving the lives, health and well-being of those already born. While eugenic policies are not alone in affecting which individuals may be conceived, many social and economic policies may do that deliberately or inadvertently, eugenics raises questions about what kinds of people should or should not be born. While one may not accept the judgements that were made in the past, to argue that, in principle, such judgement should never be made would be to condemn, among other things, all programmes for prenatal screening and diagnosis for serious medical conditions.

- *The pluralism of values and our status as designers.* Eugenic programmes are criticised for promoting a particular conception of human perfection and for failing to appreciate the essential plurality of values and ideals of human excellence. In practice, the usual eugenic ideal was people like the eugenicists themselves. Buchanan *et al* suggest that eugenicists should not be faulted for favouring individuals with high intelligence, or other such traits, but rather for the beliefs and attitudes that accompanied such elements in their programme. For example, crime and unemployment were thought to be the result of low intelligence, and people of low intellectual ability were considered of little value to themselves or others. The pluralism of ideals and values already raises difficult questions with regard to selection against serious disease: these problems are heightened by the potential selection and manipulation of behavioural traits and characteristics about the value of which there is even less consensus. Jonathan Glover has argued that the barbarous history of the twentieth century makes the improvement of human nature desirable.[17] However, a counter-argument might suggest that some of the worst policies of the twentieth century arose from the very effort to improve the human population, through Nazi racial ideology or Stalinist social engineering. While such excesses seem unlikely in a democracy, it remains the case that our own ideas about what might be the best way to improve the human species are limited by our own values, perspectives and horizons.

- *Violations of reproductive freedoms.* We have already noted the crimes of Nazi Germany, the involuntary sterilisation of tens of thousands of Americans and Europeans and the programmes of segregation. But it is worth pointing out that many eugenicists, including Francis Galton and the British Eugenics Society from the early 1930s did not favour coercion.[18] Today, China has a clearly eugenic Maternal and Infant Health Law.[19] But in many other countries reproductive freedom is sufficiently well established that the introduction of programmes for mass sterilisation and other forms of reproductive coercion seems very unlikely.[20] It is widely agreed that the elimination of individual choice and the introduction of coercion in reproductive matters are two features of past

---

17 Glover, J. (1984). *What Sort of People Should There Be?* Harmondsworth: Penguin.

18 Paul, D. B. (1998). *Controlling Human Heredity 1865 to the Present.* Amhurst, NY: Humanity Press.

19 China's Misconceptions of Eugenics [editorial]. (1994). *Nature* **367**,1–2. The law is concerned with negative eugenics, that is, with preventing those with undesirable inherited traits from reproducing.

20 Wertz, D. C. & Fletcher, J. C. Ethical decision making in medical genetics: women as patients and practitioners in eighteen nations. In Ratcliff, K.S. *et al*, editors. (1989). *Healing Technology: Feminist Perspectives.* Ann Arbor: University of Michigan Press. But see also footnote 9 in this chapter.

eugenic practices that make them morally abhorrent. Some have suggested, on libertarian grounds, that voluntarily chosen 'quality control' should be an option.[21] It should be noted that one does not have to conclude that eugenics free of coercion is morally acceptable. In Chapter 13, we discuss arguments against allowing individuals who would like to make use of techniques of prenatal selection from doing so.

- *Statism.* James Watson, one of the scientists who discovered the structure of DNA, has argued that since state policies were responsible for the eugenic crimes of the past, the role of the state in matters of inheritance should be curtailed. However, as several others have pointed out, the actions of parents, employers and insurers, among many others, can harm those with genetic diseases.[22] States can take positive actions to curb such harm. Conversely, states may be involved in funding and organising services for genetic screening and testing as well as the termination of pregnancies with fetuses found to carry genetic diseases.

- *Justice.* 'Eugenics has proved itself historically to have a cruel and always a problematic faith, not least because it has elevated abstractions – the "race", the "population", and more recently, the "gene pool" – above the rights and needs of individuals and their families'.[23] The eugenic movement believed that the human population faced a grave threat of 'degeneration' and that this justified their programmes of segregation and sterilisation. Today, in an attempt to distance current policies from that eugenic past, a line is often drawn between eugenics, as an intervention on behalf of public health and well-being, and clinical genetics as a service for individuals and families. But, this is a line that is very difficult to draw clearly. Behavioural genetics cannot disavow any social purpose, but rather has to ensure that its goals are pursued justly and fairly.

The impact of eugenic thought on research into human behaviour

Psychology in the first half of the twentieth century

2.10 It is hardly surprising that eugenic thought profoundly shaped the growth of developmental psychology and what later became known as behavioural genetics. Questions of nature and nurture dominated the developing theories. Pioneers, such as Francis Galton, initially used information about family history and pedigree to argue the hereditarian case for both high and low intellectual abilities (see Figure 2.1). As well as measuring physical characteristics, Galton devised psychological tests which led to the development of IQ tests. He attempted to measure the 'strength' of inheritance by the association of characteristics in parents and children and between other relatives. The pedigree techniques which had proved so successful in the analysis of characteristics associated with single genes (and, indeed, are used to this day for the diagnosis of Mendelian diseases) were found not to be effective for the analysis of traits like intelligence or height, which were increasingly described in quantitative rather than qualitative terms. Each family member in a pedigree can be described as having, or not having, a trait such as blue eyes or a Mendelian condition such as Huntington's disease. In the early work, mental capacities were described in the same way, with individuals classified using terms such as feebleminded or as having scientific ability (see Figure 2.1). However, in analysing mental capacities, Galton and others moved to the use of quantitative

---

21 For example, Glover, J. (1984). *What Sort of People Should There Be?* Harmondsworth: Penguin.

22 For example, Duster, T. (1990). *Backdoor to Eugenics.* New York: Routledge.

23 Kevles, D. (1985). *In the Name of Eugenics: Genetics and the Uses of Human Heredity.* Berkeley: University of California Press. pp. 300–1.

Figure 2.1: The first families of eugenics

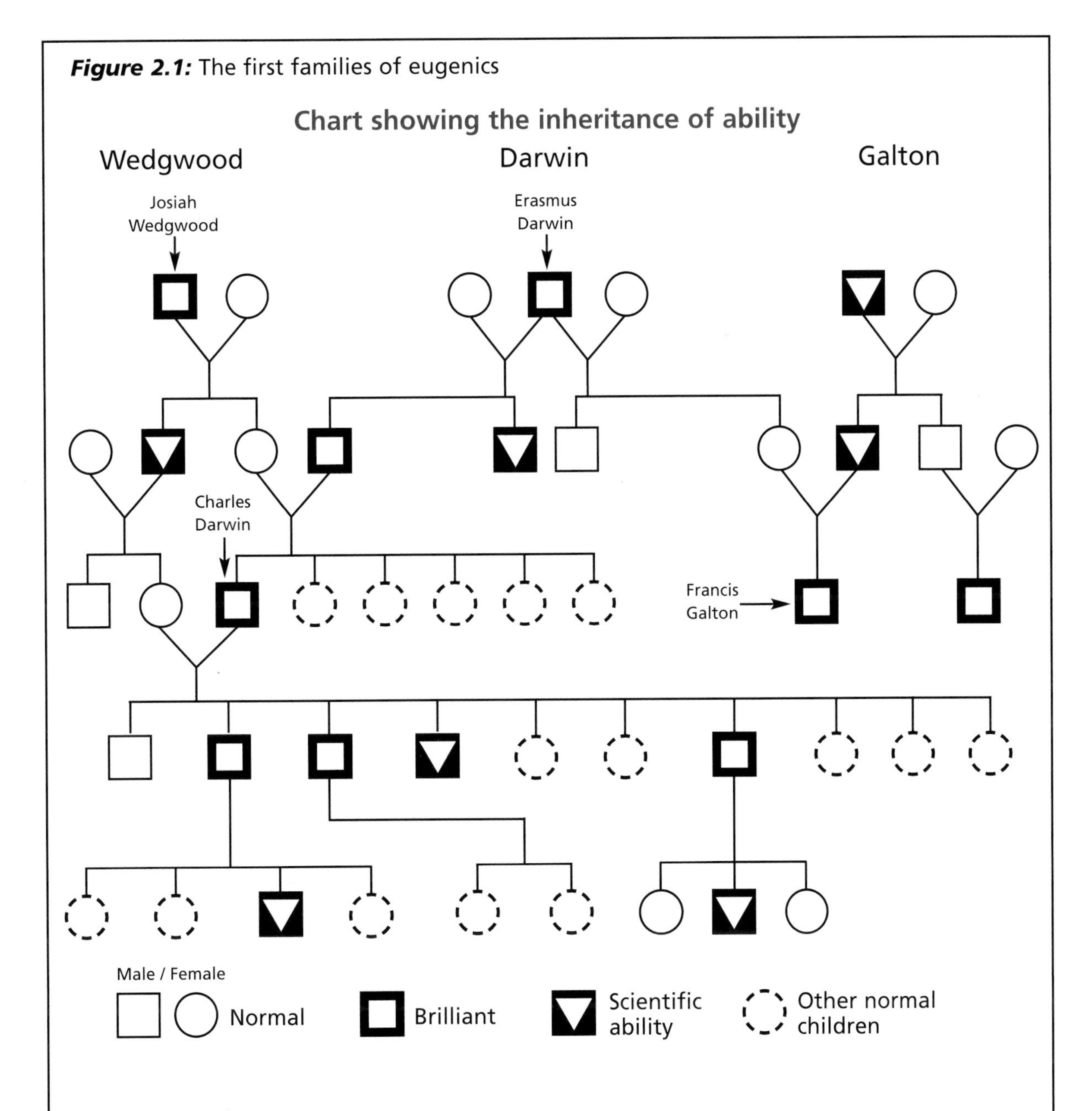

A pedigree chart showing the inheritance of ability in the Wedgwood, Darwin and Galton families which was originally published by the Eugenics Society in 1909. The names of prominent individuals were added by Resta.*

Francis Galton (1822–1911) was a founder and the first President of the Eugenics Society. On his death Major Leonard Darwin, son of Charles Darwin, became Secretary of the Society and later President. Sir Charles G. Darwin (Charles Darwin's nephew) was a Vice-President and served on the council of the Society with such luminaries as Aubrey Lewis (psychiatrist), Julian Huxley (biologist), John Maynard Keynes (economist), Richard Titmus (sociologist) and D.V. Glass (demographer).

* Resta, R. (1995). Whispered hints. *Amer. J. Med. Genet.* **59**, 131–3. It will not escape the notice of readers that, in line with prejudices of the day, no women are classified as brilliant or as having scientific ability.

measures, like IQ scores, and applied the new statistical approaches. This research led to the development of heritability scores, which are discussed in Chapter 4. Today, IQ is seen as being polygenic (influenced by many genes) in contrast with a disease like Huntington's disease which is associated with the mutation of a single gene. While pedigree methods remain a valuable way to study characteristics associated with a single gene, quantitative methods are needed for polygenic traits such as behavioural characteristics.

2.11 Galton's original question about the 'strength' of inheritance is the same as the contemporary common sense understanding of heritability. This is the extent to which inheritance (nature), on the one hand, and environmental (nurture) factors, on the other, contribute to the development of characteristics such as intelligence in an individual. Does an individual owe her high intelligence to what she has inherited from her parents or her upbringing and schooling or a particular mixture of the two? In fact, it turns out to be very difficult to answer scientifically the question posed in these terms. As we shall see in Chapter 4, what research in behavioural genetics can do is to estimate the heritability of a characteristic in a particular group of people, not an individual. This is the proportion of the variation in the characteristic in a particular population, say the variation in IQ scores for a particular group, and it is this group variation which can be apportioned between inherited factors and those in the environment. But, as we shall see later in our discussion, there is a continuing tendency to misunderstand the meaning of estimates of heritability. People often assume that it is the common sense meaning of heritability (or Galton's strength of inheritance). So, if it is stated that the heritability of IQ is 0.50, some people may assume that half their IQ (or that of anyone else in that population) is contributed by their genes and half by their nurture. As will be discussed more fully in Chapter 4, this is incorrect. The scientific meaning of an estimate of heritability of 0.50 is that half the *variation* in IQ scores between people in the group appears to result from genetic variation between them, and half the group variation from differences in their environment and upbringing.

2.12 Most of the British scientists involved in the quantitative study of individual and group differences in intellectual abilities in the first half of the century who made lasting contributions to development of the subject, were prominent eugenicists and were centrally concerned with issues of nature and nurture.[24] This tradition of research created modern parametric statistics and the scientific study of behavioural genetics.

2.13 In the first half of the century there were numerous studies of intellectual abilities often using twin designs and estimates of heritability. These set out to demonstrate that inheritance played a major part in the development of these characteristics. But such work was rather eclipsed in the 1940s and 1950s in the US by the rise of behaviourist psychology. However, the tradition continued in the UK led by psychologists such as Hans Eysenck. The behaviourists compared inputs and outputs, but they had little interest in either the evolutionary or developmental factors that might shape the mind/brain/body.

Psychology from the 1960s onwards

Individual differences

2.14 The earlier traditions of 'individual psychology' or behavioural genetics, which were based on techniques of quantitative genetics, were gradually re-established in the United States in the 1960s. Such work received enormous publicity with the publication of Arthur Jensen's

---

[24] For example, Francis Galton, R A Fisher, Karl Pearson and Cyril Burt.

article in the *Harvard Educational Review*, 'How far can we boost IQ and educational achievement?'[25] Jensen's own answer to his question was, in brief, 'very little', as he assumed that intellectual abilities were largely determined by genetic endowment. Jensen argued on the basis of estimates of heritability that difference in IQ scores generally found when comparing black and white groups were the result of genetic differences between the groups. He claimed, therefore, that they were unlikely to be able to be changed by environmental manipulations, such as the pre-school Head Start Programmes which at that time were being widely instituted in the US.

2.15 Despite the fact that Jensen's conclusions were criticised by many academics (although they did receive support from others such as Hans Eysenck in the UK), they have been very influential. Waters were further muddied because several prominent researchers in behavioural genetics involved in this research both in the US and Britain accepted support from overtly racist organisations. Critics argued that the inferences that Jensen drew from estimates of heritability were invalid and that his arguments involved a notion of genetic determinism that was unsupported by evidence. Recently, broadly similar arguments to Jensen's, which reach generally similar conclusions related to socioeconomic differences in the USA, have been put forward in *The Bell Curve*.[26] These, too, received wide international publicity and much criticism, but also support, from some social scientists, psychologists and geneticists.[27]

2.16 There continues to be a popular but mistaken belief that the level of heritability equates with the ease or difficulty of changing or altering a particular characteristic, or its immutability. However, researchers in behavioural genetics and psychologists would now agree that the ways in which different factors interrelate in the development of a characteristic are not related to its immutability. Environmental interventions, be they social, dietary, physiological or otherwise, can change the course of genetic diseases or, indeed, behavioural characteristics that are highly heritable. Conversely, there are numerous examples of social and cultural practices and behaviour that are very resistant to change.

Evolutionary psychology

2.17 In part as a reaction against the behaviourism of the 1950s and 1960s (paragraph 2.12), other approaches were developed that drew to a greater extent on biology. One example of this trend is evolutionary psychology. Evolutionary psychology takes its inspiration from the Darwinian theory of natural selection. A general aim is to see how current patterns of behaviour can be understood in terms of our evolutionary history. Where a particular pattern of behaviour is widespread and is seen across different cultures, it is often assumed that there will have been strong selection pressures favouring the development of that behaviour and so the selection of the particular genetic variants ('genes') responsible for its development. There is therefore a general inference about processes of development in the individual (ontogeny) from the presumed evolutionary process (phylogeny) that has led to the widespread occurrence of the behaviour pattern. Over the past two decades the principles of evolutionary psychology have been widely applied to the study of human behaviour. But evolutionary biology has always had its critics,

---

[25] Jensen, A. R. (1969). How much can we boost IQ and scholastic achievement? *Harvard Educ. Rev.* **39**, 1–123.

[26] Herrnstein, R. & Murray, L. (1994). *The Bell Curve: Intelligence and Class Structure in American Life*. New York: The Free Press.

[27] Devlin, B., Fienberg, S. E., Resnick, D. P. & Roeder, K., editors. (1997). *Intelligence, Genes and Success*. New York: Copernicus.

[28] Rose, H. & Rose, S. (2000). *Alas Poor Darwin: Arguments Against Evolutionary Psychology*. London: Cape.

particularly from the field of developmental biology.[28] One criticism they make is that there is no necessary connection between a possible evolutionary explanation that suggests that selection pressures may have influenced a pattern of behaviour in the past, and the processes of development that lead an individual to behave in a particular way in a particular situation.

Processes of development

2.18 There are of course many other approaches within developmental psychology which attempt, in various ways, to understand the processes of development of behaviour in individuals and to isolate factors which have significant effects. Given the complexity of the processes involved, it is perhaps not surprising that no theory of development is generally accepted. While most developmental psychologists believe that nature and nurture are both involved in the development of behavioural characteristics, there is an increasing move towards a variety of theoretical positions that do not use this conceptual dichotomy.

Conclusion

2.19 Behavioural genetics was established in the era of eugenic policies and practices; indeed, it formed a major part of the scientific foundations on which these policies were claimed to be based and the development of behavioural genetics was itself shaped by eugenic concerns. However, this does not necessarily imply that contemporary research on the genetics of behaviour is in any sense eugenic or is driven by considerations that could be considered eugenic. In fact, as we have pointed out, part of the reason for the decline in the support of eugenic policies in many countries from the 1930s onwards was scientific research which demonstrated that the policies of segregation and sterilisation of those deemed to be unfit would not achieve their stated goals. However, as a number of respondents to our consultation have suggested, there remains a view that research on the genetics of human behaviour, particularly in the area of intelligence, is necessarily eugenic or will lead to the re-establishment of eugenic policies. It is possible that contemporary understanding of the heritability of IQ and other behavioural characteristics, and increasing knowledge of the processes of inheritance of other traits, could provide a scientific foundation for a programme of positive or negative eugenics, were there to be the political will or power to construct and implement such a policy.

2.20 We conclude that historical and philosophical studies of eugenic practices and policies should be encouraged so that it may be clearly understood what was, and was not, unacceptable about the past and the ways in which this may, or may not, be distinguished from contemporary genetic policies and practices.

Section 2

Scientific background

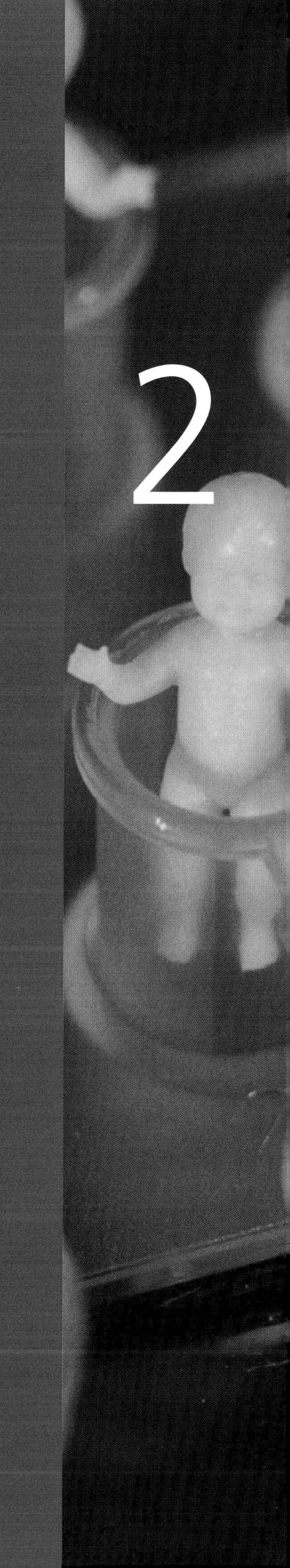

Chapter 3

Research in behavioural genetics

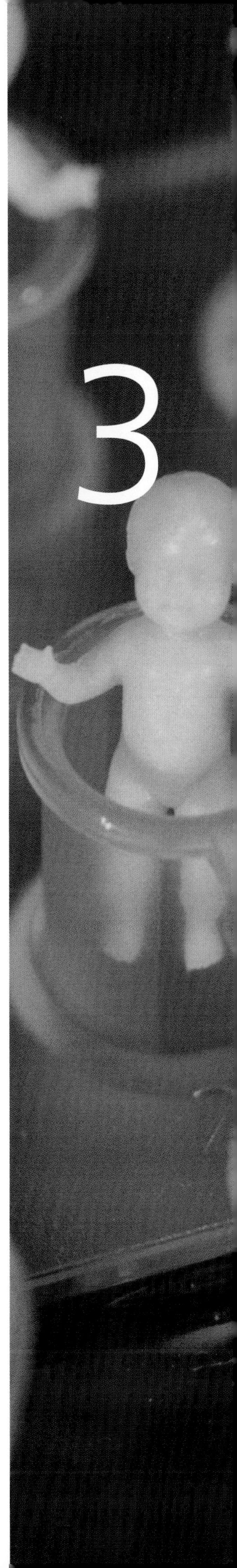

Research in behavioural genetics

Introduction

3.1 There are different ways in which researchers can study the contribution that genetic factors make to human behaviour. First, there are observational studies, which involve assessing and comparing relatives such as twins or siblings, families and adopted children. This type of research is called quantitative genetics because it aims to examine the extent to which variation in a trait is influenced by genetic factors in a population. It uses statistical methods to examine and compare groups of people, without focusing on particular genes. More detail about research in quantitative genetics is provided in Chapter 4. Secondly, researchers can try to identify differences in genes that contribute to trait variation in characteristics or traits between individuals. This type of research is called molecular genetics and its application to behavioural research is explained in Chapter 5. Thirdly, researchers can use animals to try and examine the effects of particular genes on behaviour. Chapter 6 describes this type of research. The focus of research in behavioural genetics is summarised in Box 3.1.

Box 3.1: What does research in behavioural genetics study?

Research in behavioural genetics examines the effects of genotype and environment on a range of phenotypic traits such as anxiety, intelligence, sexual orientation and antisocial behaviour.

Genotype

An individual's genotype is his or her entire complement of DNA.

Phenotype

An individual's phenotype consists of all his or her measurable or observable properties and characteristics aside from his or her genes. These could include characteristics such as hair colour, height and IQ score. Researchers in behavioural genetics often include such diverse traits as marital status, taste in music and religious beliefs as part of the phenotype.

Environment

An individual's environment is to be understood very broadly. It includes everything that influences an individual's phenotype, apart from his or her genotype. Environmental factors include where a person lives and how many siblings he or she has, but also biological factors such as to which chemicals a person might have been exposed to before and after birth.

3.2 Before examining the various types of research and their advantages and limitations, it is important to have a clear understanding of what is meant by the suggestion that genes influence, affect or contribute to human behaviour. The remainder of this chapter attempts to do this by addressing the following questions:

- What are genes and how do they work? (See Box 3.2).
- What is genetic variation?
- What do we mean by human behaviour in the normal range?
- How might genes influence human behaviour in the normal range?
- How could the behaviour of an individual be predicted from information about his or her genotype?

Box 3.2: How do genes work?

The human genome contains the genetic information required to build the human body. This information is held in code on tightly coiled threads of deoxyribonucleic acid (DNA). A DNA molecule consists of two strands that wrap round each other to resemble a twisted ladder – the famous double helix. Each strand of DNA is made up of a string of units called nucleotides, or bases. There are four different bases: adenine (A), thymine (T), guanine (G) and cytosine (C). These bases pair together – A with T, and C with G. Each base pair forms a rung of the ladder. The way these pair together causes the strands to coil up into the spiral twisted ladder (see Figure 3.1). It also allows the DNA to replicate, or copy itself.

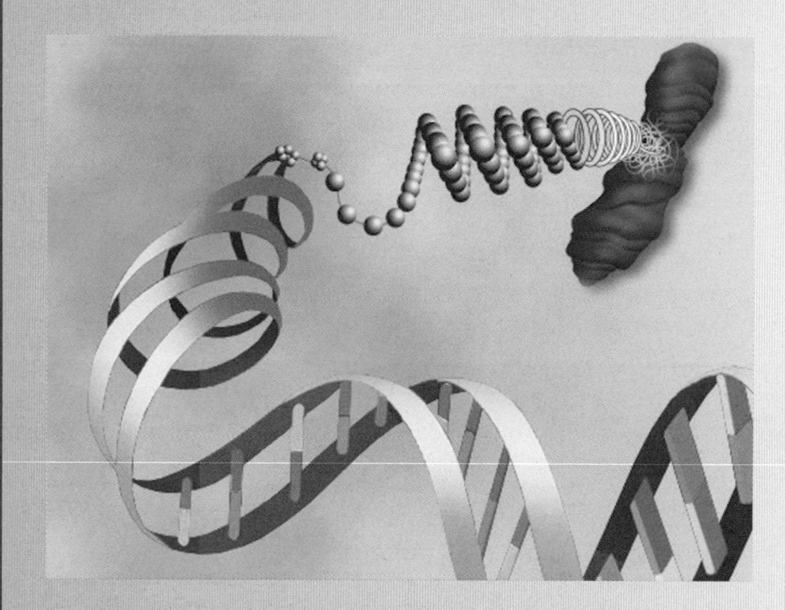

Figure 3.1:
The structure of DNA. The base pairs, A-T and C-G, form the rungs of the ladder.

A gene is a segment of DNA that contains the instructions for making a specific protein (or sometimes ribonucleic acid (RNA)). Each set of three base letters, for example ACG, is a code providing the instructions to assemble a protein. A gene may contain anything from a few hundred to over a million base pairs. Genes are assembled into chromosomes, long strands of DNA large enough to be seen down the microscope. A chromosome contains between a couple of hundred and several thousand genes, arranged in a specific order end-to-end, with sections of spacer DNA, which does not code for any genes, in between. Humans have 22 pairs of chromosomes plus the sex chromosomes (XX in the female, XY in the male). One set is from the mother and one from the father. Together, these 23 pairs make up the human genome. It is estimated that each human has about 30,000–40,000 genes, and around six billion base pairs of DNA.

Proteins carry out the work of a cell. They are made of various combinations of 20 chemical building blocks, called amino acids. The sequence of the gene determines the order that these blocks assemble together, and hence which protein is made (see Figure 3.2). Different proteins have different specialised functions, such as making muscle, binding oxygen from the air, transmitting nerve impulses, and breaking down food substances. Many proteins are enzymes, with the specialised function of synthesising, breaking down or altering other chemical molecules. Some of the products of genes, and some of the substances made by these products, are 'messengers' exported by cells to have effects on other cell types. For example, hormones are made in specialised endocrine glands, and can stimulate or suppress the functions of other cells in distant organs.

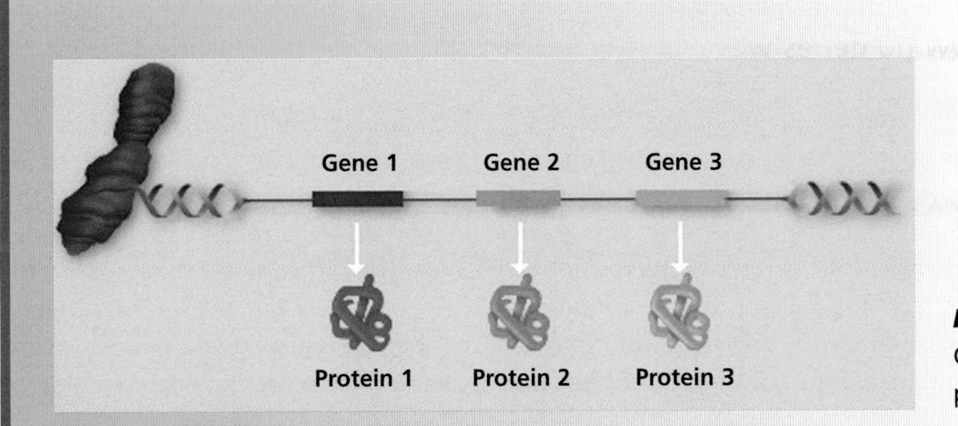

Figure 3.2: Genes make proteins

The human body consists of many different types of cell, each with a specialised function, for example skin cells and liver cells. These cells rely on different proteins to perform their specialised jobs. Nearly every cell in the body has the same genetic material. But what makes cells differ from each other is not which genes they have, but which genes are active in that cell. A protein, or part of a protein, is only produced when its corresponding gene is active. The production of proteins is also called gene expression. A gene is active when RNA, the intermediate between DNA and protein, is being synthesised. It is not yet completely understood what determines whether a gene is active or inactive, though the function of some genes is (through their encoded proteins) to turn other genes on and off. It is increasingly recognised that secondary modifications to the chemical structure of the original gene and its association with specific proteins are important factors in this process. The environment of the cell may influence these so-called epigenetic effects, which can be stably inherited through cell divisions and even through generations.[*,†]

* Pennisi, E. (2001). Behind the scenes of gene expression. *Science* **293**,1064–7. For an account of the complex etymology of the term 'epigenetics', see Wu, C.-T. & Morris, J. R. (2001). Genes, genetics, and epigenetics: a correspondence. *Science* **293**,1103–5.

† Images in this box are reprinted with permission from Roche Genetics. http://www.roche.com/pages/rgg/science-gengen-cdrom%5b2%5d+jpg_page1.html (11 June 2002).

What is genetic variation?

3.3 A comparison of the DNA sequence of corresponding chromosomes between two people chosen at random would show that the DNA sequences were almost, but not precisely, identical. On average, one in every 1,300 positions along the sequence will have different bases present at the corresponding positions. For example, some people might have an 'A' base whereas others have a 'G' base at a particular position. These two alternative possibilities are termed alleles. If the rarer of the two alleles is present in at least 1% of chromosomes in a population, it is termed a polymorphism. The simplest type of variation, where a single letter is substituted for another (as in the example above), is called a single nucleotide polymorphism (SNP). Continuing with this example, an individual's DNA sequence at a particular point could be AA, GG or AG, because the chromosomes occur in pairs. In the first two situations, the person is called a homozygote because both letters in the pair of chromosomes are the same. In the third, the person is called heterozygote because both the letters at this position are different. Most people are heterozygous at over 20 million different sites in their genome. Included in this total would be a significant proportion of SNPs, estimated to number about 11 million.[1]

3.4 Much of this variation occurs in the stretches of DNA situated between the genes and probably has no important effect on the organism. However, variation occurring near to, or within, genes could affect either the amount of protein made in a particular cell, or the sequence of amino acids in the protein. If this variation is found to correlate with a particular behaviour, or other trait, it is termed a susceptibility allele. The difficulty for the researcher is in sifting out, from the millions of polymorphisms in the human genome, the smaller number, possibly thousands, that actually contribute to variation between individuals, and which are presumed to underlie the contribution of genetic factors to differences between people.

3.5 Such 'genetic variation' arises in the first place because of damage to DNA or mistakes in copying DNA during replication. This process is called mutation. Mutation can occur in any cell, but is of particular concern when it affects eggs or sperm, as this allows the variant alleles to be passed on to future generations. However, new alleles that have major adverse effects will be eliminated rapidly from a population, because individuals carrying those alleles are less likely to reproduce. How, then, can particular alleles become common in the population and yet influence genetic susceptibility? Combinations of the following processes influence the frequency of alleles:

- *Age of onset of the trait.* An allele whose major effect occurs after the age of reproduction will be subject to very little selection because individuals carrying the allele will already have had the potential to transmit it to their offspring by the time that the effect becomes apparent.

- *Chance factors in the context of weak selection.* The rapid growth of the human population from relatively small numbers of individuals, and chance factors influencing reproductive success, could together enable mildly harmful alleles to reach a significant frequency in the population (this is termed genetic drift).

- *Strength of selection in relation to genotype.* Selection of an allele at the level of the population will be strong if the trait manifests in the heterozygote (dominance) but weaker if it manifests only in the homozygote (recessivity). A special case is when the heterozygous state has a survival benefit over either homozygote (this is termed heterozygote advantage).[2]

- *Different selection in different environments.* Alleles may be beneficial in some environmental circumstances and harmful in others. For example, they may protect from starvation but predispose to obesity. Environmental variation may then give rise to a balanced polymorphism between two alleles. Whether an allele is considered beneficial or harmful will depend on the context.

---

[1] Kruglyak, L. & Nickerson, D. A. (2001). Variation is the spice of life. *Nat. Genet.* **7**, 234–6. The remainder consists of single nucleotide variations present on less than 1% of chromosomes and other types of variation such as simple sequence repeats. The identification of these SNPs has been a significant focus of the Human Genome Project: already over 2.7 million are known (figure from dbSNP, available at: http://www.ncbi.nlm.nih.gov/SNP/snp_summary.cgi (3 July 2002)) and it is likely that virtually all these SNPs will be identified within the next few years.

[2] A well-known example is the sickle cell mutation of ß globin. The homozygous state ($ß^A/ß^A$) causes the blood disorder sickle cell anaemia, but the heterozygous state ($ß^S/ß^A$) protects against malaria and has a survival advantage over the normal ($ß^A/ß^A$) state in malaria-infested countries. The two alleles ($ß^A/ß^S$) are maintained in the population because their net effect is quite neutral. The deleterious effects become apparent in disease-based studies and beneficial effects may only be discovered later from population-based studies.

- *Pleiotropy*. Susceptibility alleles may affect different traits, which are subject to different selection pressures. For example, homozygosity for the ε2 allele of a blood protein called apolipoprotein E predisposes an individual to developing excessive fat levels in the blood, but also seems to protect the brain against the development of Alzheimer's disease.[3]

- *Genetic hitch-hiking*. When selection of an allele occurs, the adjacent segment of DNA is passively selected with it, only later becoming separated by rare recombinations.[4] This, and other factors, such as the mixing of populations, gives rise to linkage disequilibrium, which means that alleles may appear to be associated with variation in a phenotype without themselves causing that variation.

3.6 It is important to note that genetic variation in the normal range is usually neither good nor bad. Genetic variation causes people to have different natural hair colours or different blood groups, but this is not to say that a particular hair colour or blood group is 'better' than another. In the case of genetic mutations that cause diseases such as cystic fibrosis or Huntington's disease, it might be reasonable to say that these mutations are deleterious. With most forms of genetic variation, all one can say is that differences exist, not that they are deleterious or advantageous.[5]

What is meant by normal variation in human behaviour?

3.7 Many human traits are not viewed as either present or absent, but rather as continuously distributed measures which each individual in the population will show to a greater or lesser extent (for example, height, blood pressure, aggressiveness and intelligence, as measured by IQ test scores). These characteristics vary from person to person in a population and this variability is known as population variation. When the frequency of the effect is plotted against the magnitude, many of these continuously distributed characteristics show a bell-curve distribution that is known as a normal distribution (see Figure 3.3).

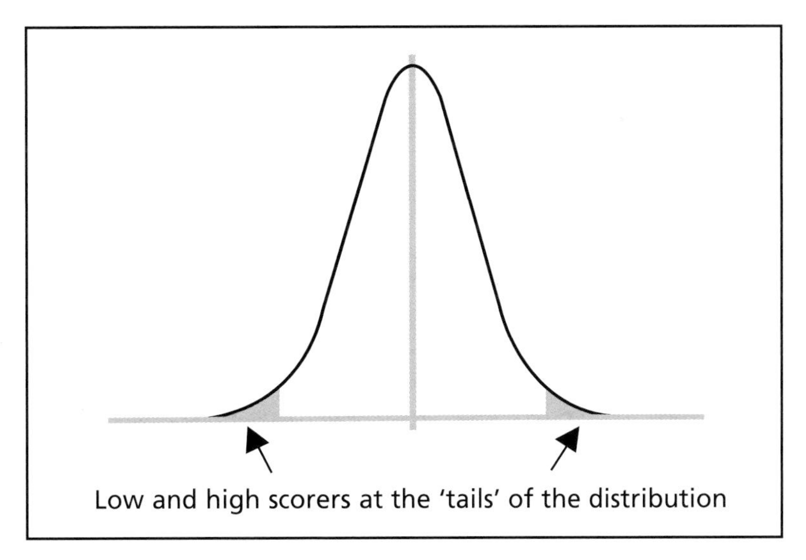

Figure 3.3: A normal distribution curve

[3] Scriver, C. R., Beaudet, A. L., Sly, W. S. & Valle, D. (2001). *The Metabolic and Molecular Base of Inherited Disease*. 8th ed. New York: McGraw-Hill. pp. 2835–62 and 5875–99.

[4] Recombination is the process by which chromosomes are broken and the fragments rejoined in new combinations, and is a vital aspect of reproduction and inheritance.

[5] Some traits that are genetically influenced may have both positive and negative aspects in an individual. For example, it has been hypothesised that people with manic depression are also more creative (for an exposition of this theory see Jamison, K. R. (1996). *Touched With Fire: Manic-Depressive Illness and the Artistic Temperament*. New York: The Free Press). Alternatively, the desirability of a trait may be perceived differently in different individuals. For example, high scores on the Psychoticism dimension of personality tests have been shown, in non-psychotic individuals, to be associated with high creativity.

3.8 Most individuals score somewhere in the middle of the population distribution, but a certain percentage will form the 'tails' of the distribution (i.e. very high or low scorers). Statisticians can quantify the 'spread' of scores in this distribution and this statistic is known as variance. Extremes of variation can be associated with an increased risk of adverse outcomes, for example high blood pressure is associated with an increased risk of a stroke, but they are not necessarily associated with illness. Such extremes might have a number of different explanations. In the case of high blood pressure, this could be due to excessive intake of salt in the diet, a combination of dietary and weak genetic factors, or a single mutation causing failure of the kidney to eliminate salt. In the field of behavioural traits, extreme scores for traits such as neuroticism or aggression may be associated with an increased risk of adverse outcomes such as mental illness.

'A gene for X'?

3.9 Having understood that there are differences in both the genotypes and the phenotypes of individuals, the next challenge is to understand how genetic variants might be related to the variations in behavioural and personality traits. It is common to hear of research that claims to identify a 'gene for aggression' or a 'gene for homosexuality'. But how could our genes *cause* us to act in a particular way? What is really meant by saying 'a gene for X'?

3.10 We all have a working knowledge of the system of causal relations that enables each of us to function in our complex world. The accumulation of this knowledge begins early in life. Once a child reaches a certain age he will push an object off the tray of his high chair and observe it falling to the floor. On discovering the effects of gravity, he will repeat the experiment over and over again to test the discovery beyond all reasonable doubt. Unfortunately, the concepts of causation that are established early in life are too rudimentary to serve well as the basis for scientific theories.

3.11 A useful way to understand what is meant by a *cause* is to think of it as a factor that increases the chance that an event occurs. So, when the child pushes its toy off its highchair, various factors combine to make the toy fall to the floor, including the movement and force of the child's hand, the weight of the toy and the effect of gravity. Together, these factors make it extremely likely that the toy will fall on the floor: they raise the chance of this happening to a very high degree. It is easy to assume that there is a one-to-one correspondence between cause and effect; that one cause leads to one effect. However, as the example of the child's toy shows, there are usually a number of causal factors that come together to make certain events more likely. These two points, the existence of more than one causal factor in a particular situation, and the idea that causes raise the chance of something happening without necessarily making that outcome inevitable or 100% likely to occur, are important in understanding how genetic factors can influence behaviour.

3.12 There are some genetic mutations that do seem always to be present when disease occurs, such as the genetic mutations that are associated with cystic fibrosis and Huntington's disease. In these diseases, an alteration in a particular gene can be said to have caused the disorder. Without the genetic mutation, the individual would not have the disorder, which means that the genetic mutation is a necessary condition for that disorder. In addition, for a very small subgroup of single-gene disorders, for example Duchenne's muscular dystrophy, the genetic mutation is also a sufficient condition: just possessing the mutation makes it certain that you will have the disorder. However, it is worth noting that even in apparently clear cases, the connection between the gene alteration and the disorder is not simple. With Huntington's disease, once the mutated gene is identified in an individual, all one can say is that the disorder will appear. Knowledge of the genetic mutation does not enable one to say how serious the disease will be for a particular individual, the precise symptoms they will experience, or exactly when it will arise in their lifetime.

3.13 Diseases in which there is a clear connection between a particular genetic mutation and a disorder are comparatively rare. Most disorders, such as breast cancer, heart disease and diabetes, are much more complicated. Often, a genetic mutation or susceptibility allele will cause a disease only in the presence of certain environmental factors, such as stress or a particular diet. The relationship between genetic and environmental factors in causing disease can be illustrated by a disorder called alpha-1 antitrypsin deficiency. If an individual with this genetic disorder takes up smoking, he or she is much more likely to develop a form of a chronic lung disease called emphysema, because of a genetic mutation which prevents the production of a normal form of a protein in the lung that protects against inflammation. However, if the individual never smokes, it is probable that he or she will never develop emphysema and may be able to have a relatively healthy life.

3.14 The connection between genes and diseases is far from straightforward, and the relationship between genes and behaviour is even more complicated. It is often difficult to establish which genes contribute to a trait and how they do so because:

- More than one genetic factor usually contributes to a particular trait.
- These multiple genetic factors may interact with each other and have different effects depending on which other factors are present in the individual's genotype.
- As well as genetic factors, many non-genetic (environmental) factors may contribute to the manifestation of a trait.
- These environmental factors may also interact with each other.
- The genetic factors may affect which environmental factors have an effect. (This is called gene–environment interaction: see Box 3.3).
- Conversely, environmental factors may affect which genetic factors have an effect.
- Certain genetic and environmental factors may go hand in hand. (This is called gene–environment correlation: see Box 3.3).
- A protein may be modified after it has been produced from a gene, and this can alter its function.
- Genes do not have a continuous effect in our bodies. They may be turned on and off, both during our overall development and within the lifetime of an individual cell.

So, while it might be correct to say that a particular genetic variant is part of the cause of a particular trait, or that it is one causal factor, it will seldom be the only cause, nor is it likely to be either a necessary or sufficient condition for the trait to be manifested. Furthermore, even if particular genes that contribute to a trait can be identified, this is only a small part of the story. There is still a need to understand the very indirect pathway between a gene, a particular protein and an individual scoring highly on an IQ test or having an aggressive personality. Our understanding of these causal pathways is at an even earlier stage than our understanding of which genes influence behavioural traits, which is itself extremely limited.[6]

3.15 In an effort to overcome this difficulty, some research focuses on 'intermediate' traits that are related to the phenotype in question but are in some sense 'nearer' the biological mechanisms and can be more objectively measured.[7] For example, in research on cognitive ability, such intermediate traits may include electrophysiological measures of brain function, behavioural measures of the speed at which information is processed or behavioural measures of the capacity of working memory in an individual (such as performance on tasks of verbal and spatio-visual working memory).[8]

Box 3.3: The relationship between genes and the environment

Gene–environment correlation

It is sometimes assumed that genetic and environmental influences act independently and additively: that separate influences add up in a linear manner to make a given outcome more likely. However, genes and environmental factors can be correlated, or interdependent. Children not only inherit genes from their parents but are also exposed to environments that are influenced by their own and their parents' genetic make-up. Thus, for example, sociable parents not only pass on genes to their children but may also provide an environment that encourages the development of sociability in their children. This is known as passive gene–environment correlation. A sociable child may actively seek out situations that serve to further increase sociability (active gene–environment correlation) or evoke responses from others that increase sociability. In both cases, the existence of the genetic variant is linked to the presence of a particular type of environment.

Gene–environment interaction

Genetic and environmental factors may interact non-additively to influence characteristics. That is, the impact of environmental factors may differ depending on a person's genetic makeup. For factors that are correlated, detecting interaction using statistical methods can be difficult. Large samples are needed. Nevertheless, studies of twins have shown that the impact of life events on, for example, depression varies depending on an individual's genetic susceptibility.*

* Kendler, K. S. et al. (1995). Stressful life events, genetic liability and onset of an episode of major depression in women. *Am. J. Psychiat.* **152**, 833–42; Silberg, J., Rutter, M., Neale, M. & Eaves, L. (2001). Genetic moderation of environment risk for depression and anxiety in adolescent girls. *Brit. J. Psychiat.* **179**, 116–21. See also Kendler, K. S. (2001). Twin studies of psychiatric illness: an update. *Arch. Gen. Psychiatr* **58**, 1005–14 for a review of gene–environment interaction in research in behavioural genetics.

[6] Rutter, M. & Silberg, J. (2002). Gene–environment interplay in relation to emotional and behavioural disturbance. *An. Rev. Psychol.* **53**, 463–90.

[7] These intermediate traits are sometimes called endophenotypes.

[8] See for example, de Geus, E. J., Wright, M. J., Martin, N. G. & Boomsma, D.I. (2001). Genetics of brain function and cognition. *Behav. Genet.* **31,** 489–95.

Describing human behaviour

3.16 Any description of a human action can be set at a level that includes information about the biological characteristics of the individual. For example, the following descriptions could all correctly refer to the same act:

- The man's brain sent messages to his leg muscles.
- The man's leg muscles contracted and then relaxed.
- The man moved his leg.
- The man kicked the dog.

3.17 Thus, it could be said that the movement of the man's muscles caused him to kick the dog, or that the movement of his leg caused him to kick the dog. If one broadens a description far enough, it will certainly include information about the physiological characteristics of the individual, since these will be involved in any human action. The important question is: which way of describing or understanding the act is the most useful? If genetic factors are one aspect of causal explanations of human behaviour, what importance should be accorded to them? The answer is likely to depend on what use the questioner wants to make of the information:

> 'It is a well known fact that we describe as the cause of an event that particular condition by which we hope to control it.'[9]

In the example above, if one wants to admonish the man for kicking the dog, an explanation at the neural or physiological level is unlikely to be relevant. We return to this important issue in the last section of this Report, in the context of moral and legal responsibility.

Predicting human behaviour from genetic information

3.18 Even if it is not known precisely how a genetic variant contributes to a behavioural trait, it might be possible to predict how likely it is that individuals with that genetic variant will display the trait in question. Here, it is important to differentiate between predicting the future development of a phenotypic trait or specific behaviour, and measuring a phenotypic trait that is already established in an individual and can be observed. For example, if there were a genetic variant, or group of genetic variants, known to be associated with lower or higher intelligence, it would be possible to measure the genotype of a baby and to make some prediction of the IQ that the baby will have as an adult. Alternatively, measuring that genotype in an adult might enable the current IQ of the adult to be estimated. A third scenario for the predictive use of genetic information would be to predict the likelihood of the future occurrence of a specific act linked to a behavioural trait, for example an act of aggression.[10]

3.19 However, in whatever context the term prediction is being used, it is highly unlikely that individual genetic variants will often be accurate predictors of behavioural traits. It is not

[9] Barton Perry, R. (1926). *General Theory of Value*. Cambridge, MA: Harvard University Press. p. 394.

[10] It is pertinent to note here that non-genetic influences are often used in attempts to predict behaviour, for example correlations between family environment and antisocial behaviour. These are discussed further in Chapter 14.

known how many genes will account for the genetic influence on a trait that is normally distributed, even if that genetic influence appears to be substantial. Behavioural traits are complex, and are likely to be the result of the expression of many different genes, which interact with each other and with the environment. No single gene is likely to account for more than a small proportion of the total variance of a given trait. Furthermore, even if it were possible to identify all the genes that contribute to the heritable component of the trait, the predictive power would still be very limited. In view of existing evidence from studies of monozygotic (MZ) twins, it appears that such genetic predictions of behavioural traits might be able to account for at most 50% of the variance (see the reviews of the evidence in Chapters 7–10 for details of particular studies). This would still leave at least half the variance in trait scores unpredictable. Whether this environmental portion of the variance will become predictable depends upon future advances in understanding which variables give rise to environmental variance. This is as yet virtually unexplored territory.

Conclusion

3.20 The complexity of human behaviour and the difficulties in understanding how genes are involved may seem overwhelming. There is wide agreement that genes do have an indirect effect on behaviour. However, some commentators have suggested that any attempt to understand the processes by which genes influence behaviour will certainly fail. We disagree. We consider that it is neither a theoretical nor a practical impossibility to identify genes that contribute to behavioural traits and to understand some of the mechanisms by which they do so. However, we note that terminology such as 'a gene for X' or 'a set of genes for X' is very misleading because it fails to convey the complexity of the role of genetic factors in causal explanations of human behaviour. Genes determine which proteins are made. They do not determine which behavioural or personality traits an individual possesses. Furthermore, the product of an individual gene will only very rarely be directly related to a complex behavioural characteristic. It will normally interact with many other genes and with many non-genetic factors, which means that the predictive capabilities of tests for any single or small number of genes will in general probably be quite limited. Nonetheless, the proteins that genes make and the way these affect our bodies and brains will be one part of an explanation of human behaviour.

Chapter 4

Quantitative genetics: measuring heritability

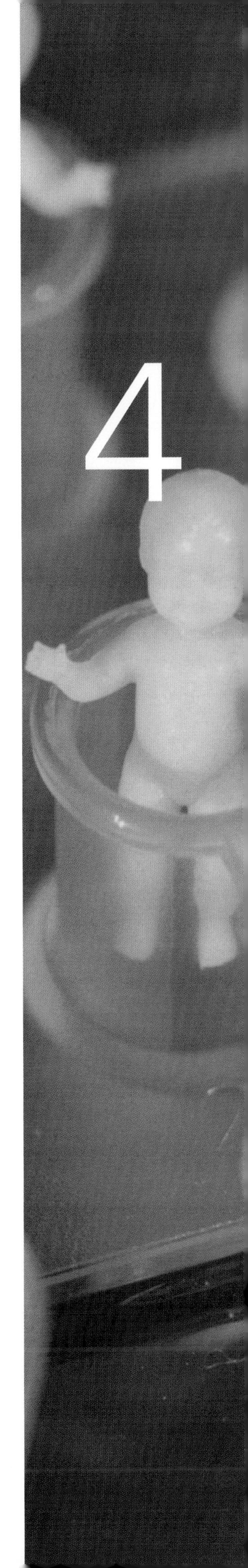

Quantitative genetics: measuring heritability

Introduction

4.1 The field of quantitative genetics originated around 1920, following statistical demonstrations that traits which are normally distributed can arise from the action of multiple genes, each with relatively small effects (either increasing or decreasing the value of the trait).[1] Various complex statistical techniques are employed in such research. In this chapter, we explain the concept of heritability, but do not provide a detailed account of the statistical methods.[2] We then go on to describe the three ways in which data about human behaviour are obtained in this field of research, namely twin, adoption and family studies.

How is population variation examined using genetic studies?

4.2 Influences on the total population variation that is observed for a particular characteristic can be subdivided into different components:

- Genetic influences
- Environmental influences
- Gene–environment correlation (see Box 3.3)
- Gene–environment interaction (see Box 3.3)

The following paragraphs 4.3 – 4.12 explain how these factors are accounted for, statistically, in quantitative research.

Genetic influences on variation

4.3 Quantitative research techniques can be used to estimate the influence of unspecified genetic factors on behaviour. This is done by using a statistical concept called 'heritability', which was first derived by plant breeders to help them reproduce desirable characteristics in agricultural products such as corn and wheat. It is a complicated concept that can be used in various ways. It is frequently misinterpreted by scientists and other commentators on research in behavioural genetics.[3]

4.4 There is a common sense notion of heritability or inheritance that is concerned with the extent to which particular characteristics in an individual are the result of what one inherits (nature), the environment and world one grows up in (nurture) or some combination of these two (see paragraph 2.10). Most developmental psychologists adopt a perspective of 'interactionism' – a process of development involving both factors. In the context of research in behavioural genetics, however, heritability has a more precise statistical definition. This defines heritability as a statistical ratio that, for a given quantitative character and against a fixed environmental background, estimates the proportion of the observational differences in that characteristic across a population that can be attributed

---

1 See paragraphs 2.10-2.11

2 For further information in this area, see: Carey, G. (2002). *Human Genetics for the Social Sciences*. London: Sage Publications; Plomin, R., DeFries, J. C., McClearn, G. E. & McGuffin, P. (2000). *Behavioral Genetics*. 4th ed. New York: Worth.

3 For a very clear discussion of concepts of heritability, see Daniels, M., Devlin, B. & Roeder, K. Of genes and IQ. In Devlin, B. *et al.* (1997). *Intelligence, Genes and Success*. New York: Copernicus.

to genetic influences. It is a statistic that refers solely to a group of individuals and does not concern the process of development in the individual.

4.5 Estimates of heritability may be divided into two types, which depend on the way in which variation within a population is accounted for. There are four aspects of variation: additive genetic variance, variance due to genetic interaction (epistasis), variance due to interaction between alleles (dominance), and variance due to environmental causes. Narrow-sense heritability is defined as the proportion of variance that can be attributed to transmissible genetic factors. Narrow-sense heritability measures the part of variance attributable in a population to the additive effect of genes, independently of interaction effects between alleles, between loci and between the genetic make-up and the environment. This provides a statistical estimate to answer the question that an animal or plant breeder will ask: if selective breeding is applied for a particular characteristic, will it work?

4.6 There is a different concept of heritability, which is also used in research in behavioural genetics that examines human populations, known as broad-sense heritability. This deals with the total variance due to genetic differences, whatever their origin (additive or interactive). Heritability in the broad-sense does not yield a figure that is predictive and therefore helpful to a breeder of plants or animals. Nor, of course, does it answer the common sense question about the extent to which genetic factors and environmental factors influence the development of characteristics in an individual. The estimate of heritability most commonly used in research studies is narrow-sense heritability, which accounts only for additive genetic variance. (All figures for heritability quoted in this Report are narrow-sense values, unless stated otherwise).

4.7 It is vital to understand that neither concept of heritability allows us to conclude anything about the role of heredity in the development of a characteristic in an individual. Heritability refers to the proportion of variation in the population attributable to genetic influences. Thus, for example, an estimate of heritability of 0.60 does *not* mean that 60% of a particular person's trait is explained by their genes. What it does mean, is that in a given population that varies for a particular trait, 60% of that variation *across the whole population* is the result of differences in their genotypes. As heritability is a proportion of the total variance, the estimate will vary depending on the variation in the population of genetic and environmental factors. For example, if there is a population of individuals who are genetically identical for all relevant genes contributing to a given trait (that is, they all carry the same alleles for those genes; clearly a hypothetical situation), the narrow-sense heritability for the phenotypic characteristic related to those genes would be zero, because any differences must, by definition, be attributed to environmental factors.

4.8 It is important to distinguish heritability from genetic determination. Novel environmental changes might have dramatic consequences on a phenotype. A standard example is height. The heritability of height in most populations is probably over 0.90, that is to say, 90% of variation in height in most human populations can be attributed to genetic factors.[4] But the

---

[4] See for example, Phillips, K. & Matheny, A. P., Jr. (1990). Quantitative genetic analysis of longitudinal trends in height: preliminary results from the Louisville Twin Study. *Acta Genet. Med. Gemellol. (Roma)* **39**: 1,143–63; Carmichael, C. M. & McGue, M. (1995). A cross-sectional examination of height, weight, and body mass index in adult twins. *J. Gerontol. A Biol. Sci. Med. Sci.* **50**, 237–44; Preece, M. A. (1996). The genetic contribution to stature. *Horm. Res.* **45 Suppl 2**, 56–8; Silventoinen, K., Kaprio, J., Lahelma, E. & Koskenvuo, M. (2000). Relative effect of genetic and environmental factors on body height: differences across birth cohorts among Finnish men and women. *Am. J. Public Health* **90**, 627–30.

average height of most Western populations increased by 1.0 cm per decade between 1920 and 1970, even though the genes in those populations could not have changed substantially. In large outbred populations, any noticeable change in the frequency of particular genes will take many centuries. The example is apposite, because a similar increase in IQ test scores also occurred throughout most of the twentieth century in most industrialised countries. At different times and places, this increase ranged from 0.3 to 10 IQ points per decade. However high the heritability of IQ might be, and it is certainly not as high as 0.90, environmental changes can potentially have a substantial impact.[5] It is worth noting that any society that succeeds in reducing differences in the environments experienced by different members of that society, for example, by improving education services in deprived areas, will probably increase the heritability of their characteristics – in this case, intelligence.

Environmental influences on variation

4.9 Environmental variance includes a proportion of variance that can be explained by shared or common environmental influences and a remaining proportion accounted for by non-shared environmental factors, random effects and error. The terms 'shared' and 'non-shared' environment refer to the effects of the environmental influence, not their origins (as previously assumed by many researchers); that is whether they increase or decrease similarity between family members for a given characteristic. For example, social disadvantage is an environmental factor to which all family members are exposed. However, its effects on a particular behaviour may appear as 'non-shared' in genetic analyses if social disadvantage has a different effect on each individual within the family; that is, if its effect is to enhance differences between family members. The categories of shared and non-shared environmental influences are statistical notions and each category contains many unidentified factors that are not necessarily specifically investigated in a quantitative research project.

4.10 Many studies in this field have reported that the proportion of variation in behavioural traits that can be attributed to factors shared by family members is relatively low. These findings have been used to claim that an individual's shared environment, particularly the family, has little effect on his or her behaviour.[6] Interestingly, an exception to this finding is in the case of antisocial behaviour. Significant effects of shared environments are routinely reported in research in behavioural genetics in this area. Moreover, many researchers have now rejected the conclusion that the role of the family in affecting behaviour is unimportant.[7]

Gene–environment correlation and interaction

4.11 In most studies in behavioural genetics, the effects of gene–environment correlation and gene–environment interaction cannot be estimated separately and are included within the estimate of heritability. This means that even when a trait is highly heritable, environmental influences may still be important in mediating the effects of the genes on behaviour. For example, in the case of gene–environment correlation, if exposure to friendly company were correlated with a person's genotype, sociability could be found to be heritable even though it may have arisen as a result of increased exposure to company.

---

[5] See Chapter 7.

[6] An influential book arguing that parenting does not matter is Harris, J. R. (1998). *The Nurture Assumption*. New York: The Free Press.

[7] Rutter, M. & Silberg, J. (2002). Gene-environment interplay in relation to emotional and behavioral disturbance. *An. Rev. Psychol.* **53**, 463–90.

4.12 Since estimates of heritability in traditional studies in quantitative genetics might be due not just to the direct effect of genes, but also to the indirect effects of environmental factors that correlate with genes and that have an effect contingent on genotype, they are likely to overestimate the contribution of genetic factors to variation. Because of the complex relationship between genetic and environmental factors, it can be difficult for statistical approaches to model them accurately, meaning that the many complicated relationships that may exist between genetic and environmental factors are often over-simplified.

Family, twin and adoption studies

4.13 Family, twin and adoption studies are used to examine the contribution of genetic and environmental influences on traits and disorders. Each of these methods has its own merits and disadvantages, but as for all research, consistent findings from different types of studies allow for greater confidence in drawing conclusions.

Family studies

4.14 Family studies are designed to examine whether the chance of having a particular characteristic is increased in the relatives of those who are have the characteristic, compared to the relatives of those who do not. An increased incidence in relatives of affected individuals indicates that the trait is familial, that is, that it appears to run in families. For continuously distributed characteristics, rather than calculating relative risks, researchers estimate the similarity of biological relatives in families for these traits by calculating a correlation coefficient. A correlation of zero indicates no similarity and a positive correlation indicates similarity between relatives. Total similarity would result in a maximum correlation of 1. A significant positive correlation suggests that the trait is familial (but not necessarily genetic).

4.15 Family studies of behavioural characteristics such as personality, IQ test scores and childhood behaviours have consistently shown that family members are more similar to each other than unrelated individuals. It is also clear from family studies that these sorts of characteristics show a complex pattern of inheritance (such that they are sometimes termed complex traits), which suggests that they are influenced by a number of different genes in combination with environmental influences. That a characteristic is common to family members could be due either to genes that relatives share, or to environmental factors that impact on all family members in a way that makes them more similar. Thus, findings from family studies alone do not provide conclusive evidence of a genetic contribution. Twin and adoption studies allow us to disentangle, to some extent, the effects of genes and shared environmental factors.

Studies of twins

Methods

4.16 Monozygotic (MZ) twins come from the same fertilised egg and are genetically identical, that is, they have 100% of their genes in common. Non-identical or dizygotic (DZ) twins, like other siblings, share, on average, 50% of their genes. A greater similarity or correlation between MZ twins than DZ twins indicates a genetic influence. Studies of twins allow researchers to examine what proportion of the total phenotypic variance is explained by genetic factors, shared environmental factors and non-shared environmental factors.

4.17 Studies of twins are based on a number of assumptions. One is that pairs of MZ and DZ twins experience very similar environments. This assumption, called the equal environments assumption, has been criticised. Indeed, there is evidence that MZ twins do experience a more similar environment than DZ twins. In most studies, it is assumed that the equal environments assumption is correct when the degree to which twins share an environment has been measured by questionnaire, but these measures do not necessarily include the relevant environmental factors. There is increasing evidence that many environmental factors that are relevant for behaviour are more often shared by MZ twins than DZ twins.[8] Studies of twins also ignore the possible role of prenatal environment. Whether subsequently separated or not, twins, unlike other siblings, have shared the same prenatal environment at the same time.[9]

4.18 Another criticism is that findings in twins may not be so easily extrapolated to non-twins (singletons). Twins experience greater intrauterine and perinatal adversity, and the experience of being brought up as a twin is unusual. However, twins do not appear to differ markedly from singletons for most types of characteristics, other than in showing delays in the acquisition of language.

4.19 Despite the fact that MZ twins share the same genome, they are never truly identical. They differ in behaviour and physique as well as in intellectual abilities and personality traits. Some of these differences will be due to random or chance effects, others due to environmental influences that are not shared by the twins. However, although the assumption is made that MZ twins are genetically identical, the process of MZ twinning is complex and it is now known that there are various biological mechanisms that can lead to genetic differences between them.

4.20 Overall, although there are criticisms of the twin method, these are not sufficient to cast doubt on the usefulness of this study design. Nevertheless, there are clearly good reasons to use a variety of research strategies in examining the contribution of genetic and environmental influences to behaviour before drawing conclusions.

Interpretation of twin study findings

4.21 Studies involving a large number of pairs of twins can be useful in providing basic information about what sorts of factors influence variation in a trait, and in refining definitions of characteristics. Studies of twins are increasingly being used to assess the contribution of environmental factors and to examine the pathways mediating the effects of environmental factors on behavioural traits. This type of design has also been used to examine the overlap of different traits (for example, studies of twins suggest that common genetic factors influence both anxiety and depressive symptoms), and in examining the underlying influences on normal variation compared with extremes. Caution, however, is also needed to avoid over-interpreting the meaning of heritability. There is a considerable literature discussing these concerns and we highlight two key areas:

---

[8] Rutter, M., Pickles, A., Murray, R. & Eaves, L. (2001). Testing hypotheses on specific environmental causal effects on behavior. *Psychol. Bull.* **127**, 291–324.

[9] There is another potentially important difference in the prenatal environments of twins. All DZ twins, and some MZ twins, are surrounded by different sacs or chorions in the uterus. But some MZ twins are monochorionic: they share the same chorion. If monochorionic MZ twins experience a more similar prenatal environment than dichorionic twins, this might explain why MZ twins as a group resemble one another more closely than DZ twins. The possibility is open to a simple test: dichorionic MZ twins should resemble one another less than monochorionic MZ twins, and no more than DZ twins. However, studies that have focused on these different types of twin do not yet provide conclusive evidence either way.

- *Studies of twins focus on populations, not individuals*
  Studies of twins have revealed that variation in many different characteristics is heritable. Estimates of heritability and the proportion of variance attributable to environmental factors only refer to the population studied. Thus, for example, many studies of twins have used representative twins born within a defined geographical area, in general a sound strategy. However, findings will refer to the population studied and may not generalise to other groups, for example, to those exposed to severe adversity or from different age and ethnic groups.

- *Extremes versus normal variation*
  In population-based samples of twins, most participants do not show extreme scores. The origins of severe or extreme behaviours may be different from those for characteristics within the normal range and thus the estimates of heritability and environmental variance obtained from twin study samples may not necessarily apply to groups of extremely high or low scorers. However, a type of statistical analysis known as 'extremes analysis'[10] allows for the testing of whether the relative contribution of genes and environment for extremely high or extremely low scores differs from that for variation across the normal range. For example, it may be that genetic factors influence normal variation in a trait, but that environmental factors are more important for extremes. This type of analysis has suggested that the magnitude of genetic and environmental influences on high levels of overactivity and inattention in children appears to be no different from that on 'normal variation' in these types of symptoms.[11] However, very large sample sizes are needed to pick up differences between normal variation and extremes.

Adoption studies

4.22 Adoption studies involve studying the biological and adoptive relatives of individuals who have been adopted. If individuals who are genetically related (biological relatives) are more similar for a particular characteristic than adoptive relatives, this suggests that genetic factors influence that trait. If relatives who are genetically unrelated are more similar for that trait, this is suggestive of a contribution from environmental factors. Adoption studies provide a powerful means of examining genetic and environmental influences and investigating gene–environment interaction. However, two difficulties with such studies are that adoptees are not placed randomly into adoptive families (they tend to be chosen to provide environments that are low-risk), and adoption is an unusual event in itself.

4.23 For traits such as intelligence, personality and antisocial behaviour, adoption studies have added to evidence from studies of twins in demonstrating a genetic contribution to variation. Adoption studies have also demonstrated important effects of gene–environment correlation. For example, adoption studies have found that the adoptive parents of children who are thought to be at increased risk of antisocial behaviour because their biological parents show similar behavioural traits, display

[10] DeFries, J. C. & Fulker, D. W. (1988). Multiple regression analysis of twin data: etiology of deviant scores versus individual differences. *Acta Genet. Med. Gemellol. (Roma)* **37**, 205–16.

[11] Stevenson, J. (1992). Evidence for a genetic etiology in hyperactivity in children. *Behav. Genet.* **22**, 337–44.

increased negative parenting.[12] This is thought to provide a demonstration of how an environmental factor (negative parent response) may be influenced by the characteristics of the child and illustrates the complexity of the relationship between genetic and environmental factors.

4.24 Adoption studies have also shown that genes and environment can have an interactive influence; that is the effects of environmental adversity are much more marked when there is also genetic susceptibility. For example, analysis of data from three adoption studies showed significant increased adolescent antisocial behaviour in adoptees when they were both at increased genetic risk and then exposed to an adverse environment. This increased risk was significantly greater than the effects of genetic and environmental factors acting alone.[13]

Current uses of quantitative genetic studies

4.25 Quantitative genetic research is traditionally regarded as a way of examining whether or not a particular disorder or characteristic is genetically influenced. Since virtually every human characteristic is genetically influenced to some extent, attention is turning to using quantitative research to answer other questions. So why do researchers still conduct studies that involve estimates of heritability? The objective of family, twin and adoption studies is now much broader than simply examining whether genes influence a particular trait. These methods are now used to examine a much wider range of issues that are clinically and scientifically relevant, such as:

- *Examining the contribution of psychosocial factors.* For example, examining to what extent parenting factors might increase the risk of behavioural problems, even when genetic influences are taken into account.

- *Examining how psychosocial/environmental influences moderate genetic effects.* For example, as mentioned earlier (Box 3.3), studies of twins have shown that the impact of life events on depression varies depending on genetic susceptibility.

- *Examining why two traits may go hand in hand.* This type of analysis has shown that anxiety and depression often occur together and are influenced by the same set of genes.

- *Examining the relationship between symptoms within the normal range and extremes.* This type of work has shown that some traits (for example, Attention Deficit Hyperactivity Disorder symptoms) lie along a continuum, with similar genetic effects on high scores and on symptoms within the normal range. Findings for other traits have been different. For example, the relative contribution of genes and environment to variation in IQ scores appears to differ for very low IQ scores compared to scores in the normal range.

---

[12] Ge, X. *et al.* (1996). The developmental interface between nature and nurture: A mutual influence model of child antisocial behaviour and parenting. *Dev. Psychol.* **32**, 574–89; O'Connor, T. G., Deater-Deckard, K., Fulker, D., Rutter, M. & Plomin, R. (1998). Genotype–environment correlations in late childhood and early adolescence: Antisocial behavioural problems and coercive parenting. *Dev. Psychol.* **34**, 970–81.

[13] Cadoret, R. J., Cain, C. A. & Crowe, R. R. (1983). Evidence for gene-environment interaction in the development of adolescent antisocial behavior. *Behav. Genet.* **13**, 301–10.

Conclusion

4.26 In summary, family, twin and adoption study designs each have different strengths and weaknesses. It is important to recognise the limitations of any type of study design, to maintain a critical approach to interpreting findings and to avoid over-interpretation (see Box 4.1). Nevertheless, when findings from different studies are consistent, research in quantitative genetics provides a useful method for studying the factors that influence different human characteristics.

Box 4.1: Central points regarding research in quantitative genetics

- Quantitative genetics involves statistical methods that attempt to distinguish the effects of genetic and environmental factors on variation in certain behavioural traits, which can be quantitatively measured, between groups of individuals.

- The subjects of the research are usually twins, siblings, adopted children, and families.

- The statistics such as estimates of heritability generated by the research refer to groups of people, not to individuals. Nor do they refer to particular genes or regions of DNA or to specific environmental factors. This requires further research and additional measurement.

- Estimates of heritability and other statistical techniques are useful in understanding the relative contribution of different types of influence and their relation to each other. They are also useful for understanding why some types of behaviour often occur together. They do not, however, lead directly to predictive information regarding individuals, nor do they give reliable estimates of how strongly predictive a genetic test might be if it were developed.

Chapter 5

Identifying genetic factors contributing to individual differences in behaviour

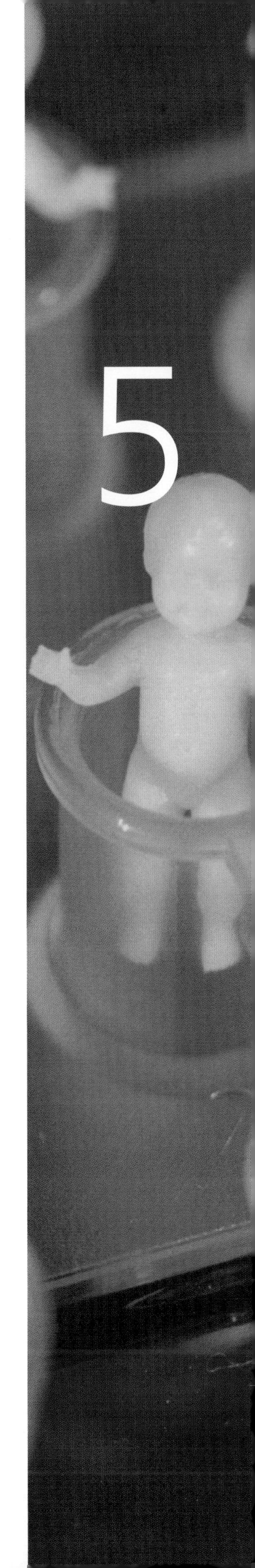

Identifying genetic factors contributing to individual differences in behaviour

Introduction

5.1 Estimates of heritability (see Chapter 4) provide evidence that genetic factors contribute, to a greater or lesser extent, to variation in behavioural traits. A great deal of effort is currently being made to identify these factors using molecular genetic approaches. This chapter reviews these methodologies. Research in molecular genetics is different from research in quantitative genetics in that it attempts to identify the function of particular genes, whereas research in quantitative genetics examines unspecified genetic influences.

5.2 Research focused on examining the genetic contribution to normal variation in behavioural traits is a branch of neuroscience. It thus represents another method used to seek understanding of how the brain works. Research in molecular genetics can also play a role in psychosocial and epidemiological research, enabling confounding genetic effects to be identified and controlled for, and to allow for further study of the non-genetic factors that influence a characteristic. A further reason for undertaking research on normal variation is that it will provide information relevant to disorders and diseases. As already observed, there may be common genetic influences on behaviour in the normal range, such as anxiety, and disorders, such as clinical depression. Further, a particular genetic influence may be linked both to behaviour in the normal range, as well as to extremes of that behaviour.

Approaches to identifying susceptibility alleles

5.3 Attempts to identify susceptibility alleles that influence traits represent various blends of 'bottom-up' and 'top-down' approaches. The 'bottom-up' approach starts with knowledge of the biochemistry of the system in question, and investigates, in a logical fashion, how the system may be varied. With behaviour, the problem is that in most cases, the biochemistry is understood imperfectly, if at all.[1]

5.4 If there is some background biochemistry to direct researchers, a 'candidate gene' approach can be taken, by studying genetic variation that is known to affect the function of proteins suspected of having a role in behaviour, for example, those that act in the brain. An example of this approach is the dopamine D4 receptor (DRD4), which is discussed in paragraphs 5.9 - 5.10.

5.5 The next level of approach is to identify a variation in the relevant gene that is speculated to affect the function of the protein. The best candidates for polymorphisms to study are those that involve amino acid substitutions that are chemically significant, or are surmised

---

[1] One exception to this statement relates to alcoholism. Alcohol is rapidly broken down in the body, or metabolised, to form acetaldehyde, a highly toxic chemical that causes nausea, facial flushing, dizziness, headaches and other unpleasant symptoms. In most gene pools, individuals possess variant alleles of the aldehyde dehydrogenase gene that enables acetaldehyde to be easily broken down. However, there is a particular variant allele of the ALDH gene, common in people from South East Asia, that leads to a slow-metabolising form of the protein, ALDH2*2. When these individuals (particularly ALDH 2*2 homozygotes) drink alcohol, they experience toxic levels of acetaldehyde and the accompanying symptoms. Possession of one or two slow-ALDH alleles protects against alcoholism. In fact, from hundreds of individuals screened, only a single Asian alcoholic was reported to be an ALDH2*2 homozygote (Chen, C.-C. *et al.* (1999). Interaction between the functional polymorphisms of the alcohol-metabolism genes in protection against alcoholism. *Am. J. Hum. Genet.* **65**, 795–807). Thus, this single gene confers substantial protection against alcoholism. This is a rare example of a single gene that is conclusively linked to a behavioural trait.

to affect the levels of expression of proteins that have a role in brain function. An indirect way to determine an effect on function is to try to find an association between the protein variation and behaviour; then, if a significant association is found, to try to establish what the functional effect might be.

5.6 Finally, the most extreme 'top-down' approach (the hypothesis-free method) examines the relationship between genetic variation of unknown function (usually in the form of multiallelic variants, termed microsatellites,[2] or SNPs) and the behaviour under study. A significant association might indicate one of three things:

(i) the effects of chance;

(ii) that the variation serves as a proxy signal for a nearby variant that influences the behaviour that occurs through a process termed linkage disequilibrium, which describes the tendency for closely spaced markers to be inherited together, only becoming separated by rare recombinations;

(iii) that the variation might itself be influencing the behaviour (for example, the variation might turn out to lie in a region outside a gene, influencing the gene's expression).

Linkage studies

5.7 Two general methodologies are used to find or test for susceptibility alleles. These are linkage and association studies. Linkage studies follow the inheritance of traits through families in comparison with polymorphic genetic markers. The consistent co-inheritance of variation at a polymorphic locus with a trait would support the hypothesis that the trait was influenced, at least in part, by genetic variation close to the polymorphism being studied. Conversely, the random inheritance of the polymorphism and the trait would be evidence against linkage. Linkage analysis in large families has been very successful in the identification of single gene disorders, but is less applicable to the study of behaviour, which does not segregate in a simple dominant or recessive fashion.

5.8 Simplified types of linkage analysis, for example, using pairs of affected siblings, have the advantage that they do not assume a particular mode of inheritance. Also they can better accommodate variation in the trait along a continuous scale (rather than as present/absent categories) in a so-called quantitative trait locus (QTL) design. This approach has been used to map susceptibility alleles for traits (including behaviour) in animals. In humans, relatively large samples (several hundred pairs of siblings) are required, and even these only have the power to detect quite major effect sizes.[3] Perhaps for this reason, linkage studies have not been applied very widely to the study of behaviour. A notable exception, though, is the early reported linkage between male homosexuality and genetic variation in the Xq28 region of the X chromosome,[4] which remains controversial (see paragraphs 10.14 – 10.17).

---

[2] Microsatellites contain tandem repeats of a simple sequence such as the dinucleotide CA, that vary in number and are usually of no functional significance. At a particular locus, one person might have (for example) 10 CA repeats on one chromosome and 14 on the other. Another person might have 11 and 13 repeats on their two chromosomes. Because these repeat lengths are usually stably inherited from generation to generation, differences in the distribution of repeat lengths between two populations may indicate differences in their genetic origins.

[3] Risch, N. & Merikangas, K. (1996). The future of genetic studies of complex human diseases. *Science* **273**, 1516–17.

[4] Hamer, D. H., Hu, S., Magnuson, V. L., Hu, N. & Pattatucci, A. M. (1993). A linkage between DNA markers on the X chromosome and male sexual orientation. *Science* **261**, 321–7.

However, several further linkage studies are in progress, examining, for example, anxiety, depressive symptoms and neuroticism.

Association studies

5.9 Association studies are more commonly used for genetic studies of behaviour. In its simplest form, an association study compares the frequency of a particular genetic variant in a cohort of cases (a group of people with a particular behavioural characteristic) with a matched set of controls (a similar group of people not displaying the characteristic). In the study of behaviour, 'cases' as such may not exist, since behavioural traits are unlikely to be easily categorised as present or absent; QTL designs can accommodate this. Two major advantages of association over linkage studies are, first, that they are more powerful for detecting susceptibility alleles of small effect size, such as those anticipated in genetic influences on behaviour, and second, that the samples are easier to collect because only single affected individuals are needed in each family. An example of an association study is the occurrence of different genetic variants of the DRD4 gene in novelty-seeking behaviour. As dopamine is a key neurotransmitter, this DRD4 polymorphism is a plausible candidate as a contributor to genetic variation in behaviour.

5.10 Two highly influential papers published in 1996 suggested that a particular allele of DRD4 was associated with novelty-seeking behaviour.[5] However, the effect of the allele was modest: the papers concluded that this polymorphism accounted for only 3–4% of overall variation in novelty-seeking. Nevertheless, this work sparked a deluge of studies of possible associations of DRD4 with many aspects of behaviour, including alcoholism, drug abuse and Attention Deficit Hyperactivity Disorder (ADHD). A subsequent critique concluded that the associations with novelty-seeking that were originally reported, as well as those with alcoholism and drug abuse, were not statistically robust. However, a weak association might exist between the 7-repeat allele and ADHD,[6] a conclusion also supported by a recent meta-analysis.[7]

5.11 A frequent criticism of association studies is that if there are subtle, but undetected differences in the populations from which the cases and matched controls were sampled, then differences in allele frequency might simply reflect the background evolutionary differences between the two samples, rather than reflecting true trait-specific differences. This problem is termed stratification. One way to avoid this is to incorporate parents or siblings into the design and examine differences in the frequency with which the two parental alleles are passed down to the offspring (transmission disequilibrium tests). This approach provides a 'halfway house' between linkage and association.

[5] The allele is called the 7-repeat allele, because it contains seven repeats of a particular series of 48 base pairs found in the gene. Other alleles have been identified that contain between two and eleven repeats of this section. Ebstein, R. P. *et al.* (1996). Dopamine D4 receptor (D4DR) exon III polymorphism associated with the human personality trait of Novelty-seeking. *Nat. Genet.* **12**, 78–80; Benjamin, J. *et al.* (1996). Population and familial association between the D4 dopamine receptor gene and measures of Novelty-seeking. *Nat. Genet.* **12**, 81–4.

[6] Paterson, A. D., Sunohara, G. A. & Kennedy, J. L. (1999). Dopamine D4 receptor gene: novelty or nonsense? *Neuropsychopharmacol.* **21**, 3–16. The authors state that 'evidence for the role of DRD4 in novelty-seeking is inconclusive, with a number of methodological concerns'.

[7] Faraone, S. V., Doyle, A. E., Mick, E. & Biederman, J. (2001). Meta-analysis of the association between the 7-repeat allele of the dopamine D(4) receptor gene and attention deficit hyperactivity disorder. *Am. J. Psychiatry* **158**, 1052–7.

5.12 Another major problem with association studies is that the testing of very large numbers of loci will lead to numerous spurious associations for purely statistical reasons, using normal criteria for significance. A common approach to combat this effect is to carry out a replication study, in which potential associations identified in an initial screen are re-examined in an independent group of individuals.

5.13 In practice, two approaches have been dominant in the study of behaviour. The first are association studies employing variants in candidate genes of either known or potential functional significance. This has been the most popular approach to date.[8] The second is to use a whole genome, hypothesis-free approach to study association, in which all gene variants are of interest, not just selected candidates. Research by Plomin *et al* on the attempted identification of QTLs for general cognitive ability (*g*) provides one of the first examples of a fully hypothesis-free, genomic approach to the study of a behavioural trait (see paragraphs 7.15 – 7.24).[9] It also illustrates many of the difficulties with this approach.

Identification of alleles that influence behaviour

5.14 The robust replication of a linkage or association identifies a small segment of the genome that contains a susceptibility allele, but does not necessarily identify the allele that actually influences the behavioural trait. This is inevitably the case for linkage, which examines gene loci, not specific alleles. In the case of association, the occurrence of linkage disequilibrium complicates the interpretation as the identified allele might be a neutral hitch-hiker with another (unidentified) allele close by. The next step in a linkage approach is to reduce the extent of the chromosomal segment which needs to be examined, by recruiting additional families and testing additional markers. The DNA sequence of the defined interval is then scrutinised for regions likely to encode genes; a list of 'candidate genes' is drawn up and the DNA sequence of each is obtained, looking for sequence changes from normal. In the case of association, attempts are made to identify all the SNPs near the site showing the initial association, then all the SNPs are tested to determine whether any show a stronger association with the trait than the allele originally identified.

5.15 As may be deduced from this abbreviated account, the identification of alleles that have an influence on complex traits is by no means straightforward, even when a robust linkage or association can be identified. Whereas in research involving animals this process is facilitated by the use of specific breeding strategies, this is clearly impossible in humans. Moreover, in contrast to Mendelian traits, it is unlikely that any specific allele will be both necessary and sufficient to cause the trait, so the genetic evidence for causation will be of a statistical nature. Further evidence of a causal link must be sought through functional studies. Most often these will involve experiments on animals, discussed in Chapter 6.

Scaling up the analysis: new methods in genetics

5.16 The past few years have witnessed the move of genetics from small-scale science conducted in individual laboratories to a larger-scale approach similar to that employed for many years in substantial physics projects as well as in industry. This has been prompted by various factors, including the availability of the sequence of the human genome, the development of partially

---

8 An example is provided by the work of Comings, D. E. *et al.* (2000). A multivariate analysis of 59 candidate genes in personality traits: the temperament and character inventory. *Clin. Genet.* **58**, 375–85.

9 Plomin, R. *et al.* (2001). A genome-wide scan of 1842 DNA markers for allelic associations with general cognitive ability: a five-stage design using DNA pooling and extreme selected groups. *Behav. Genet.* **31**, 497–509.

automated high-throughput technologies for analysing DNA sequence and its variation, and the strategic move of the pharmaceutical industry into genetics, as well as the sheer complexity of human genetic variation. It can be anticipated that this trend will continue apace.

5.17 Apart from the use of rapid methods of analysing genotypes involving large numbers of samples (essential for the approaches outlined above), another technology that promises to yield significant insights is the use of gene chips or microarrays. The best validated application of this technology is for simultaneous examination of the expression of thousands of different genes from a particular source of tissue. DNA sequences from these genes are arrayed onto a glass slide or synthesised chip, then RNA (the intermediate between DNA and protein) from the tissue of interest is prepared and matched by hybridisation to the array. This enables widespread changes in gene expression to be examined. Such methods are likely to come into widespread use in behavioural genetics. It is anticipated that they will lead to a more sophisticated view both of the biology of behavioural processes and to new ways of classifying these processes. Large-scale proteomics approaches, which examine changes in protein, rather than RNA, expression, are also being developed.

Conclusion

5.18 It is likely that there will be a significant increase in the application of molecular genetics to the study of behaviour. It can be anticipated that very large amounts of data about the function of particular genes will be generated over the coming years, and many claims will be made about the significance of these data. Box 5.1 contains a number of points that should be borne in mind when evaluating such claims.

Box 5.1: Central points about research in molecular genetics

- Research in molecular genetics tries to identify variation in particular genes that influences behaviour, by examining the DNA of individuals.

- This is difficult because there are usually many genes involved, each of which may only have a small effect. Many associations between a genetic variant and a behavioural trait have been reported but have not been successfully repeated by other researchers.

- In most cases, the research does not explain how the gene influences the behaviour. However, some researchers predict that they will overcome these difficulties and that genes that influence behaviour will be reliably identified.

- When associations are reported by researchers, it is important to consider the following questions:
  - How convincing is the evidence, in terms of both statistical analysis and the supposed pathway of causation, that the claim is correct? Much more credibility can be attached to findings that have been independently replicated by a different research group, and first reports of gene–behaviour associations should be treated with caution until they are replicated.
  - Over what range of populations and environmental conditions has the effect been tested?
  - If claims are made about the practical application of the findings to influence human behaviour, what is the size of the effect of the genetic variant? Is it large enough to have any relevance for the testing of individuals?
  - What are the implications for the pathway of causation of the behaviour?

Chapter 6

Research in behavioural genetics involving animals

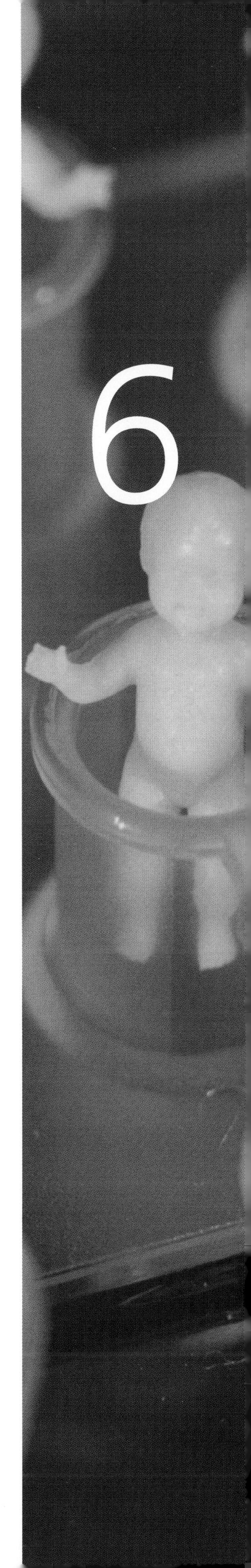

Research in behavioural genetics involving animals

Introduction

6.1 One method of investigating human behaviour is to examine similar traits in animals. Although they have obvious limitations, animal 'models' of human behaviour have frequently been an effective tool for scientists. Such models are useful in understanding disease, but can also be informative about the contribution of genetic factors to some normal behavioural traits. Many species are used in both genetic and psychological research into behaviour, including primates, mice, rats, birds, fish and fruit flies. The different traits being studied in these animals include: intelligence/learning,[1] novelty seeking,[2] anxiety,[3] impulsivity,[4] aggression,[5] hyperactivity,[6] addiction,[7] social interaction,[8] sexual orientation,[9] emotionality,[10] depression and neuroticism.[11]

6.2 This chapter sets out various types of model that researchers use and points to possible advantages and problems with the use of animal models that should be borne in mind when evaluating the results of such research. The chapter focuses predominantly on research involving mice, since much research in behavioural genetics uses mouse models of human behaviour. Although primates are much closer to humans in terms of their behaviour, there are various reasons why non-human primates have not been used as often to study the genetics of human behaviour. Research involving primates tends to pose

---

1 Dobkin, C. *et al.* (1997). FMR1 knockout mouse has a distinctive strain-specific learning impairment. *Neurosci.* **100**, 423–9; Fisch, G. S., Hao, H. K., Bakker, C. & Oostra, B. A. (1999). Learning and memory in the FMR1 knockout mouse. *Am. J. Med. Genet.* **84**, 277–82; Tang, Y. *et al.* (1999). Genetic enhancement of learning and memory in mice. *Nature* **401**, 63–9.

2 Tang, Y. *et al.* (1999). Genetic enhancement of learning and memory in mice. *Nature* **401**, 63–9; Dulawa, S. C., Grandy, D. K., Low, M. J., Paulus, M. P. & Geyer, M. A. (1999). Dopamine D4 receptor-knock-out mice exhibit reduced exploration of novel stimuli. *J. Neurosci.* **19**, 9550–6.

3 König, M. *et al.* (1996). Pain responses, anxiety and aggression in mice deficient in pre-proenkephalin. *Nature* **383**, 535–8; Smith, G. W. *et al.* (1998). Corticotropin releasing factor receptor 1-deficient mice display decreased anxiety, impaired stress response, and aberrant neuroendocrine development. *Neuron* **20**, 1093–102.

4 Cardinal, R. N. *et al.* (2001). Impulsive choice induced in rats by lesions of the nucleus accumbens core. *Science* **292**, 2499–501.

5 De Felipe, C. *et al.* (1998). Altered nociception, analgesia and aggression in mice lacking the receptor for substance P. *Nature* **392**, 394–7; DeVries, A. C., Young, W. S. III & Nelson, R. J. (1997). Reduced aggressive behaviour in mice with targeted disruption of the oxytocin gene. *J. Neuroendocrinol.* **9**, 363–8; Ledent, C. *et al.* (1997). Aggressiveness, hypoalgesia and high blood pressure in mice lacking the adenosine A2a receptor. *Nature* **388**, 674–8.

6 Accili, D. *et al.* (1996). A targeted mutation of the D3 dopamine receptor gene is associated with hyperactivity in mice. *Proc. Natl. Acad. Sci. USA* **93**, 1945–9.

7 Crabbe, J. C. (1996). Elevated alcohol consumption in null mutant mice lacking 5-HT1B serotonin receptors. *Nat. Genet.* **14**, 98–101; Ledent, C. *et al.* (1999). Unresponsiveness to cannabinoids and reduced addictive effects of opiates in CB1 receptor knockout mice. *Science* **283**, 401–4; Maldonado, R. *et al.* (1997). Absence of opiate rewarding effects in mice lacking dopamine D2 receptors. *Nature* **388**, 586–9; McBride, W.J. & Li, T.K. (1998). Animal models of alcoholism: neurobiology of high alcohol-drinking behaviour in rodents. *Crit. Rev. Neurobiol.* **12**, 339–69; Nestler, E. J. (2000). Genes and addiction. *Nat. Genet.* **26**, 277–81; Rocha, B.A. *et al.* (1998). Increased vulnerability to cocaine in mice lacking the serotonin-1B receptor. *Nature* **393**, 175–8.

8 Ferguson, J. N. *et al.* (2000). Social amnesia in mice lacking the oxytocin gene. *Nat. Genet.* **25**, 284–8; Gendreau, P. L., Petitto, J. M., Petrova, A., Gariepy, J. & Lewis, M. H. (2000). D(3) and D(2) dopamine receptor agonists differentially modulate isolation-induced social-emotional reactivity in mice. *Behav. Brain Res.* **114**, 107–17; Lijam, N. *et al.* (1997). Social interaction and sensorimotor gating abnormalities in mice lacking Dvl1. *Cell* **90**, 895–905.

9 McGraw, K. J. & Hill, G. E. (1999). Induced homosexual behaviour in male house finches (Carpodacus maxicanus): the 'prisoner effect'. *Ethol. Ecol. Evol.* **11**, 197–201.

10 Flint, J. *et al.* (1995). A simple genetic basis for a complex psychological trait in laboratory mice. *Science* **269**, 1432–5.

11 Flint, J. *et al.* (1995). A simple genetic basis for a complex psychological trait in laboratory mice. *Science* **269**, 1432–5.

greater ethical problems than animal models using rodents.[12] Monkeys do not breed rapidly nor do they have large numbers of offspring. The time and costs involved in producing and rearing them would be prohibitive. Many strains of mice already exist that have been bred selectively to display particular traits. For these reasons, the mouse currently remains the most commonly used organism for studying the genetics of human behaviour.

6.3 Many genes involved in fundamental biological processes have been conserved as species have evolved. In other words, many genes are similar in different species. Due to the fact that many genes that play an important role in development and the proteins they produce tend to be very similar in mice and humans, considerable evidence has been gathered from research involving mice as a guide to the human case. However, when considering the findings of various studies, it is vital to remember that conservation of a gene across the two species does not necessarily mean that the gene itself, the timing of its expression in the organism or its function will be exactly equivalent in mice and humans.[13]

How are animal models created?

6.4 Before it became possible to manipulate specific genes in animals, researchers examined the effect on behaviour of preventing particular parts of an animal's brain from influencing its behaviour in the normal way. Today, changes in an animal's genetic make-up can be produced in several ways, either by selecting animals which show natural variation or by inducing variation through genetic manipulation.[14] The main methods are:

- variation induced in individual animals by surgery, conditioning, diet and so on, which is not due to the animals' genotype;
- selective breeding (i) of naturally-occurring traits, where animals are specifically chosen for mating based on an observed behavioural trait; and (ii) of animals exposed to pre- or post-natal rearing environments which are either enriched or impoverished;
- variation induced in specific genes by (i) the deletion or 'knocking out' of a gene; (ii) the under- or over-expression of a gene; (iii) transferring a gene to create a transgenic animal; (iv) exposure to radiation or drugs. Variation can be as subtle as changing just one base pair; this sometimes has effects as profound as those of knocking out the whole gene.

6.5 Selective breeding capitalises on the genetic variation that is present either in unmodified mice or in those which have been produced by cross-breeding two or more inbred strains. Measurements of behavioural traits may be used to divide groups of animals which do not have similar genotypes into sub-groups with, for example, high or low aggression, or high or low levels of exploratory activity. Selective breeding from animals with the most extreme manifestations of the trait in question is then undertaken for a number of generations.

[12] Some of these issues were discussed in *Animal to human transplants: the ethics of xenotransplantation*, Nuffield Council on Bioethics (1996). The issue of the ethics of research involving animals is outside the scope of this Report, but will be the subject of a future Report by the Council.

[13] Fougerousse, F. *et al.* (2000). Human–mouse differences in the embryonic expression patterns of development control genes and disease genes. *Hum. Mol. Genet.* **9**, 165–73.

[14] See for example Flint, J. (1996). Annotation: behavioural phenotypes: a window on the biology of behaviour. *J. Child Psychol. Psyc.* **37**, 355–67; Heintz, N. (2000). Analysis of mammalian central nervous system gene expression and function using bacterial artificial chromosome-mediated transgenesis. *Hum. Mol. Genet.* 9, 937–43; Hunter, A. J., Nolan, P. M. & Brown, S. D. M. (2000). Towards new models of disease and physiology in the neurosciences: the role of induced and naturally occurring mutations. *Hum. Mol. Genet.* **9**, 893–900; Kempermann, G., Georg Kuhn, H. & Gage, F. H. (1997). More hippocampal neurons in adult mice living in an enriched environment. *Nature* **386**, 493–5.

Often, by the end of a selection experiment, animals may have become inbred. Groups of animals that have similar genotypes but that differ in terms of a particular phenotype can also be created by inbreeding animals that have little genetic ancestry in common. These are powerful methods for identifying genetic differences between strains; however, the genetic diversity that is present is limited, compared to that which occurs naturally, as a result of using inbred mice.

6.6 Mutations can be induced at random in the genome through irradiation using X-rays, or by the use of mutagenic chemicals. Several large-scale projects are under way, in which thousands of mice are exposed to mutagenic chemicals. Their offspring are then screened for a wide range of characteristics, including behavioural and neurobiological abnormalities. After finding such mutants, they can be bred to create a line of animals with the characteristics in question. Mutagenesis is of relevance when it produces animals that have abnormal phenotypes similar to complex traits of interest to the investigator (for example, increased anxiety). Once such a mutant line is established, further research may be able to identify the mutation that causes the trait. It is not yet clear how frequently complex traits can be mimicked by induced mutations, nor how useful such experiments will be in uncovering the genetic basis of the complex trait itself.

Box 6.1: The 'Doogie mice'

Here, we provide a brief description of a much-publicised research project investigated memory and learning in genetically modified mice.[*] The study was undertaken to investigate a potential treatment for the memory and learning problems of patients with Alzheimer's disease, but its extrapolation to the enhancement of normal variation in these traits, which are components of intelligence, was focused on both by scientists and the popular press. The genetically modified mice were nicknamed 'Doogie' after the intellectually precocious star of a popular TV programme, Doogie Howser MD.

The mice were genetically altered so that they over-expressed a gene that has an effect in the brain and is thought to be involved in learning. The modified mice were then compared to unmodified mice in various tasks. These tested the ability of the mice to recognise objects they had previously seen, to remember events that had caused an emotional response, to learn relationships between an electric shock and a particular outcome and to succeed in spatial learning. The genetically modified mice were normal in all respects, except for learning and memory. They showed normal growth, normal body weight and normal mating behaviour, but appeared to have enhanced learning capacity. When tested three to six months after birth, the genetically modified mice showed a greater tendency for exploratory behaviour, a stronger preference for novel situations and superior abilities to code and store information. The researchers concluded that over-expression of the gene resulted in a better long-term memory. However, it is very difficult to measure the precise effects of the over-expression of the gene in the brain. Moreover, the enhancement effects in one experiment lasted only three days, and in others for merely a few hours, so the claims should be treated with great caution.

Nevertheless, the scientific and popular press was rapid in hailing these results as pointing to the existence of a 'gene for learning', a 'gene for intelligence' or even simply 'the IQ gene'[†] that might subsequently be enhanced in humans. Even the original press release, issued by Princeton University, to which the researchers were affiliated, claimed that 'the finding also shows that genetic improvement of intelligence and memory in mammals is now feasible, thus offering a striking example of how genetic technology may affect mankind and society in the next century'. This was based on the hypothesis that overexpression of the gene might help the brain to retain the extensive capacity for learning that young children possess naturally early on but gradually lose with age. This example attracted media coverage of increasing exaggeration throughout the world and points to the risks of generalising the tentative results of a relatively restricted experiment on mice to the human case.

More recent experiments on the same strain of genetically modified mice have suggested that there is an additional, unintended effect of this manipulation, namely an increased susceptibility to persistent pain. This illustrates that attempts at genetic enhancement may have unexpected side effects.[‡]

[*] Tang, Y. *et al.* (1999). Genetic enhancement of learning and memory in mice. *Nature* **401**, 63–9.

[†] See, for example, Lemonick, M. D. (1999). Smart Genes? *Time Magazine* 13 Sept.

[‡] Wei, F. *et al.* (2001). Genetic enhancement of inflammatory pain by forebrain NR2B overexpression. *Nat. Neurosci.* **4**, 164–9.

What are the benefits of using animals to study the genetics of human behaviour?

6.7 One of the obvious advantages of research involving mice is that the human and mouse genomes are very similar, so that many human genes have counterparts in mice. Mice breed very rapidly and plentifully, so programmes of breeding can be more easily implemented. Many organs in mice are also very similar to those in humans. Thus, discovering the parts of the body and brain in which a known or candidate gene is expressed (called expression analysis) can be done in the laboratory with a reasonable expectation that this will usually be similar in the human case. A particular advantage is that scientists can study gene expression throughout the development of the mouse before birth and in early postnatal life, which makes it possible to chart where and when genes are expressed. Some genes are expressed early in development and never again, whereas others are expressed later. The earlier in development that a gene is expressed, the greater the ability to understand its function. This may enable the planning of timely intervention during periods at which the brain is most receptive to alteration. New treatments can be tried out when the function of genes and their products are fully identified. For example, using mouse models in which genes related to the human hearing system have been knocked out, researchers may be able to establish the best period of time for inserting cochlear implants.

6.8 Fairly complex behaviours in mammals can be dependent on the presence and functioning of the chemicals produced by specific genes. For example, studies in prairie voles have suggested that two chemicals in the brain, the neuropeptides oxytocin and vasopressin, 'play important roles in behaviours associated with monogamy, including affiliation, paternal care and pair bonding'.[15] Some prairie vole species are monogamous. They have been shown to have a higher density of oxytocin receptors in specific parts of the brain than do closely related non-monogamous species. The specific behaviours related to the

[15] Young, L. J., Lim, M. M., Gingrich, B. & Insel, T. R. (2001). Cellular mechanisms of social attachment. *Horm. Behav.* **40**, 133–8.

development of social bonds, but not other general behaviours, appear to be altered when animals are treated by injection of substances that block the binding of these neuropeptides to the relevant cells in the brain.[16] What is much less clear, currently, is the extent to which similar mechanisms may or may not exert some influence on human behaviour, even with regard to disease, let alone within the normal range. It is important to emphasise that the absence of current evidence of this nature is not evidence that such effects could not exist. On the contrary, if animal evidence suggests a neurobiological mechanism underlying certain complex behaviours, it is entirely plausible that at least some residue of these mechanisms will eventually also be discovered in human beings. For example, the sleep disorder narcolepsy has been found to have the same chemical basis in mice, dogs and humans.[17]

What are the problems with using animals to study the genetics of human behaviour?

6.9 While human genes have many homologues in mice, their patterns of expression are often dissimilar both spatially and temporally.[18] Indeed, time-dependent processes differ significantly between the two species.[19] Although specific genes may be similar, interactions between genes, as well as with the internal and external environments, may be different. Identical genes may have different functions within the development of the brain in different species and may be expressed at varying times and at different developmental stages. It may be that haploinsufficiency (having one instead of the normal two copies of a gene) in mice turns out to be less detrimental than in humans. Such potential differences must always be taken into account.[20] Generalisations from mouse to human can sometimes, therefore, be premature and need to be examined with caution.

6.10 In scientific experiments, caution should always be exercised in interpreting the results. Unless replicated, reported findings cannot be taken at face value, because sometimes outcomes differ even in ostensibly identical conditions. For example, one group of researchers set up a comparison of results from three different laboratories that studied genetically modified mice in which the gene involved in regulating a chemical in the brain (a neurotransmitter called serotonin), had been knocked out.[21] Each of the three laboratories had identical strains of mice and conducted the experiments starting at exactly the same time, on the same day and under the same laboratory conditions, using the same mouse feed and the same behavioural tests. The results were, in some respects, surprising. For example, in a simple test of anxiety (a maze in which animals could either stay 'safe', relatively hidden in areas with high walls, or else venture out into 'more dangerous' open areas), the differences between genetically modified mice and the controls, varied as a

---

16 Insel, T. R. (1997). A neurobiological basis of social attachment. *Am. J. Psychiat.* **154**, 726–35.

17 Overeem, S., Mignot, E., Gert van Dijk, J. & Lammers, G. J. (2001). Narcolepsy: clinical features, new pathophysiologic insights, and future perspectives. *J. Clin. Neurophysiol.* **18**, 78–105.

18 Fougerousse, F. *et al.* (2000). Human–mouse differences in the embryonic expression patterns of development control genes and disease genes. *Hum. Mol. Genet.* **9**, 165–73.

19 Doyle, J. L., DeSilva, U., Miller, W. & Green, E. D. (2000). Divergent human and mouse orthologs of a novel gene (WBSCR15/Wbscr15) reside within the genomic interval commonly deleted in Williams syndrome. *Cytogenet. Cell Genet.* **90**, 285–90.

20 Keverne, E. B. (1997). An evaluation of what the mouse knockout experiments are telling us about mammalian behaviour. *BioEssays* **19**, 1091–8.

21 Crabbe, J. C., Wahlsten, D. & Dudek, B. C. (1999). Genetics of mouse behaviour. *Science* **284**, 1670–2.

function of the laboratory. One laboratory's modified mice showed more activity in the open areas of the maze, the second laboratory's modified mice showed less, and in the third laboratory there was no difference in activity between the modified mice and the controls. These results presumably result from uncontrolled differences, for example in handling, in the odour of the handlers or in the composition of the water supplied to the mice. Some of these kinds of differences, particularly handling, might well be expected to affect the emotional responses of the mice and hence change their behaviour in this simple anxiety test. Results that have been replicated under different conditions or using several different ways of assessing anxiety are therefore likely to be more reliable than those resulting from a single measurement.[22] Of course this caveat does not just apply to genetic studies. The results obtained are always likely to depend in part on the environment in which the test is conducted. Note also that knocking out a gene that is expressed in the brain, for example, might have no consequences of behaviour in mice, while damage to the equivalent genes might by contrast critically affect behaviour in the human case. This is because the effects of the expression of the same gene across two species may differ.

6.11 Genetic effects are usually very dependent on context (both in terms of other genes and of environmental factors), such that even after breeding for a specific behavioural change, it may be significantly altered by subsequent experience. In sum, environmental factors clearly interact with an animal's genotype to produce the final phenotype. Furthermore, genetic effects can be beneficial in one environment, but damaging in another. For example, in the fruit fly, a number of sites on particular chromosomes (QTLs) have been identified that contribute to variations in lifespan. However, research has revealed that the effects of these QTLs vary as a function of sex and of larval environment. Some even have antagonistic effects on life span in the different sexes and across different environments.[23]

6.12 Another factor relevant to the problems of generalising from mouse to human is the fact that the mouse repertoire of behaviour measurable in the laboratory is comparatively limited. Often the effects of genetically modifying an animal are only studied with respect to a single hypothesis about the function of the gene in question, despite the fact that the gene may be pleiotropic (that is, have more than one effect) and be expressed in several parts of the body and brain.

6.13 When investigating intelligence in mice, most researchers focus on spatial memory in a task called the water maze, in which the mice have to remember where a submerged platform is located in a tank of water. How comparable is the enhancement of the mouse's learning capacity and thus performance in the water maze task (which is by no means a natural environment for mice) to improvements in, say, human memory in all its multiple forms? Other measurements less often used, but perhaps more analogous to human behaviour, might be speed of processing or the time one takes to react to a novel stimulus.[24] Researchers are now tending to use a wider range of tests in comparing mice to humans.

---

[22] For example, Turri, M. G., Henderson, N. D., DeFries, J. C. & Flint, J. (2001). Quantitative trait locus mapping in laboratory mice derived from a replicated selection experiment for open-field activity. *Genetics* **158**, 1217–61.

[23] Leips, J. & Mackay, T. F. C. (2000). Quantitative trait loci for life span in *Drosophila melanogaster:* interactions with genetic background and larval density. *Genetics* **155**, 1773–88.

[24] It is important to note that although mouse models have been used to make claims about enhanced performance, faster is not always better in the human case. One might, for instance, be able to speed up a mouse's search for hidden objects by altering one of its genes. Should it therefore be concluded that such enhancement would be beneficial in the human case? Not necessarily. People with autism, for instance, are significantly faster than matched controls on a visual search task (O'Riordan, M. A., Plaisted, K. C. & Baron-Cohen, S. (2001). Superior visual search in autism. *J. Exp. Psychol. Hum. Percept. Perform.* **27**, 719–30), but this enhanced speed is actually detrimental to cognition and contributes to the tendency of people with autism to focus on specific features at the expense of context and overall configuration.

Indeed, it is becoming increasingly clear that good genetic research requires one to define and measure the traits under study effectively.

Conclusion

6.14 In conclusion, we have seen that research involving animals is one method of investigating influences on behaviour. While there are many similarities, in terms of genetics, between some animals and humans, the results of studies involving animals cannot be taken to apply in a straightforward way to human behaviour. Box 6.2 summarises the central themes that have emerged in this chapter.

Box 6.2: Central points about animal models of human behaviour

- Animal models have greatly advanced our understanding of how genes have an effect in the organism and of how the brain develops.
- Animal models can be created by various techniques including selective breeding and the direct manipulation of specific genes.
- Although there are many similarities with regard to genetics between human and non-human animals, there are also considerable differences in the expression of their genes both within the organism and over time.
- It is difficult to equate directly the richness of complex human traits such as intelligence, personality and sexual orientation with the behaviour of animals. This may limit the potential value of the research.
- For these reasons, caution should be exerted when hypothesising that genes studied in research involving animals will have the same effect in humans.

Section 3

Reviews of the evidence

Chapter 7

Review of the evidence: intelligence

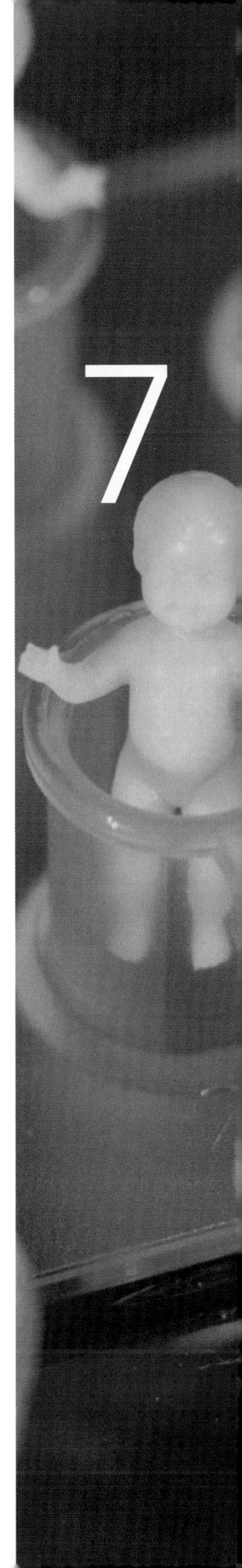

Review of the evidence: intelligence[1]

Background

7.1 The first tests that aimed to measure intelligence were developed at the start of the twentieth century. The Simon–Binet test was commissioned by the French government to identify children who would not benefit from ordinary schooling because of low intelligence. It was subsequently adapted by researchers in the US to measure average and above-average intelligence as well. Other tests have been developed in different contexts than education, for example in military recruitment. The use of such tests has often aroused controversy and criticism, particularly when combined with claims about the biological basis of variation in test scores. There have been several prominent examples of claims that differences in IQ between racial groups are due to genetic factors rather than social or environmental ones and, further, that this ought to inform social policy. While it is often claimed that on average, black individuals score slightly lower on IQ tests than white individuals, who in turn score lower than people from East Asia, there are also studies which show that, if black individuals and white individuals are closely matched on socioeconomic status, the differences in IQ are substantially reduced.[2] The potential abuse of information about genetic influences on behaviour is discussed further in Chapters 13-15. Here, it suffices to observe that research into genetic influences on intelligence has been associated, historically, with significant concerns about misuse of the information and unfair discrimination.

Trait definition and measurement

7.2 Psychologists measure intelligence using a range of tests called IQ (Intelligence Quotient) tests. However, there is considerable disagreement about whether these tests do in fact measure intelligence, and even whether intelligence can be measured by a test at all. Many critics have suggested that intelligence is too complex to be measured by such tests:

> 'IQ psychologists ... like to think that intelligence can be measured as if it were ... a simple scalar quantity ... Unfortunately for IQ psychologists this is not so ... Intelligence ... is a complicated and many-sided business. Among its elements are speed and span of *grasp*, the ability to see implications and conversely to discern a *non sequitur* and other fallacies, to discern analogies and formal parallels between outwardly dissimilar phenomena or thought structures, and much else besides. One number will not do for all these.'[3]

7.3 However, IQ tests come in a variety of forms. Some require an individual to engage in reasoning in order to solve novel problems, which may be presented in verbal, numerical or diagrammatical form. Others test general knowledge or the extent of an individual's

---

1 The material in this chapter is taken from a paper commissioned by the Nuffield Council on Bioethics from Professor N. J. Mackintosh, Department of Experimental Psychology, University of Cambridge. The paper is available on the Council's website: www.nuffieldbioethics.org.

2 See, for example, Nichols, P. L. & Anderson, V. E. (1973). Intellectual performance, race and socioeconomic status. *Soc. Biol.* **20**, 367–74. The authors conclude that 'socioeconomic differences are largely responsible for the usually reported differences in intellectual performance'.

3 Medawar, P. (1982). *Pluto's Republic*. Oxford: Oxford University Press. Another common criticism of IQ tests arises from the 'Flynn effect', first noted by Professor James Flynn in 1987 (*Psychol. Bull.* **101**, 171) that the average IQ of individuals has been rising steadily since the measurement was first introduced. In January 2002 he reported that the Flynn Effect is particularly great in Britain, which has seen a 27 point increase in average IQ since World War II, compared to a 24 point rise in the US.

vocabulary. Yet others measure how quickly an individual can solve a series of very simple problems, as well as whether he or she is capable of solving seriously difficult problems regardless of time pressure. The very diversity of questions asked in the various IQ tests makes it hard to accept that *none* of them succeeds in measuring any aspect of intelligence. But the important observation is that scores on all these different kinds of test are positively correlated. In general, people who score highly on tests of general knowledge or vocabulary will also tend to obtain high scores on tests of abstract reasoning or numerical series-completion tasks. Similarly, those who are poor at memorising a series of rapidly presented numbers will also be poor at seeing whether two three-dimensional diagrams are really views of the same object viewed from different angles and slow to delete all the 'X's in a list of random letters of the alphabet.

7.4 There are two implications of this observation. One, first noted by Spearman[4] but now accepted by most testers of IQ, is that the statistical technique of factor analysis,[5] when applied to people's scores on a variety of IQ tests, will always yield a substantial general factor, which accounts for much of the variation in their scores.[6] Spearman labelled this factor '*g*', for general intelligence, and argued that the reason why different IQ tests correlate with one another is because they all measure, to a greater or lesser extent, a single underlying psychological or even neurological, process. The second implication is that if IQ tests fail completely to measure intelligence, it should be possible to produce a different test, or set of tests, that does measure intelligence, but does not correlate with existing IQ tests. Given the diversity of existing tests that do correlate with one another, the challenge is not a trivial one, and has not yet been met.

7.5 If performance on every kind of IQ test correlates with performance on every other kind of test, it clearly follows that the score a person obtains on one test will be similar, but not identical, to the score they obtain on another. Correlations between different kinds of test range from about 0.35 to about 0.85. It must equally follow, therefore, that a single, short test will not tell us all that we might want to know about a person's IQ.

7.6 Different types of IQ test may all be partly measuring a factor of general intelligence. But they are also measuring partially distinct cognitive abilities. Factor analysis of scores on a large range of tests invariably reveals not only a general factor, but also a number of more specific 'group factors', caused by the fact that clusters of sub-tests show high correlations within the cluster, but lower correlations with sub-tests in other clusters. The general consensus is that one can distinguish between at least the following kinds of test:

- measures of abstract reasoning or 'fluid' intelligence (Gf)
- vocabulary and general knowledge, or 'crystallised intelligence' (Gc)

---

4 Spearman, C. (1927). *The Abilities of Man*. London: Macmillan.

5 Factor analysis refers to a group of statistical procedures, based on correlation, which attempt to reduce a large amount of data to the smallest number of factors which can adequately account for the variance between individuals on the measures in question. Factor analysis is an important tool for areas of behavioural genetics where the underlying components are difficult to discern (e.g. personality assessment). Strictly speaking, factors are not traits as they merely represent regularity in the available data. The establishment of a valid trait from factor analysis requires additional inferences to be made.

6 See paragraphs 4.5 - 4.8 for a definition of heritability. Carroll, J. B. (1993). *Human Cognitive Abilities*. Cambridge: Cambridge University Press; Gould, S. J. (1996). *The Mismeasure of Man*. New York: Norton.

- visuo-spatial ability (Gv)
- retrieval or memory (Gr)
- speed of processing (Gs).

7.7 It has been argued that there are important aspects of human intelligence that IQ tests fail to measure, such as creativity, practical intelligence, social intelligence and emotional intelligence. Some of these constructs are more securely grounded than others, and not all of them are wholly independent of IQ. However, those who support IQ tests require only that their tests should measure some reasonably important aspects of intelligence. They can readily allow that their tests leave some aspects unmeasured.

7.8 The claim of those who support IQ tests must be, however, that the tests do measure some important aspects of intelligence. They have attempted to prove this by showing that people's IQ scores are correlated with, or predict, many other things about them: how well they are now doing and will do later at school, how long they will stay in full-time education, the kind of job they will obtain and how well they will perform that job. Schoolchildren's IQ scores correlate in the range 0.50 to 0.70 with their current and subsequent educational attainment: for example, the correlation between 11-year-olds' IQ scores and their GCSE grades at age 16 is over 0.50.[7] Studies in the US have shown that the correlation between children's IQ scores and their occupational status as adults is also about 0.50. Moreover, these correlations cannot simply be attributed to the pervasive influence of family background. Although there is a correlation of around 0.30 between IQ scores and socioeconomic status, Herrnstein and Murray showed that children's IQ scores were substantially more powerful predictors of their subsequent educational and occupational attainments than was their family background.[8] Their analyses have been vehemently criticised, and some of these criticisms require some qualification of their arguments.[9] But their central conclusion stands: IQ scores do predict, independent of family background, significant things about people's lives. The prediction is far from perfect: even correlations of 0.50 leave much unexplained. Moreover, many of these correlations, for example, between IQ and measures of actual performance of a job are usually substantially lower than this. This is hardly surprising. No one could sensibly doubt that success, whether at school or in the adult world, depends on many other things besides intelligence, including hard work, ambition, social skills and plain luck. But IQ is also a significant factor.

Current findings: quantitative genetics

7.9 Both testers of IQ and researchers in behavioural genetics agree that the heritability of IQ is relatively high.[10] That there is a genetic influence on IQ is suggested by two findings:

(i) Monozygotic (MZ) twins resemble one another more closely than dizygotic (DZ) twins or siblings, and full siblings resemble one another more closely than half siblings.

---

7 Brody, N. (1992). *Intelligence*. New York: Academic Press; Jensen, A. R. (1998). *The g Factor*. Westport, CT: Praeger.

8 Herrnstein, R. J. & Murray, C. (1994). *The Bell Curve*. New York: Free Press.

9 Devlin, B. *et al*., editors. (1997). *Intelligence, Genes and Success*. New York: Springer-Verlag.

10 See the following for summaries of research in this field: Devlin, B., Daniels, M. & Roeder, K. (1997). The heritability of IQ. *Nature* **388**, 468–71; Plomin, R., DeFries, J. C., McClearn, G. E. & McGuffin, P. (2000). *Behavioral Genetics*. 4th ed. New York: Worth; Sternberg, R. J., editor. (2000). *Handbook of Intelligence*. Cambridge: Cambridge University Press; Chipuer, H. M., RoVine, M. & Plomin, R. (1990). LISREL modeling: Genetic and environmental influences on IQ revisited. *Intelligence* **14**, 11–29.

(ii) Individuals who are genetically-related continue to resemble one another even when living apart.

Two other observations suggest that environmental factors have an effect:

(i) For all kinship categories, those living together resemble one another more closely than those living apart.

(ii) Unrelated people living together, adoptive parents and their adopted children or two adopted children living in the same family, show a modest correlation in IQ.

The data suggest, therefore, that both genetic and environmental sources of variation contribute to variations in IQ. This may not seem a startling conclusion, but it is still disputed by some critics, including those who question the validity of estimates of heritability and the methodologies of quantitative genetics.[11]

7.10 Adoption studies have also provided evidence for genetic influences on IQ. Children given up for adoption before the age of 6 months continue to resemble their biological mother in IQ. Critics have appealed to 'selective placement' to explain this, arguing that such children live in adoptive homes carefully selected by adoption agencies to match their biological parents' circumstances. If this were a sufficient explanation, it would follow that the resemblance between adopted children and their adoptive parents in IQ should be *at least* as high as that between these children and their biological parents. However, research suggests that this is not true, and in two recent American studies, the correlation with the biological parents has been considerably higher than with the adoptive parents.[12]

7.11 DZ twins resemble one another in IQ somewhat more than other siblings. An obvious explanation is that, being the same age, they spend more time together and share more experiences than siblings of different ages. In one small study, separated DZ twins were found to resemble one another more closely than separated siblings. This suggests that the shared prenatal environment may also be important.[13] An alternative explanation is that some children classified as full siblings may in fact have different biological fathers. Both blood group and DNA tests suggest that not all putative fathers are the actual biological fathers of their children.

7.12 The evidence from research in quantitative genetics strongly suggests that a significant part of the observed variation in IQ is genetic in origin: the heritability of IQ is substantially greater than zero. How much greater? A sufficiently accurate answer is that in modern Western societies it is probably about 0.50, with a range of possible values from, say, 0.35 to 0.75. For some time, this has been the consensus of virtually all researchers in behavioural genetics.[14] However, this finding does not provide any information about

---

[11] See Chapter 4 (paragraphs 4.7-4.8). How, M. J. A. (1997). *IQ in Question*. London: Sage; Wahlsten, D. & Gottlieb, G. The invalid separation of effects of nature and nurture: Lessons from animal experimentation. In Sternberg, R. J. & Grigorenko, E. L., editors. (1997). *Intelligence, Heredity and Environment*. Cambridge: Cambridge University Press. pp. 163–92.

[12] Loehlin, J. C. *et al*. Heredity, environment, and IQ in the Texas Adoption Project. In Sternberg, R. J. & Grigorenko, E. L., editors. (1997). *Intelligence, Heredity and Environment*. Cambridge: Cambridge University Press. pp. 163–92; Plomin, R., Fulker, D. W., Corley, R. & DeFries, J. C. (1997). Nature, nurture, and cognitive development from 1 to 6 years: A parent–offspring adoption study. *Psychol Sci* **8**, 442–7.

[13] Devlin, B., Daniels, M. & Roeder, K. (1997). The heritability of IQ. *Nature* **388**, 468–71

[14] Plomin, R., DeFries, J. C., McClearn, G. E. & McGuffin, P. (2000). *Behavioral Genetics*. 4th ed. New York: Worth.

which genes influence intelligence, how many genes might be involved, or how the genes have their effect.

7.13 Interestingly, there is some evidence that the heritability of IQ increases with age. Although it might seem more plausible to suppose that an infant's or young child's intelligence is affected by their genetic make-up, and that the cumulative effect of environmental experience should become more important as children grow older, it is possible that some of the genes associated with variations in IQ are not 'switched on' until adolescence. Another possibility is that the genetic effects on IQ are mediated by the environment as we develop, in other words, that we actively select environments that complement our genotypes, and that the environment responds to us differently depending on our genotypes. If this is true, it could mean that the effects of our genes are reinforced over time and thus appear to be more important as we get older.

Current findings: molecular genetics

7.14 Some progress has been made in identifying genes linked to instances of mental retardation. One example is Fragile X syndrome, a disease caused by a small section of base pairs on the X chromosome being repeated too many times. However, as one commentator has noted: 'Not a single gene involved in the development of mental retardation has been shown to be associated with normal variation in IQ'.[15] This is consistent with the general belief that mild 'familial' retardation is the lower end of normal variation in IQ, but serious retardation is usually due to quite specific, relatively rare causes – whether genetic or environmental in origin.

7.15 If this is true, it will be necessary to search specifically for individual genes associated with normal variation in IQ. The behavioural geneticist Robert Plomin and his colleagues have been engaged in just such a search for the past ten years. The difficulties should not be underestimated. Normal variations in IQ are expected to be influenced by the combined action of a number of genes, rather than by any one 'major' gene.[16] As we have already noted, although factor analysis yields a general factor *g*, IQ is not a unitary construct, and must therefore be influenced by many different genes. Suppose, for the sake of argument, that the heritability of IQ is 0.50 in today's Western populations. This means that half the observed phenotypic variation in IQ can be ascribed to genetic differences between members of those populations. Suppose also that there are 25 genes associated with this variation in IQ, and that each has an equal, additive effect. Then each will be associated with 2% of the observed variation in IQ. That is a small effect, not easily distinguished from chance fluctuation.

7.16 The history of the search for genes that influence such characteristics as schizophrenia or manic depression provides ample warning of some likely problems. It is all too easy to find some genetic differences between two groups of people selected for their difference in some phenotypic trait. Chance alone is almost bound to produce some small differences. They are not worthy of serious consideration unless replicated in further independent samples. With some false starts, Plomin's group does appear to have

[15] Grigorenko, E. Heritability and intelligence. In Sternberg, R. J., editor. (2000). *Handbook of Intelligence*. Cambridge: Cambridge University Press.

[16] Weiss, V. (1992). Major genes of general intelligence. *Pers. Individ. Dif.* **13**, 1115–34, has argued for a 'major gene' account of variation in IQ, but does not suppose that only one gene is involved.

satisfied this minimum requirement. One study compared two groups of about 50 children, between 6 and 15 years old, one of average IQ (a mean of 103), a second of high IQ (a mean of 136).[17] A systematic search of the long arm of chromosome 6 found a significant difference between them in the frequency of different alleles of the IGF2R gene.[18] This difference was replicated in a second sample of 12-year-old children, 50 with an average IQ (a mean of 101) and another 50 with an estimated IQ of at least 160. The probability of the difference arising by chance in both groups was less than 1 in 1,000. The same four groups of children were also used in a second study that employed a different technique (DNA pooling across participants) to perform a systematic search of chromosome 4.[19] Eleven differences were found between the initial pair of high and average groups, and three of these were confirmed in the second pair of groups. A more recent and perhaps more stringent study, however, has been less successful. The initial pair of high and average IQ groups was formed by combining the two pairs of groups from the earlier studies. A large number of differences in the frequency distribution of microsatellite alleles were found between these two groups (each comprising 101 individuals). However, very few of these differences were replicated in a second pair of groups, and none in a third sample.[20]

7.17 At present, the most one can say is that some differences in the frequencies of particular alleles at particular loci have been found between high and average IQ groups, and that some of these differences have been replicated in new samples. It will be important to see if independent groups of researchers, studying quite different populations (all the participants in these studies were white, non-Hispanic Americans, most of them living in the Midwest), can replicate these differences. It is, moreover, important to note that the effects observed, even if statistically significant, are very small. The critical allele 5 was found in less than half of the high-IQ children in the initial study, and in nearly one quarter of the average IQ group. As the authors properly acknowledge: 'IGF2R is not *the gene* for *g* but may be one of many genes responsible for the high IQ heritability of *g*.'

7.18 Finding genes associated with variations in IQ is not really surprising. If the heritability of IQ is approximately 0.50, there must be such genes. The importance of the research is that it may make it possible to work out *how* genetic differences lead to differences in IQ. That endeavour has barely started. IGF2R is an insulin growth factor gene. There is some, rather contentious, evidence implicating defective glucose metabolism in Alzheimer's disease, and some equally contentious animal studies have suggested that insulin may be involved in learning and memory.[21] However, this is a great distance from ascertaining the way in which variation in the IGF2R gene influences variation in IQ.

7.19 It is extremely unlikely that researchers will find one or two genes that have a sizeable impact on variation in IQ within the normal range. The discovery of genes with small effects will be very much harder than the discovery of mutations associated with serious mental

---

17 Chorney, M. J. *et al.* (1998). A qualitative trait locus associated with cognitive ability in children. *Psychol. Sci.* **9**, 159–66.

18 IGF2R (insulin-like growth factor II receptor).

19 Fisher, P. J. *et al.* (1999). DNA pooling identifies QTLs on chromosome 4 for general cognitive ability in children. *Hum. Mol. Genet.* **8**, 915–22.

20 Plomin, R. *et al.* (2001). A genome-wide scan of 1842 DNA markers for allelic associations with general cognitive ability: a five-stage design using DNA pooling and extreme selected groups. *Behav. Genet.* **31**, 497–509.

21 Wickelgren, I. (1998). Tracking insulin to the mind. *Science* **280**, 517–19.

retardation. It may also be very much more difficult to uncover their mode of action. It seems reasonable to suggest that there may be some readily detectable differences between the brains of those with an IQ below 50 and those with an IQ of 100 or more. Indeed, some such differences have already been observed. It seems rather less likely that a gene associated with a 1% to 2% variation in IQ in the normal range will have such easily discernible effects on brain function. Indeed, the search for correlations between any measure of the brain and variations in IQ in the normal range has been long and remarkably unproductive.

7.20 The only *securely* replicated correlation is that between IQ and the overall volume of the brain – where the correlation is about 0.40.[22] But we do not know whether that effect is genetic: improved nutrition and a more stimulating environment will both cause a significant increase in the volume of rats' brains and improve their learning ability, and it is entirely possible that these and other environmental variables have a similar impact on the human brain.[23] One recent study assessed the heritability of brain structure rather than cognitive ability.[24] The researchers compared the density of grey matter (brain cell bodies) at specific regions in the brains of twins and other individuals. Their findings suggest that grey matter density is much more clearly correlated with intelligence at some cortical sites than at others. This area of genetic research requires considerably more detailed studies before firm conclusions can be drawn.

7.21 The search for genes associated with variation in IQ will be made more difficult, to the extent that genetic effects on IQ are not additive. We used earlier the illustrative possibility that IQ was affected by 25 genes, each with an equal, additive effect (paragraph 7.15). But some genetic effects, dominance and epistasis, are not additive. A recessive allele at a particular locus will have one effect on the phenotype if it is accompanied by a dominant allele at that locus, and a quite different effect if accompanied by the same recessive allele. Many harmful recessive genes are maintained in the population because, although harmful or even lethal when two copies are present, they may be beneficial if they are accompanied by a dominant allele which blocks the harmful consequence. Epistasis refers to the possibility that phenotypic characteristics are affected by particular combinations of alleles at different loci. For example, it might be the case that allele 5 of the IGF2R gene is associated with high IQ only if it is accompanied by particular alleles at other loci. In their absence, it is accompanied by normal or even low IQ. If that were true, it would clearly be difficult to detect, and replicate, substantial effects.

7.22 Is the genetic variance underlying variation in IQ mostly additive? We noted in Chapter 4 that much research in behavioural genetics assumes this to be the case. But two relatively sophisticated attempts to model IQ variation, while both concluding that the overall broad-sense heritability of IQ is about 0.50, also argue that additive genetic variance accounted for no more than about 30% of the overall variation in IQ, while non-additive effects accounted for some 20%.[25]

---

22 Vernon, P. A. et al. The neuropsychology and psychophysiology of human intelligence. In Sternberg, R. J., editor. (2000). *Handbook of Intelligence*. Cambridge: Cambridge University Press; Deary, I. J. (2000). *Looking Down on Human Intelligence*. Oxford: Oxford University Press.

23 Renna, J. M. & Rosenzweig, M. R. (1987). *Enriched and Impoverished Environments*. New York: Springer-Verlag.

24 Thompson, P. M. et al. (2001). Genetic influences on brain structure. *Nat. Neurosci.* **4**, 1253–8.

25 Devlin, B., Daniels, M. & Roeder, K. (1997). The heritability of IQ. *Nature* **388**, 468–71; Chipuer, H. M., RoVine, M., & Plomin, R. (1990). LISREL modeling: Genetic and environmental influences on IQ revisited. *Intelligence* **14**, 11–29.

7.23 Although we observed in paragraph 7.3 that performance on one kind of IQ test is often positively correlated with performance on others, thus ensuring that factor analysis will find a sizeable general factor, this *g* is certainly not the entire answer to the question of IQ. The cognitive abilities measured by tests of Gf, Gc, Gv and so on are partially independent of one another. This is particularly true at higher levels of IQ: scores on different types of IQ test are more strongly correlated in people of below average IQ, than in those of above average IQ.[26] Thus a high-IQ group may contain some people with much higher scores on one kind of test, and other people with higher scores on another kind of test. If the genes associated with variations in scores on these different tests are different, there will be that much less chance of finding genes consistently associated with a high IQ score. To that extent, the strategy of comparing a high-IQ group with an average-IQ group may be problematic.

7.24 There is evidence for the heritability of different cognitive abilities, independent of any general factor.[27] However, Plomin and others have argued that multivariate genetic analysis[28] establishes that, to a significant extent, the same genes affect different cognitive abilities.[29] To the extent that scores on tests of different cognitive abilities are all positively correlated, it is indeed possible that all cognitive abilities depend on a common underlying process – the substrate of *g*, and that genetic effects on *g* are common to all tests. But that is certainly not a necessary conclusion. It is true that tests of different cognitive abilities are all correlated: but the reason for the correlations between various pairs of tests may be different. The general factor extracted by factor analysis is no more than a mathematical representation of the fact that all these tests correlate with one another: it does not prove that there is a single reason why they should do so, in other words, that there is any process or processes common to all tests. It is entirely possible that the genes associated with what one pair of tests shares in common are different from those genes associated with what is common to other pairs of tests.

Directions for future research

7.25 The strategy of the research programme of Plomin and his colleagues has been to identify alleles associated with high, as opposed to average, IQ. A different strategy might be able to locate genes associated with below average IQ, in the range 80 to 100. As noted earlier, since scores on tests of different cognitive abilities are more highly correlated in those of below-average, rather than above-average, IQ, there would seem to be more chance of such research finding genes associated with variations in *g* or any general factor of intelligence. There is, however, a growing belief that the genetic variance in IQ in the lower range of scores may be due to mildly deleterious mutations rather than genes that are associated with variation in IQ scores in the normal range.[30] Recent evidence suggests that the number of such mutations which all people carry and the rate at which new mutations

[26] Detterman, D. K. & Daniel, M. H. (1989). Correlations of mental tests with each other and with cognitive variables are highest for low IQ groups. *Intelligence* **13**, 349–59.

[27] Alarcon, M. *et al*. (1998). Multivariate path analysis of specific cognitive abilities data at 12 years of age in the Colorado Adoption Project. *Behav. Genet.* **28**, 255–64.

[28] Multivariate genetic analysis involves the simultaneous analysis of a number of phenotypes, which allows for the covariance between phenotypes to be broken down into genetic and environmental sources. This attempts to establish how well the genetic or environmental values of one phenotype predict the genetic or environmental values of another phenotype.

[29] Petrill S. A. (1997). *Current Directions in Psychological Science* **6**, 96–9.

[30] Alarcon, M. *et al*. (1998). Multivariate path analysis of specific cognitive abilities data at 12 years of age in the Colorado Adoption Project. *Behav. Genet.* **28**, 255–64.

occur in each generation are much higher than previously supposed.[31] If such mutations act to increase susceptibility to pathogens or other environmental factors, or decrease in any way the overall efficiency of the individual, one would expect them to contribute to a below-average IQ, and that variation in IQ in this range may be caused by variation in the number and nature of such mutations. This would help to explain why there is a significant correlation, after controlling for social class, between IQ and such physical factors as overall health and bodily symmetry.[32] If all this is true, it will be very difficult to identify particular alleles associated with below-average IQ in the population as a whole: a whole range of different genotypes, with quite different mildly deleterious mutations, may be implicated.

[31] See Kondrashov, A. S. (1995). Contamination of the genome by very slightly deleterious mutations: why have we not died 100 times over? *J. Theor. Biol.* **175**, 583–94 and Sunyzev, S. *et al.* (2001). Prediction of deleterious human alleles. *Hum. Mol. Genet.* **10**, 591–7. The latter comes to the conclusion that 'the average human genotype carries approximately 10^3 damaging non-synonymous SNPs that together cause a substantial reduction in fitness'. In other words, every one of us is genetically defective to some extent.

[32] Lubinski, D. & Humphreys, L. G. (1992). Some bodily and medical correlates of mathematical giftedness and commensurate levels of socioeconomic status. *Intelligence* **16**, 99–115; Furlow, B. F., Armijo-Prewitt, T., Gangestad, S. W. & Thornhill, R. (1997). Fluctuating asymmetry and psychometric intelligence. *Proceedings of the Royal Society of London B.* **264**, 823–9.

Chapter 8

Review of the evidence: personality

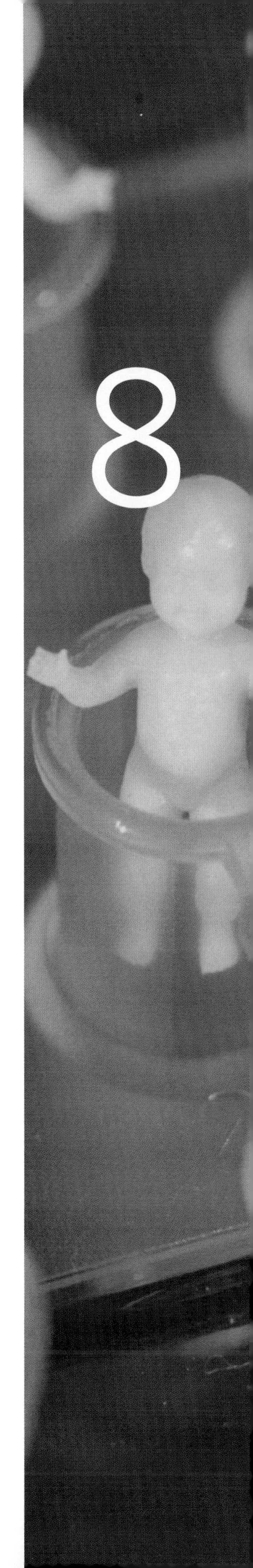

Review of the evidence: personality

Background

8.1 Personality has long been a focus of research in various disciplines. Many measures of personality originated outside psychiatry. For example, the first personality measure, devised in 1919, was used in determining mental fitness for military service. Since then many measures of personality, of differing quality, have been developed, such as the Minnesota Multiphasic Personality Inventory (MMPI). However, it should be noted that the prime purpose of psychological tests of personality was not for use in psychiatry but rather to build a theory of personality.

Trait definition and measurement

8.2 Different aspects of personality can be described at different levels. One can either choose the highest level, at which all the traits are independent of one another, or a variety of lower levels, at which the traits are to varying degrees correlated with each other. Genetic research into personality has largely concentrated on the first, highest level; what might be termed 'global' traits.

8.3 The dominant view at present puts the number of independent personality traits at five; this is called the 'Big Five' model of personality. The 'Big Five' traits are: Neuroticism, Extraversion, Agreeableness, Conscientiousness and Openness to Experience (see Table 8.1).[2] Each trait has a normal distribution of scores. These five traits, or factors, are commonly referred to as 'dimensions of personality'. There is disagreement among psychologists about the number of core personality traits; alternative views range from three to seven. The British psychologist Hans Eysenck originally suggested three – Neuroticism, Introversion and Psychoticism. However, in the Big Five Model, Psychoticism is broken down into three separate factors (Agreeableness, Conscientiousness and Openness to Experience). Impulsivity (sensation-seeking) is also sometimes separated out. It is important to note that these traits are used for descriptive convenience, rather than because there is evidence that they have distinct biological causes or pathways that affect personality.

Table 8.1: The 'Big Five' Personality Traits

Trait	Descriptors at high end of scale	Manifestation of trait
Neuroticism	Anxious Depressed Feeling guilty Having low self-esteem Tense Shy	Individuals with high scores on this trait are likely to develop one of a range of neurotic psychiatric disorders, including generalised anxiety disorder, agoraphobia, major depression and obsessive-compulsive disorder. There is

[1] The material in this chapter is taken from a paper commissioned by the Nuffield Council on Bioethics from Professor Jeffrey Gray, Emeritus Professor at the Institute of Psychiatry, Kings College London. The paper is available on the Council's website: www.nuffieldbioethics.org.

[2] Since terms such as Neuroticism are also in common usage, we adopt the practice of psychologists of capitalising the first letter of each trait in order to indicate that we are referring to these traits as they are defined and studied by psychologists.

	Moody Agitated Suspicious Hostile Emotional	considerable comorbidity between these neurotic disorders (but not between them and the psychotic disorders, such as schizophrenia or mania).[3]
Introversion–Extraversion[4]	Sociable Lively Active Assertive Carefree Dominant Venturesome Optimistic Impulsive Sensation-seeking	Individuals with high scores for Introversion tend to be quiet and reserved, introspective, distant except with intimate friends, reliable, non-impulsive, serious, liking order, emotionally restrained, non-aggressive, moral and somewhat pessimistic. High scorers on Extraversion in contrast tend to be sociable, impulsive, sensation seekers, liking of change, easy going, optimistic, aggressive and can be unreliable.
Agreeableness	Trusting Straightforward Altruistic Compliant Modest Tender-minded	Individuals with high scores on this trait are straightforward and frank, co-operative, yielding rather than aggressive in conflict, modest and unpretentious, caring, nurturing, and supportive and tend to see others as honest and trustworthy.
Conscientiousness	Productive Orderly Dependable Having a high level of aspiration Consistent Rational	Highly conscientious people are goal-oriented and efficient. They are dependable, well-organised, methodical and focused. Being rule-oriented, they avoid disorder and impulsive behaviour.
Openness to Experience	Given to fantasy Aesthetically reactive Sensitive to interpersonal cues Concerned with philosophical problems Moralistic Socially poised	High scorers are flexible and broad-minded individuals who are creative, imaginative and intellectual. They like to try new options, seek out variety and find reward in learning and developing new ideas. They avoid situations that are highly , structured, rigid or controlled.

[3] Quantitative genetics research has shown that the genetic influences on Neuroticism affect almost exclusively its comorbidity with other traits as distinct from the liability to any one particular disorder. The studies show also that scores on self-report scales of Neuroticism provide a good measure of the heritable component of the comorbidity of neurotic disorders. Thus, this trait is best regarded as one of susceptibility to the entire gamut of neurotic disorders, with the actual nature and occurrence of such a disorder depending upon life events.

[4] This is the best established of all personality traits. Like Neuroticism, Extraversion has been embedded in several, experimentally testable, neurobiological theories and progress is being made towards identifying the underlying brain mechanisms.

8.4 Most research indicates that the two most robust traits are those of Neuroticism and Introversion–Extraversion. These are highly replicable, they account for a considerable portion of the variance across a very wide range of measures, and they can each be reliably measured by relatively short self-report scales ideally suited to large-scale genetic studies.

8.5 Using factor analysis, it is possible to determine how many independent factors or traits exist within a given body of data, but not how these factors are related. Thus, from the results of descriptive studies alone, we are unable to tell whether a given dimension of personality merely provides us with a convenient set of coordinates within which to locate an individual's personality (as, say, East–West and North–South are used as convenient sets of coordinates within which to fix spatial location), or whether it has a basis in underlying causal reality (as, say, up–down has a basis in the force of gravity). Because of this ambiguity, many of the trait terms used in personality research (even when they all operate at the highest, dimensional, level) do not reflect entirely different traits, but rather rotations of one another. For example, the trait of novelty-seeking blends some lower-order traits that, in alternative descriptive systems, make up Extraversion with others that make up Psychoticism.

8.6 A further problem is that different investigators may refer to what is essentially the same dimension by different names (often reflecting different theories into which the dimension has been embedded). There are no clear pre-existing signposts to suggest for which personality traits researchers will most likely find genetic influences. However, if there is a substantial heritable component to a given personality trait, then this can itself provide both an external criterion by which to validate the factor purporting to represent the trait as well as a theoretical framework for prediction and experiment to establish its causal reality. For example, if research in quantitative genetics shows a substantial genetic influence on variation in Neuroticism, this simultaneously provides support for the reality of the underlying trait of Neuroticism, for the tests by which it is measured, and for the factor-analytic solution that has yielded the factor of Neuroticism.

Current findings: quantitative genetics

8.7 The two most important conclusions to emerge to date from quantitative genetic studies of personality are of broad generality. First, across a range of traits, heritability estimates from twin studies lie in the range 0.30–0.50[5] (though estimates from adoption studies are consistently lower, suggesting that non-additive genetic variance may have an important role in personality).[6] This is the result obtained for Neuroticism, Extraversion, Conscientiousness, Openness to Experience and Agreeableness (though in the latter case, heritability in one study was estimated at only 0.12). Sensation-seeking has been reported to have somewhat higher heritability, about 0.60. This consistency in the pattern of results is surprising. Between them, these findings, extending as they do over the entire Big Five model, cover all known personality traits. Thus, the genetic contribution to personality is thought to be substantial and appears to be roughly equal across all aspects of personality.

---

[5] Plomin, R., DeFries, J. C., McClearn, G. E. & McGuffin, P. (2001). *Behavioral Genetics*. 4th ed. New York: Worth.

[6] Bouchard, T. J. Jr. & Loehlin, J. C. (2001). Genes, Evolution, and Personality. *Behav. Genet.* **31**, 243–73. Another interesting feature of heritability calculations that the authors discuss is the variation between sexes.

8.8 There is no *a priori* reason to expect all personality traits to be influenced equally by genetic causes. However, the results obtained to date are mutually consistent and apparently robust. It is possible that the uniformity of genetic influence is an artefact due to the imperfect alignment of personality traits derived from descriptive, factor-analytic studies. Future research combining genetic and factor-analytic methods may be able to improve this alignment. In that case, traits would emerge with greater estimates of heritability than the 0.30–0.50 that have emerged so far, but these would be balanced by others with lesser estimates of heritability (with the total genetic contribution across the whole of personality space necessarily being conserved).

8.9 Secondly, quantitative genetics research has shown that when considering the environmental effects on personality, non-shared environmental factors have the largest effect (see paragraphs 4.9–4.10 which explain the difference between shared and non-shared environment).[7] However, unless specific measures of environmental risk factors are included in these studies, little can be surmised as to what these influences might be, or even the degree to which they are likely to yield to systematic analysis.

Current findings: molecular genetics

8.10 A large number of genes are known to influence brain function. Moreover, in the present state of knowledge, a plausible hypothesis can be constructed to link almost any of the known genes with virtually any aspect of personality. And many other genes with influence on the brain remain to be discovered and so cannot yet serve as candidates.

8.11 There are many grounds for believing that levels of anxiety, psychoticism or impulsivity may in part reflect differing levels of functioning of particular neurotransmitters in the brain. Prominent in this respect are the monoamine transmitters: dopamine, serotonin and noradrenaline. Thus, an experimenter may investigate whether trait scores differ as a function of a polymorphism in a gene that determines, for example, the rate of synthesis or transport of one of these neurotransmitters or the structure of the receptors upon which the neurotransmitter acts.

8.12 There has recently been a flurry of studies that claim to identify particular genetic influences on personality traits. Associations have been reported between: (i) novelty-seeking and a polymorphism in the gene for the D4 receptor (one of several different types of receptor) for dopamine;[8] and (ii) anxiety and a polymorphism in the gene for the serotonin transporter.[9] (The serotonin transporter terminates the action of serotonin by transporting it from the synaptic junction back into the cell that has just released it.) There have since been numerous attempts to replicate these findings, with very mixed results. Several of these experiments, especially those reporting negative outcomes, have used samples too small to yield conclusive results. However, there have now been a sufficient number of positive replications of the initial report concerning

---

[7] Riemann, R., Angleitner, A. & Strelau, J. (1997). Genetic and environmental influences on personality: a study of twins reared together using the self- and peer-report NEO-FFI scales. *J. Pers.* **65**, 449–76.

[8] Ebstein, R. P. *et al.* (1995). Dopamine D4 receptor exon III polymorphism associated with the human personality trait of novelty-seeking. *Nat. Genet.* **12**, 78–80; Benjamin, J. *et al.* (1996). Population and familial association between the D4 dopamine receptor gene and measures of novelty-seeking. *Nat. Genet.* **12**, 81–4. See also paragraphs 5.9-5.10.

[9] Lesch, K. P. *et al.* (1996). Association of anxiety related traits with a polymorphism in the serotonin transporter gene regulatory region. *Science* **274**, 1527–31.

the serotonin transporter gene that this finding is reliable.[10] These studies concur in showing that alleles of the serotonin transporter gene which result in reduced serotonin re-uptake are associated with higher anxiety. These results are, however, unexpected, given that drugs which reduce serotonin re-uptake, such as Prozac, are used to alleviate both depression and anxiety. As noted in paragraph 5.10, the evidence for a link between the DRD4 gene and novelty-seeking does not seem convincing, despite the initial findings.

Quantitative trait loci (QTL) research

8.13 Several studies of QTLs for Neuroticism are in progress around the world. QTL studies in humans, that use sibling pairs and linkage strategies, require very large numbers; around 20,000 pairs of siblings who either both score high (or low) on the trait (concordant pairs), or one of whom scores high and the other low (discordant pairs).[11] Results from these studies are likely to become available in the next year. In the light of the results from rodent studies (see paragraphs 8.14 – 8.16) it is likely that at least some of these results will be positive. However, to move beyond the identification of a QTL to the actual gene with which it is associated remains a very difficult technical problem that has not so far been achieved for any QTL thought to affect human behaviour.

Current findings: research involving animals

8.14 Numerous animals have been tested in genetic studies of personality, including primates, rats, mice and even fish. The most developed animal model is that of Emotionality, which is used as an analogue of the human trait of Neuroticism. Neuroticism has been embedded within several neurobiological theories which can be tested experimentally; and there has been good progress in understanding the nature of the systems in the brain whose functioning most likely underlies scores on the trait. Across a wide range of behavioural tests with good credentials as putative measures of anxiety, rodents which obtain high scores on one test are likely also to get high scores on the others. Furthermore, it has proved possible to inbreed and selectively breed strains of mice or rats such that they reliably obtain high (or low) scores on such tests, generation after generation. It remains to be demonstrated, however, that the genes which influence Emotionality in rodents are similar to those that determine human Neuroticism.

8.15 The first QTL study of a behavioural trait, reported by Flint *et al*,[12] investigated Emotionality in mice. This study was an important demonstration of principle. Nearly 1,000 mice were derived from intercrossing two highly inbred, selectively bred strains with very high and very low scores on behavioural tests of Emotionality. The intercrossing mixes the genes from these two parental strains; and the DNA markers can then be used to determine which genes

10 Greenberg, B. D. *et al.* (2000). Association between the serotonin transporter promoter polymorphism and personality traits in a primarily female population sample. *Am. J. Med. Genet. (Neuropsychiatric. Genet.)* **96**, 202–16; Sher, L. *et al.* (2000). Pleiotropy of the serotonin transporter gene for seasonality and neuroticism. *Psychiatr. Genet.* **10**, 125–30; Osher, Y. *et al.* (2000). Association and linkage of anxiety-related traits with a functional polymorphism of the serotonin transporter gene regulatory region in Israeli sibling pairs. *Mol. Psychiatry* **5**, 216–19; Melke, J. *et al.* (2001). Serotonin transporter gene polymorphisms are associated with anxiety-related personality traits in women. *Am. J. Med. Genet. (Neuropsychiatric. Genet.)* **105**, 458–63; Jang, K. J. *et al.* (2001). Covariance structure of neuroticism and agreeableness: a twin and molecular genetic analysis of the role of the serotonin transporter gene. *J. Pers. Soc. Psychol.* **81**, 295–304; Du, L., Bakish, D. & Hrdina, P. D. Gender differences in association between serotonin transporter gene polymorphism and personality traits. *Psychiatr. Genet.* **10**, 159–64.

11 Risch, N. & Merikangas, K. (1996). The future of genetic studies of complex human diseases. *Science* **273**, 1516–17.

12 Flint, J. *et al.* (1995). A simple genetic basis for a complex psychological trait in laboratory mice. *Science* **269**, 1432–5.

in the offspring have been inherited from each strain. QTLs were identified by correlations between these markers and scores on various behavioural tests for Emotionality. Three QTLs were identified, having the important property of *pleiotropy*: that is, each was associated with several different behavioural measures, rather than with any single item of behaviour. The QTL with the greatest effect was situated on chromosome 1. This finding has since been replicated several times. Additional analysis using quantitative genetics techniques assessed the amount of the variance in scores on the tests that could be attributed to genetic factors to be, at most (depending on the particular behavioural measure), about 30%. Importantly, the additive effects of the identified QTLs, taken together, were able to account for nearly all of this genetic variance. Finally, the study confirmed the conclusion, derived from mathematical simulations, that (given a large enough sample size) the QTL approach is able to identify QTLs that account for a very small portion of the phenotypic variance – as little as about 3% in the Flint *et al* study.

8.16 Even for the well-replicated research on the QTL on chromosome 1, however, it has not yet been possible to identify the gene involved; although subsequent work has narrowed down the relevant chromosomal region. Until the gene in question has been identified, it is not possible to test its effects in humans. If the gene were identified in both animals and humans, this would permit investigation of the causal chain by which the gene contributes to the specification of values on the trait. In this respect, the rat is preferred to the mouse, since much more is known about the behavioural functions of the brain in rats. Flint's group have now identified a QTL in the rat which appears to be related to Neuroticism, since it has pleiotropic effects across a large battery of behavioural tests that are sensitive to the effects of drugs used in human beings to reduce anxiety.[13]

Future directions for research

8.17 Future research in behavioural genetics in the field of personality traits is likely to focus on the use of molecular genetic research techniques to identify candidate genes and regions of DNA that have an effect. If such genes are identified, they could provide the basis for experiments aimed at determining the neurobiological pathways by which genetic influences are brought to bear. Detailed knowledge of the genes that affect personality would then, in turn, provide the basis for investigation of non-genetic influences on personality.

[13] Fernandez-Teruel, A. *et al*. (2002). A quantitative trait locus influencing anxiety in the laboratory rat. *Genome Res.* **12**, 618–26.

Chapter 9

Review of the evidence: antisocial behaviour

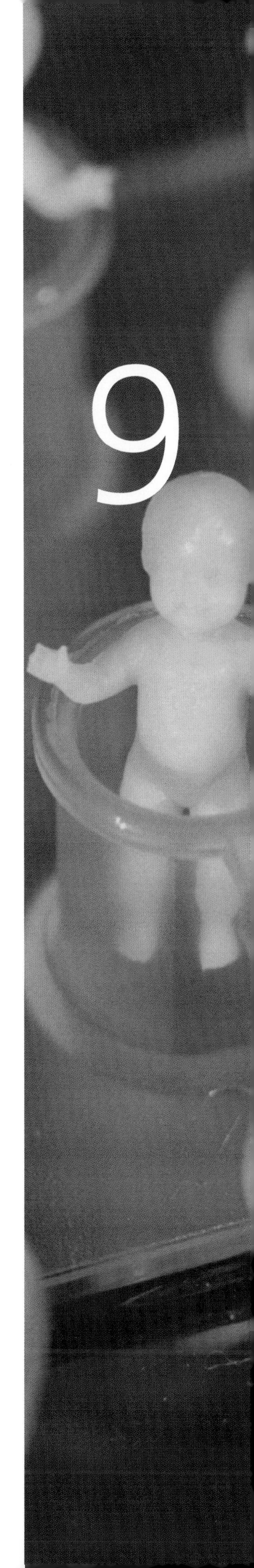

Review of the evidence: antisocial behaviour

Background

9.1 Various biological explanations of antisocial and criminal behaviour have been offered historically but none have stood up to rigorous analysis or offered successful or acceptable solutions to the continuing problems caused by such behaviour. It is widely accepted that crime and antisocial behaviour are the results of many different influences, some of which, such as deprivation and poverty, are already the target of existing interventions. This chapter explores attempts by researchers in behavioural genetics to examine a potential genetic contribution towards such behaviour.

Trait definition and measurement

9.2 Antisocial behaviour is studied by different disciplines, each of which has its own perspective on the definition and measurement of what is antisocial. Mental health clinicians, criminologists and personality psychologists conceptualise and measure antisocial behaviour somewhat differently, but all three fields share in common the underlying assumption that antisocial behaviour is behaviour that violates the rights and safety of others.

9.3 Mental health clinicians interested in pathological behaviour conceptualise antisocial behaviour as a mental disorder. As a result, their definitions require that the behaviour is seriously harmful to others, involves a number of different types of antisocial acts, or has persisted over a long time period. The primary labels assigned to antisocial pathology are: *conduct disorder*, in young people under 18; *antisocial personality disorder*, in adults; and *psychopathy*, also in adults. These clinical definitions tend to apply to fewer than 5–10% of the population, depending on age. Such mental disorders are typically measured as diagnostic categories (either the individual meets the criteria for the disorder, or not). However, there are instruments that measure these disorders as continuous distributions, in which the number of different symptoms exhibited is counted. Examples of dimensional instruments that have been used in research in behavioural genetics with children include the Achenbach Child Behaviour Checklist for externalising behaviours and the Rutter antisocial scale. An example of a dimensional measure used in research with adults is the Minnesota Multiphasic Personality Inventory (MMPI) psychopathy scale, which was discussed briefly in paragraph 8.1 in relation to personality tests. Information about the presence or absence of symptoms is usually gathered about young children through reports from parents and teachers, about older children and adolescents through parents, teachers and self-reports, or about adults through self-reports or clinical records.

9.4 Criminologists conceptualise antisocial behaviour as behaviour that is against the law. As a result, their definitions do not require there to be serious harm, a variety of acts or persistence. Nonetheless, in practice most criminologists discriminate between the minor offender who commits a one-off offence and the more extreme alternatives, namely

[1] The material in this Chapter is taken from a paper by Professor Terrie Moffitt, Institute of Psychiatry, King's College London. The paper is available on the Council's website: www.nuffieldbioethics.org.

violent, proficient or persistent recidivistic offenders, because the latter are of greater concern in policy terms. The primary labels assigned are: *delinquency*, in juveniles, whose age is legally defined; and *crime*, in adults. These legal definitions tend to apply to between 20–30% of the population, depending on age. These constructs are sometimes measured as legal categories (either the individual has been convicted at court, or not). However, they are more commonly measured as continuous distributions, in which the number of different illegal behaviours committed and the frequency with which they have been committed are counted. Information about the presence or absence of illegal acts is usually gathered through self-reports or police records (about older children and adolescents), or through self-reports or court conviction records (about adults).

9.5 Personality psychologists conceptualise antisocial traits in terms of attitudes, beliefs, interests and preferences that indicate an inclination to take advantage of or harm others, or a willingness to break the law. As a result, their definitions do not require that any antisocial act has occurred. Personality psychologists think of the 'aggressiveness' of humans as a characteristic analogous to the 'brittleness' of glass; always there, but not necessarily expressed. Although older personality measures that were labelled 'aggression' sometimes included items asking about actual physical acts, it has been shown that such acts are not integral to the measures. The primary labels assigned are *hostility*, which refers to temper, *socialisation*, which includes such traits as conscientiousness and honesty, or *aggression*. Definitions of personality traits tend to apply to the entire population; the high end of an 'aggression' scale may indicate enthusiasm for aggression whereas the low end may indicate timidity. These personality constructs are virtually never measured as discrete categories, because a fundamental assumption about personality traits is that they are continuously distributed in the population. They are generally measured using checklists which count the number of different antisocial attitudes endorsed by the respondent. Examples of dimensional instruments that have been used in research in behavioural genetics include the Multidimensional Personality Questionnaire (MPQ) aggression scale, the Buss–Durkee hostility scales, and the California Psychological Inventory (CPI) socialisation scale. Information about antisocial personality traits is usually gathered through self-reports about older adolescents and adults.

9.6 Although the discussion above highlights differences between the three ways of conceptualising and measuring antisocial behaviour, research that has crossed disciplines has repeatedly shown that clinical, legal and personality measures are moderately to strongly related to each other. For example, aggressiveness measured in adolescence is strongly correlated with later court conviction for violent criminal offending in adulthood, as well as with psychiatric diagnosis of antisocial personality disorder.[2,3] Moreover, as we shall see, estimates of genetic and environmental influences on the three types of measure are more similar than different.

9.7 Classifying individuals into dichotomous categories based on their antisocial behaviour is fraught with difficulty and generally classification is not strongly reliable. Is an individual a psychopath, or not? Is an individual a criminal, or not? Does he or she have a diagnosis

[2] Moffitt, T. E., Krueger, R. F., Caspi, A. & Fagan, R. W. (2000). Partner abuse and general crime: How are they the same? How are they different? *Criminology* **38**, 201–35.

[3] Krueger, R. F., Caspi, A., Moffitt, T. E., Silva, P. A. & McGee, R. (1996). Personality traits are differentially linked to mental disorders: A multi-trait/multi-diagnosis study of an adolescent birth cohort. *J. Abnorm. Psychol.* **105**, 299–312.

of conduct disorder, or not? Does he or she have a diagnosis of antisocial personality disorder, or not? Assigning a person to such categories is a matter of deciding that his or her behaviour has surpassed some cut-off point along a continuous measure of antisocial behaviours. The cut-off points are more arbitrary than based on evidence. Unreliable assignment arises frequently because individuals' scores fall just above or below cut-off points. Quantitative genetic theory, psychometric theory and accumulated research findings suggest that a truer, and more reliable, measure of individual differences in antisocial behaviour is obtained when the natural continuum is not arbitrarily cut into categories. For this reason, we consider antisocial behaviour in this Report as a trait that is normally distributed and therefore able to be measured as part of variation in the normal range.

9.8 The advantages of the principle of continuous dimensional measures do not apply only to research in behavioural genetics. Rather, measures of antisocial behaviour that sample a variety of behaviours are more useful in other types of research as well. For example, longitudinal research shows that the variety of different antisocial acts a child has exhibited is the single best predictor of his or her adult outcome.[4] There is therefore a growing consensus that measures of antisocial behaviour should gather data about a large number of different behaviours covering a wide range of antisocial severity, and should include a period of observation that allows enough time for research participants to exhibit the behaviours.

Current findings: quantitative genetics

Antisocial behaviour

9.9 Estimates of heritability for antisocial behaviour from recent research in quantitative genetics cluster around 0.50. The most reliable estimates come from contemporary studies in the Netherlands, Britain, Norway, Sweden, Australia and the US, because these studies examine large, representative samples using sophisticated quantitative modelling techniques. A complementary meta-analysis of 51 twin and adoption studies yielded an estimate of heritability of 0.41 for the genetic influence on antisocial behaviour.[5] Estimates of heritability below 0.20 tend to emerge from studies with unusual design features; for example, observational measures, small sample sizes, very wide age ranges, small groups of girls, or adults being asked to report childhood symptoms retrospectively. Similarly, some, but not all, studies yielding estimates above 0.70 have non-optimal designs, such as small sample sizes or adults being asked to report their childhood symptoms retrospectively.

9.10 The sizes of estimates of heritability vary somewhat across different types of measures of antisocial involvement. Overall, this variation appears to be systematic. It reflects the fact that (all other aspects of methodology being equal) higher estimates of heritability are obtained from studies using measures that sample the most different types of antisocial behaviours. Measures that sample many behaviours yield more accurate estimates because their scores are less contaminated with error, and also because they are more sensitive to

---

4 Robins, L. N. (1978). Sturdy childhood predictors of antisocial behaviour: replications from longitudinal studies. *Psychol. Med.* **8**, 611–22.

5 Rhee, S. H. & Waldman, I. D. (2002). Genetic and environmental influences on antisocial behavior: a meta-analysis of twin and adoption studies. *Psychol. Bull.* **128**, 490–529.

the full range of behaviour in the population. The lowest estimates of heritability emerge from observational measures, which sample only a narrow type of behaviour such as hitting a doll or arguing with a parent, over brief spans of time, usually minutes. The next lowest estimates emerge from measures of official offending in juveniles, which also sample a narrow range of behaviour, namely illegal behaviour, which is seldom detected. Fewer than half of juveniles who offend are arrested, and of those arrested 75% are arrested only once or twice. Medium estimates of heritability tend to emerge from measures of self-reported offending, symptoms of conduct disorder and official offending in adults, all of which tend to aggregate across a moderately wide sample of behaviours and moderately long periods of ascertainment.

9.11 The largest estimates of heritability tend to emerge from studies using measures able to array individuals along a continuum from non-antisocial to severely and persistently antisocial. These are studies using other-reported delinquent or aggressive behaviours (such as the Child Behaviour Check List (CBCL) externalising scale), and self-reported personality traits (such as the MPQ aggression scale). These studies tend to include a very large number of items inquiring about a variety of antisocial attitudes and behaviours. Some of these items, such as robbery, are exhibited rarely by people, but others, such as enjoying violent films, are exhibited commonly. As a result, the instruments are sensitive to population variation in the severity of antisocial behaviour.[6] Overall, the distribution of more than 100 estimates of heritability from recent papers approximates a bell-shaped normal curve. This distribution is to be expected from a sample of more than 100 imperfect estimates of a true effect that equals 50% in nature.

9.12 As well as the possibility that genes influence antisocial behaviour, it is also possible that antisocial experience can influence how genes are distributed in the population. This is an implication of the finding that men and women mate on the basis of similarity between the partners' antisocial behaviour (this is called assortative mating), and that couples in which both people exhibit antisocial behaviour tend to have more children than the norm.[7] Assortative mating on a genetically-influenced phenotype, such as antisocial behaviour has consequences for genetic variation in the population. Because people form unions with other people like themselves, the result is that families differ more from each other on average than they would if people mated randomly. If successive generations mate assortatively, genes relevant to the phenotype will become concentrated within families. Consider height as an example. Whole families clearly differ from other families in terms of height, yet families are made up of persons who are similar in height. Part of the explanation for this phenomenon is likely to lie in the positive assortative mating that occurs for this trait.

[6] A study of 14,500 Danish adoptee families provides a good example of the importance of measures that sample different acts along a dimension to improve sensitivity to features of antisocial behaviour such as severity, frequency and persistence (Mednick, S. A., Gabrielli, W. F. & Hutchings, B. (1984). Genetic factors in criminal behaviour: evidence from an adoption cohort. *Science* **224**, 891–3). When adoptee family members were classified simply as 'not convicted' or 'convicted' (a legal status applying to nearly one quarter of Danish males), the estimate of heritability was modest. However, when the number of convictions in an individual's life-time from age 15 to 50 was considered, stronger estimates of heritability emerged for individuals who had repeatedly been convicted on many successive court dates, presumably reflecting what criminologists call a 'crime career'.

[7] See for example Farrington, D. P., Barnes, G. C. & Lambert, S. (1996). The concentration of offending in families. *Leg. Criminol. Psychol.* **1**, 47–63; Rowe, D. C. & Farrington. D. P. (1997). The familial transmission of criminal convictions. *Criminology* **35**, 177–201; Farrington, D. P., Jolliffe, D., Loeber, R., Stouthamer-Loeber, M. & Kalb, L. (2001). The concentration of offenders in families, and family criminality in the prediction of boys' delinquency. *J. Adolescence* **24**, 579–96; Kreuger, R. F., Moffitt, T. E., Caspi, A., Bleske, A. & Silva, P. A. (1998). Assortative mating for antisocial behaviour: development and methodological implications. *Behav. Genet.* **28**, 173–86.

9.13 Another important insight from research in behavioural genetics is that while genes influence tendencies towards antisocial personality and antisocial behaviour, they have relatively little influence on the probability of becoming officially designated as a delinquent at any particular court appearance. The designation of 'delinquent' is a characteristic influenced by the behaviour of co-offenders, police, parents, lawyers and judges, not merely by the behaviour of the young person.

Violence

9.14 Public debate about the implications of heritability for criminal responsibility often focuses on violent crime. Findings about genetic effects on violence are rare and inconsistent. Three studies report evidence of a value of zero for the heritability for violence,[8] whereas three studies report evidence that heritability for violence is about the same as for non-violent antisocial behaviour (0.50).[9]

9.15 Two main difficulties arise in the study of individual differences in official records of conviction for violent crime. First, even in the largest samples, official convictions for violent crime occur at very low rates. Inconsistent findings arise from such low indicators, because they cannot be reliably aggregated. Secondly, contrary to popular assumption, offenders designated 'violent' by virtue of court conviction are not necessarily the most serious, persistent criminals at the antisocial extreme. To illustrate, studies of murderers reveal that approximately half have lengthy histories of repeated assaults, rapes, robberies and other offence types, but the other half have committed a single extreme act after a lifetime free from crime. This indicates that the most serious of violent offences, homicide, as a legally constructed status, captures individuals likely to be quite heterogeneous in their genetic dispositions. Low base rates and heterogeneous participants may explain why studies using conviction data have found no heritability for violence.

9.16 The antidote to studying convictions is to use measures of violence that inquire about violent behaviours that have physical differences and cover a range of severity (fighting, hurting animals, robbery, hitting, aggravated assault using a weapon, gang-fighting, rape and domestic abuse). It is also helpful to use a reporting period long enough for research participants who are violently inclined to exhibit these relatively rare behaviours. This approach was used in two studies of self-reported violence in twins and siblings, which yielded significant estimates of heritability.[10]

9.17 Researchers in behavioural genetics usually do not single out violence for separate analysis. Researchers are dissuaded from doing so by the strong psychometric evidence that antisocial behaviour is a unified construct and therefore a separate research focus on violence is not warranted. Most studies of the structure of antisocial behaviour have

---

[8] Bohman, M., Cloninger, R., Sigvardsson, S. & von Knoring, A. L. (1982). Predisposition to petty criminality in Swedish adoptees. I. Genetic and environmental heterogeneity. *Arch. Gen. Psychiatr.* **39**, 1233–41; Mednick, S. A., Gabrielli, W. F. & Hutchings, B. (1984). Genetic factors in criminal behaviour: evidence from an adoption cohort. *Science* **224**, 891–3; Sigvardsson, S., Cloninger, C. R., Bohman, M. & von Korring, A. (1982). Predisposition to petty criminality in Swedish adoptees. III. Sex differences and validation of the male typology. *Arch. Gen. Psychiatr.* **39**, 1248–53.

[9] Heritability is reported as 50% in Cloninger, C. R. & Gottesman, I. I. Genetic and environmental factors in antisocial behaviour disorders. In Mednick, S. A., Moffitt, T. E. & Stack, S. A., editors. (1987). *The Causes of Crime: New Biological Approaches.* Cambridge: Cambridge University Press. pp. 92–109; 32% in Rowe, D. C., Almeida, D. M. Jacobson, K. C. (1999). School context and genetic influences on aggression in adolescence. *Psychol. Sci.* **10**, 277–80; 55% in Rushton, J. P. (1996). Self-report delinquency and violence in adult twins. *Psychiatr. Genet.* **6**, 87–9.

[10] Rowe, D. C., Almeida, D. M. & Jacobson, K. C. (1999). School context and genetic influences on aggression in adolescence. *Psychol. Sci.* **10**, 277–80; Rushton, J. P. (1996). Self-report delinquency and violence in adult twins. *Psychiatr. Genet.* **6**, 87–9.

suggested that items measuring physical aggression belong together with items assessing stealing, lying, fraud, vice, reckless irresponsibility and other forms of antisocial behaviour.[11]

9.19 Many studies in behavioural genetics have examined measures known to be strong, specific predictors of physical violence. For example, many have used the MPQ aggression scale and have reported strong estimates of heritability. The MPQ aggression scale measures attitudes, values, and beliefs that are consistent with approval of the use of physical violence.[12] Longitudinal research shows that the MPQ aggression scale empirically predicts future conviction for violent crime.[13]

9.20 Overall, the question of genetic influences for violent crime has not interested researchers in behavioural genetics as much as it has the general public. As a result, the evidence base is not sufficient to answer the question decisively. However, there is good evidence of heritability for antisocial traits and behaviours associated with risk for engaging in violent crime, and this suggests that heritable liability for violence is a reasonable hypothesis. An area overlooked by research in behavioural genetics is violence within relationships, a type of violence for which there are reliable aggregate measurement tools.

Sex differences

9.21 Differences between the sexes in heritability of antisocial behaviour may exist, but are small. It is unclear as yet whether these small differences should be interpreted as substantive, or as artefacts of sex differences in measurement. On balance, the results of model tests in large samples suggest that estimates of heritability may be slightly higher among males than females, but that sex-specific models of heritability cannot be justified.[14]

9.22 Estimates of heritability may be slightly smaller for females because measurements of antisocial behaviour among females represent less of the full range of antisocial severity, relative to measurements among males. The antisocial behaviour performed by females is less serious and less frequent than that of males, and females participate in antisocial activities for a much shorter period of the life course than males.[15] The relative rarity and brevity of females' antisocial behaviour makes it difficult to obtain strong aggregate measures of it, and this may influence estimates of heritability downwards for females.

---

[11] Moffitt, T. E., Krueger, R. F., Caspi, A. & Fagan, R. W. (2000). Partner abuse and general crime: How are they the same? How are they different? *Criminology* **38**, 201–35; Blumstein, A., Cohen, J., Das, S. & Moitra, S. (1988). Specialization and seriousness during adult criminal careers. *J. Quan. Criminol.* **4**, 303–45; Farrington, D., Snyder, H. & Finnegan, T. (1988). Specialization in juvenile court careers. *Criminology* **26**, 461–85.

[12] Do not be misled by the names of measures; most scales labelled 'aggression', including the MPQ, do not measure *physical* aggression.

[13] Moffitt, T. E., Krueger, R. F., Caspi, A. & Fagan, R. W. (2000). Partner abuse and general crime: How are they the same? How are they different? *Criminology* **38**, 201–35.

[14] Gjone, H. & Stevenson, J. (1997). The association between internalizing and externalizing behaviour in childhood and early adolescence: Genetic or environmental common influences? *J. Abnorm. Child Psychol.* **25**, 277–86; Eaves, L. *et al.* (1997). Genetics and developmental psychopathology: 2. The main effects of genes and environment on behavioural problems in the Virginia study of adolescent behavioural development. *J. Child Psychol. Psychiatr.* **38**, 965–80; Taylor, J., McGue, M., Iacono, W. G. & Lykken, D. T. (2000). A behavioural genetic analysis of the relationship between the socialization scale and self-reported delinquency. *J. Pers.* **68**, 29–50; Finkle, D. & McGue, M. (1997). Sex differences and nonadditivity in the heritability on the Multidimensional Personality Questionnaire scales. *J. Pers. Soc. Psychol.* **72**, 929–38.

[15] Moffitt, T. E., Caspi, A., Rutter, M. & Silva, P. A. (2001). *Sex Differences in Antisocial Behaviour: Conduct Disorder, Delinquency, and Violence in the Dunedin Longitudinal Study.* Cambridge: Cambridge University Press.

Current findings: molecular genetics

9.23 Strong estimates of heritability for a behavioural trait are generally taken to recommend further genetic research at the molecular level, to identify specific genes associated with the trait, and to ascertain their functions in relation to the brain. Antisocial behaviour is not currently a high priority for research in molecular genetics, because it is not as strongly heritable as disorders such as autism or schizophrenia. Nonetheless, molecular genetic research into antisocial behaviour will be pursued because antisocial behaviour forms part of a syndrome alongside two disorders that are currently of great interest in molecular genetics: Attention Deficit Hyperactivity Disorder and substance-dependence. Antisocial behaviour is a complex disorder, quantitatively distributed in the population, and as a result, antisocial behaviour must be influenced by many genes of small effect.

9.24 There is one study that has claimed to find an association between a genetic variant and forms of antisocial behaviour. In the 1980s, researchers became interested in a particular family in the Netherlands. Many of the male members of the family behaved in a notably violent and aggressive manner, and a considerable number had been involved in serious crime including rape and arson. Analysis of the family pedigree led researchers to look for a gene on the X chromosome that might be linked to this tendency in the men. They focused on a gene responsible for producing a protein called monoamine oxidase A (MAOA), involved in regulating the metabolism of serotonin in the brain. The male members of the family who engaged in aggressive behaviour were found to have abnormally low levels of MAOA in their bodies, and a defect in the gene was identified in these men in 1993.[16] They were also found to have lower than average IQs of around 80.

9.25 In August 2002, a study was published which investigated the link between MAOA and antisocial behaviour in a group of 500 male children.[17] The study examined the genotypes of the boys and identified a variant in the MAOA gene that was associated with high levels of MAOA activity in the brain, and another that was associated with low levels. The researchers found that children with the genotype conferring low levels of MAOA activity were significantly more likely to grow up to exhibit antisocial behaviour than those with high levels, but only if they were also maltreated and abused as children. In other words, it was the interaction between the genetic variant and the environment to which the children were exposed that was important. Children with low levels of MAOA activity who were not maltreated did not display antisocial behaviour. Nor did children with high levels of MAOA activity who were maltreated. The researchers stated that their findings 'may partly explain why some victims of maltreatment grow up to victimise others'. This research is particularly interesting because it demonstrates the connection between genetic and environmental influences on behaviour. We discuss its implications further in paragraphs 14.34 – 14.44 in the context of predicting future criminal and antisocial behaviour.

Current findings: research involving animals

9.26 The relevance of animal models of aggression for human antisocial behaviour has not yet been fully established. However, rodents offer the clear advantage of experimental manipulation to test effects of specific genes on aggression. Genetic research into

[16] Brunner, H. G., Nelen, M., Breakefield, X. O., Ropers, H. H. & van Oost, B. A. (1993). Abnormal behavior associated with a point mutation in the structural gene for monoamine oxidase A. *Science* **262**, 578–80.

[17] Caspi, A. *et al.* (2002). Role of genotype in the cycle of violence in maltreated children. *Science* **297**, 851-4.

aggression in animals (such as selective breeding of highly aggressive mouse strains, or studies of enhanced aggression in mice with 'knockout' manipulations of the genome) is proceeding rapidly, which should lead to findings in molecular genetics in the related area of human antisocial behaviour.[18]

9.27 One example of such a study was reported in May 2002, which claimed to have identified a genetic mutation that caused violent behaviour in mice.[19] The mutation, nicknamed 'fierce', has a range of effects in mice including extremely violent behaviour towards other mice, significant brain defects and physical differences such as decreased size, body fat and eye abnormalities.[20] A counterpart of the gene does exist in humans, but its precise function is not known.

Future directions for research

9.28 Quantitative research techniques are useful for revealing the contribution of environmental factors to antisocial outcomes in humans. This is a priority for future research because it may indicate the possibility of strategies for prevention. Researchers in behavioural genetics are beginning to include in their research, measures of the environmental factors that are thought to contribute to antisocial behaviour, such as the maltreatment of children, poverty and inconsistent discipline. Studies will hope to ascertain how the environments of young people interact with their genetic vulnerabilities, to exacerbate or protect against their risk for antisocial behaviour. Longitudinal research will follow samples of twins and adoptees as they age, to explore the changing balance between genetic and environmental factors that influence antisocial behaviour over the course of an individual's life. Because 'crime' itself is not inherited, researchers are working to investigate which features of personality and cognitive function may be associated with antisocial behaviour. With regard to molecular research techniques, research into MAOA-related genotypes is likely to continue (see paragraphs 9.24–9.25), along with research into other genes identified in research involving animals, and genes known to have functional significance in the brain. Importantly, quantitative and molecular work is converging on the possibility that genes act to augment the resistance of young people to environmental factors that would otherwise increase the likelihood of antisocial behaviour.

---

[18] For a review see Maxson, S. C. Genetic influences on aggressive behavior. In Pfaff, D. W., Berrettini, W. H., Toh. H. J. & Maxson, S. C., editors. (2000). *Genetic Influences on Neural Behavioural Functions*. New York: CRC Press. pp. 405–15.

[19] Young, K. A. *et al.* (2002). Fierce: a new mouse deletion of Nr2e1; violent behaviour and ocular abnormalities are background-dependent. *Behav. Brain Res.* **132**, 145–58.

[20] An interesting observation about this study is that the researchers did not set out to identify genes that influenced violent behaviour – they were studying reproduction. This illustrates the point made in Chapters 3 and 4 that findings related to behavioural traits are likely to emerge as a result of genetic research into disorders, making it difficult to prevent this kind of knowledge from being discovered.

Chapter 10

Review of the evidence: sexual orientation

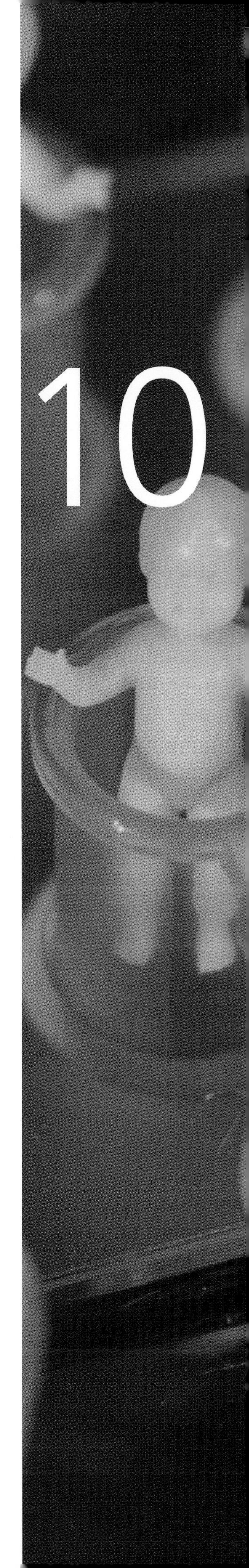

Review of the evidence: sexual orientation

Background

10.1 There has always been considerable interest in biological explanations of homosexuality, as in other aspects of human behaviour. Until the 1970s, homosexuality was classified as a mental disorder in many Western countries, which meant that much research was aimed at developing 'cures' for the 'disease'.[1] Today, the vast majority of countries do not classify homosexuality as a disease. Nevertheless, attitudes towards homosexuals are often negative, hostile and discriminatory. Homosexual behaviour remains illegal in over 40 countries across Africa, Asia, Europe, the Middle East and the Americas, and in some, it is punishable by death.[2] Even in those countries in which homosexuality is not illegal, it is often the case that homosexual couples are not awarded the same legal rights and recognition as heterosexual couples.

10.2 There remains considerable controversy about whether sexual orientation is a matter of choice and whether it is possible to change one's sexual orientation. A recent Gallup poll conducted in June 2001 on Americans' attitudes towards homosexuality asked 'In your view, is homosexuality something a person is born with or is homosexuality due to other factors such as upbringing or environment?' 40% of respondents said that it was something a person was born with, while 39% felt that it was the result of environmental factors. This was the first time that opinion had been equally split since the first poll in 1977, at which time the respective figures were 13% and 56%. During the period 1977–2001, there was also a gradual increase in adherence to the belief that homosexuality is an acceptable alternative lifestyle, though approximately half of those questioned in 2001 still thought it was not. Various polls have shown that people who believe homosexual orientation cannot be changed, is biologically based or is not a choice are more likely also to believe that there should not be social or criminal sanctions against homosexual behaviour.[3]

Trait measurement and definition

10.3 The scale most commonly used to measure sexual orientation is the Kinsey Scale, which was developed in 1948. This measures sexual behaviour and fantasies on a continuum from 'exclusively heterosexual' to 'exclusively homosexual' (see Box 10.1). Individuals obtain scores of between zero and six, with zero and one usually classed as heterosexual and five and six classed as homosexual, for the purposes of the research. There is an additional category for individuals with no sexual contacts or reactions. Other measures, such as the

[1] Most countries use one of two classification and diagnostic systems for psychiatric illness: the Diagnostic Statistical Manual for Mental Disorders (DSM), published by the American Psychiatric Association, or the International Classifications of Diseases, Mental Disorders Section (ICD). Homosexuality was removed from the DSM in 1973. A new 'disorder' of ego-dystonic homosexuality was included in the 3rd edition in 1980 but was removed six years later after considerable criticism. Homosexuality was included as a psychiatric disorder in the ICD until the publication of its 10th edition in 1993.

[2] The International Lesbian and Gay Association. (September 1999). International Lesbian and Gay Association World Legal Survey 1999. http://www.ilga.org/Information/Legal_survey/ilga_world_legal_survey%20introduction.htm. (9 August 2002).

[3] See, for example, Whitley, B. E., Jr. (1990). The relationship of heterosexuals' attributions for the causes of homosexuality to attitudes toward lesbians and gay men. *Pers. Soc. Psychol. B.* **16**, 369–77; Piskur, J. & Degelman, D. (1992). Effect of reading a summary of research about biological bases of homosexual orientation on attitudes toward homosexuals. *Psychol. Report.* **71**, 1219–25.

Klein Sexual Orientation Grid, include a wider range of variables such as sexual attraction, self-identification, emotional preferences, social preferences and lifestyle. However, these more detailed measures complicate the analysis of data and are thus used less commonly.

Box 10.1: The Kinsey scale of sexual orientation

0 Exclusively heterosexual
1 Predominantly heterosexual/only incidentally homosexual
2 Predominantly heterosexual but more than incidentally homosexual
3 Equally heterosexual and homosexual
4 Predominantly homosexual but more than incidentally heterosexual
5 Predominantly homosexual/only incidentally heterosexual
6 Exclusively homosexual

10.4 Scales such as the Kinsey Scale are designed for self-reporting. In many studies of the biological basis of sexual orientation, data about family members and relatives are also collected. Often this is done by administering questionnaires or interviews, but in some cases, research participants are asked to estimate the sexual orientation of their relatives based on their own experience of them. The correlation of self-reports by relatives and reports about their relatives by research participants is usually high, but does leave open the possibility that some individuals will be assigned to the wrong group.

10.5 There are numerous ways in which biological features could, in theory, influence sexual orientation. For example, they could affect sexual orientation directly by influencing the physical development of the brain. Alternatively, they could operate indirectly by affecting personality and temperament, which in turn could affect an individual's development and interaction with environmental factors. These biological influences need not be genetic; they could, for example, be chemical or hormonal. However, it should be remembered that the control of hormones is largely mediated through genetic factors. This section summarises the results of key research into genetic and other biological influences on human sexual orientation.

Current findings: quantitative genetics

Families

10.6 The rate of homosexual orientation in the general population has been variously estimated between 2% and 10% depending on the criteria used, with 4–5% being the most common estimate for males, and around 2–4% for females.[4] Calculations of the rate of homosexuality are made difficult by the fact that some individuals may not wish to divulge their sexual orientation to a third party, and because of the various ways in which sexual orientation can be defined and measured.

10.7 A number of studies have calculated the rate of homosexual orientation among siblings where one sibling is homosexual.[5] Most studies show that the rate of homosexuality among

[4] See for example Le Vay, S. (1993). *The Sexual Brain*. Cambridge, MA: MIT. p.108. The British National Survey of Sexual Attitudes and Lifestyles (2000) found rates of up to 8.5% in males aged 26–44.

[5] Bailey, J. M. & Pillard, R.C. (1995). Genetics of human sexual orientation. *An. Rev. Sex Res.* **6**, 126–50.

the brothers of a male homosexual appears to be around 9%, though one study found a much higher rate of 22%. The rate of homosexuality among the sisters of a male homosexual appears to be around 5%. Findings of the rate of homosexuality among the sisters of a homosexual female range from 6% to 25%.[6] The rate of homosexuality among the brothers of a homosexual female appears to be around 10%. These results indicate that homosexual males may be more likely to have homosexual brothers than homosexual sisters. Homosexual females may be more likely to have homosexual sisters than homosexual brothers. This suggests that the factors influencing homosexual orientation may be different for males than for females.

Twins and adopted siblings

10.8 In recent years, three studies have examined the concordance rates for sexual orientation among monozygotic (MZ) and dizygotic (DZ) twins and their biological and adoptive siblings. These studies show that there is a significant genetic influence on sexual orientation. However, although all the studies show the same general trend, there is considerable variation in the levels of concordance identified. This may be explained by the sampling methods used. The studies that found the highest concordance rates were those obtained in samples recruited through homophile publications rather than selecting participants from the general population, which may have led to biased samples. Further, an obvious point, but one worth making, is that even the highest concordance rates found for identical twins are in the region of 50%, which indicates that environmental factors are at least as important as genetic factors in explaining variation in sexual orientation.

Male homosexuality

10.9 Bailey and Pillard found that 52% of the MZ co-twins of male homosexual twins were also homosexual or bisexual.[7] For DZ male twins, this fell to 22%, which suggests that genetic factors may be influential. The researchers estimated the heritability of male homosexuality and bisexuality to be between 0.31 and 0.74. Analysis of the various models of the possible influences on sexual orientation developed by the researchers showed that genetic influences were always statistically significant, while non-shared environmental influences were sometimes significant, and shared environmental influences were never significant.

10.10 The study also found that 11% of the adopted brothers of homosexual or bisexual male twins were also homosexual or bisexual, and that 9% of non-twin biologically-related brothers of homosexual or bisexual male twins were homosexual or bisexual. If the rate of homosexuality in the general population is estimated at around 4%,[8] the higher rate of concordance for homosexuality in adopted siblings than in the general population points to a substantial environmental contribution. However, since there is no agreed rate of homosexual orientation in the population, and since this research assessed rates of homosexuality and bisexuality together, this conclusion must be treated with caution.

---

[6] Pillard, R. C. & Weinrich, J. D. (1986). Evidence of familial nature of male homosexuality. *Arch. Gen. Psychiat.* **43**, 808–12.

[7] Bailey, J. M. & Pillard, R. C. (1991). A genetic study of male sexual orientation. *Arch. Gen. Psychiat.* **48**, 1089–96. The researchers defined a score of greater than 1 on the Kinsey scale as homosexual or bisexual, treating homosexuality and bisexuality as one group for their research.

[8] Gebhard, P. H. Incidence of overt homosexuality in the United States and Western Europe. In Livingood, J. M., editor. (1972). *NIMH Task Force on Homosexuality: Final Report and Background Papers.* Rockville, MD: National Institute of Mental Health. Other estimates range from 2 to 10%. Female homosexuality is less prevalent, perhaps about half as common as male homosexuality.

10.11 It is interesting to note the discrepancy between concordance rates between DZ twins (22%), and those for DZ twins compared to their non-twin brothers (9%). Since DZ twins and their non-twin siblings are genetically similar to the same degree, the difference in concordance points to an important environmental factor that makes non-identical twins more similar than siblings. Bailey and Pillard acknowledge this possibility but observe that another study found the concordance rates to be more similar and note that their results could be explained by sampling fluctuations. Another interesting feature of their study is that non-twin biological brothers show the lowest rates of concordance, lower even than adopted siblings, which seems, at first impression, to contradict a biological explanation. It is possible that this finding is the result of ascertainment bias, or some other feature of the research: in any case, it strongly suggests that further studies are needed before firm conclusions can be made.

10.12 More recently, Kendler *et al* conducted a study that used a random sample of approximately 3,000 people. The researchers found a concordance rate of 32% for non-heterosexual orientation in MZ twins.[9] For DZ twins of the same sex, the chance of the second twin also being homosexual or bisexual fell to 13%. The researchers estimated that the heritability of male sexual orientation was between 0.28 and 0.65.

Female homosexuality

10.13 Bailey *et al* found that 48% of MZ co-twins of female homosexual twins were also homosexual.[10] For DZ female twins, the chance of the second twin also being homosexual fell to 16%; 6% of adoptive sisters of female homosexual twins were also homosexual. The homosexual female twins studied reported concordance rates of 14% with their non-twin sisters. The researchers calculated the heritability of sexual orientation to be between 0.27 and 0.76.

Current findings: molecular genetics

10.14 In the light of the evidence from family, twin and adoptive studies which suggests that genetic factors, along with environmental factors, may influence sexual orientation to some degree, attempts have been made to identify the particular genes involved. The most well-known research is that of Dean Hamer, who received considerable publicity in the early 1990s and was widely reported as having discovered the 'gay gene'. Hamer studied 40 pairs of homosexual brothers who all had family histories that indicated a high rate of homosexuality on the mother's side.[11] He interpreted this to mean that a genetic influence on sexual orientation might be found on the X chromosome in these families. In 33 of the 40 sibling pairs, he identified significant similarities in the genetic markers in a particular region of the X chromosome called Xq28, which contains 4 million base pairs and approximately one hundred genes. Since male children only inherit one X chromosome from their mothers, who have two X chromosomes, the probability of both brothers in a sibling pair having inherited the same part of the X chromosome is only 50%. Thus, the finding of 82% of sibling pairs with shared DNA in this region was found to be significant.

[9] Kendler, K. S., Thornton, L. M., Gilman, S. E. & Kessler, R. C. (2000). Sexual Orientation in a US National Sample of Twin and Nontwin sibling pairs. *Am. J. Psychiat.* **157**, 1843–6.

[10] Bailey, J. M., Pillard, R. C., Neale, M. C. & Agyei, Y. (1993). Heritable factors influence female sexual orientation. *Arch. Gen. Psychiat.* **50**, 217–23.

[11] Hamer, D. H., Hu, S., Magnuson, V. L., Hu, N. & Pattatucci, A. M. L. (1993). A linkage between DNA markers on the X chromosome and male sexual orientation. *Science* **261**, 321–7.

10.15 Two years after Hamer's original study, his group of researchers replicated the Xq28 finding, but with less significant results, and using a smaller number of families.[12] They found that 67% of homosexual brothers had inherited the same Xq28 region as each other. The researchers also found that there was no significant linkage for homosexual female siblings.

10.16 In 1998, Sanders *et al* replicated the work in a study involving 54 homosexual sibling pairs. They found that 66% of the pairs of brothers shared the Xq28 region. Their work was presented at the American Psychiatric Association Annual Meeting in Toronto in 1998 but has not yet been formally published. In a similar-sized sample to the Sanders *et al* study, Ebers and Rice found no indication that Xq28 contained a gene that influenced sexual orientation.[13] They examined 52 pairs of homosexual brothers and found that only 46% shared the Xq28 region, which was not statistically significant. Their study differed from the original work in that it did not select participants on the basis of evidence of maternal transmission. However, the researchers argued that even if this methodology were applied, their data would still fail to yield significant results.

10.17 In 1999, Hamer combined the data from these four studies and estimated the percentage of brothers who shared the Xq28 region at 64%. While this result is less significant than his initial result, Hamer's meta-analysis of DNA linkage data continues to support the hypothesis that Xq28 may contain genes that have a role in sexual orientation in males, but indicates that the association is not as strong as was first suggested.

Current findings: research involving animals

10.18 Homosexual behaviour in animals has been widely reported,[14] but research into the genetic basis of such behaviour is less common. One study involving fruit flies showed that by manipulating an individual gene, male fruit flies could be made to initiate homosexual courtship.[15] It is interesting to note that the male fruit flies that had not been genetically modified nevertheless also engaged in courtship and sexual behaviour with the 'homosexual' fruit flies. However, the issue of the extent to which human traits can be meaningfully compared to animal behaviour seems particularly pertinent in the context of sexual orientation, in view of the many facets of this trait in humans, beyond overt, observable behaviours:

> 'flies do not have beliefs and desires. This is a quite serious objection to the view that flies have sexual orientations in anything like the sense that humans do and, thereby, the views that flies can be useful models of human sexual desire'.[16]

---

[12] Hu, S. *et al*. (1995). Linkage between sexual orientation and chromosome Xq28 in males but not in females. *Nat. Genet.* **11**, 248–56.

[13] Rice, G., Anderson, C., Risch, N. & Ebers, G. (1999). Male homosexuality: absence of linkage to microsatellite markers at Xq28. *Science* **23**, 665–7.

[14] See, for example, Vines, G. (1999). Queer Creatures [editorial]. *New Scientist* 7 August.

[15] Zhang, S.-D. & Oswald, W. F. (1995). Misexpression of the white (w) gene triggers male–male courtship in *Drosophila*. *Proc. Natl. Acad. Sci. USA* **92**, 5525–9.

[16] Stein, E. (1999). *The Mismeasure of Desire: the Science, Theory and Ethics of Sexual Orientation*. Oxford: Oxford University Press. pp. 167–9.

Current findings: other biological influences

10.19 The research into genetic influences on sexual orientation does not provide any information about the mechanisms by which genes might influence behaviour. However, a number of studies have examined physiological features that may be correlated with sexual orientation. In 1991, LeVay conducted research into an area of the brain called the anterior hypothalamus, which contains four cell groups called the interstitial nuclei of the anterior hypothalamus (INAH).[17] The INAH neurons had already been shown to be larger in men than in women, and LeVay hypothesised that they could be relevant in sexual behaviour. His research found that a particular group of neurons called INAH3 was significantly larger in heterosexual men than in homosexual men. However, his research was criticised for using as its sample the brains of men who had died of AIDS, since it was possible that the disease may have affected their brains, and for having a small sample of only 41 people. Le Vay noted that his research left open the question of whether 'the structural differences were present at birth and later influenced the men to become gay or straight, or whether they arose in adult life, perhaps as a result of the men's sexual behaviour'.[18]

10.20 The same year, other researchers showed that a bundle of nerves that connects a small region of the right and left sides of the brain, the anterior commissure, is bigger in homosexual men than in heterosexual men.[19] However, evidence of a correlation between aspects of brain structure and a behavioural trait does not by itself provide any guidance on which came first, or whether both are influenced by an entirely separate variable. The idea of neuroplasticity – that experience itself changes the way the brain is formed – is an important concept.

10.21 Other researchers have examined the possibility that exposure to particular hormones and chemicals before birth may be linked to sexual orientation later in life. In 1994, it was reported that homosexual men have a leftward asymmetry in the number of ridges on their fingerprints.[20] Fingerprint ridge development takes place before birth and is influenced by androgens released from the mother to the fetus. Androgens are also thought to be responsible for finger length, and a recent study showed that the ratio of second finger length to fourth finger length is greater in women than in men; women's fingers are on average more similar in length.[21] Homosexual women had a significantly smaller ratio than heterosexual women (in other words, their hands were more like men's hands) but no significant difference was found between homosexual men and heterosexual men. However, as the researchers noted, there is considerable overlap and it is not possible to use finger ratios to predict sexual orientation with any accuracy.

10.22 In 1998, Ellis reported that very high levels of stress during the second trimester of pregnancy increases the probability that a male child is homosexual.[22] Other findings

---

17 Le Vay, S. (1991). A difference in hypothalamic structure between heterosexual and homosexual men. *Science* **253**, 1034–7.

18 Le Vay, S. (1993). *The Sexual Brain*. Cambridge, MA: MIT. p.122.

19 Allen, L. S. & Gorski, R. A. (1992) Sexual orientation and the size of the anterior commissure in the human brain. *Proc. Natl. Acad. Sci. USA* **89**, 7199–202.

20 Hall, J. A. Y. & Kimura, D. Dermatoglyphic asymmetry and sexual orientation in men. *Behav. Neurosci.* **108**, 1203–6.

21 Williams, T. J. *et al.* (2000). Finger-length ratios and sexual orientation. *Nature* **404**, 455–6.

22 Ellis, L., Ames, M. A., Peckham, W. & Burke, D. (1988). Sexual orientation of human offspring may be altered by severe maternal stress during pregnancy. *J. Sex Res.* **25**, 152–7. See also Ridley, M (1993). *The Red Queen*. London: Penguin. pp. 264–5.

include an increased rate of left-handedness among homosexuals,[23] worse performance on visuospatial tasks by homosexual men compared to heterosexual men,[24] and an association, at least in women, between sexual orientation and exposure prenatally to particular hormones.[25] The findings in this area of research into sexual orientation has led some commentators to conclude that hormones have a key role in sexual orientation: 'The "gay gene" ... is widely expected to turn out to be a series of genes that affect the sensitivity of certain tissues to testosterone.'[26]

Critical assessment of the validity of this evidence

10.23 There are numerous problems with genetic and other biological research into sexual orientation which mean that any reported findings must be viewed with caution. First, studies in molecular genetics have relied on very small sample sizes, usually fewer than 100 homosexual participants. Recruiting enough participants to obtain sufficient statistical power appears to be difficult, and the problem of small samples may account for the failure to replicate the Xq28 finding conclusively. Twin studies face similar problems of sample size, of which the researchers are aware. In reporting research that tested 71 identical twin pairs and 37 non-identical twin pairs, Bailey *et al* state 'we urge that our results be evaluated cautiously ... they are not conclusive'.[27]

10.24 Secondly, the method of recruitment of participants has been criticised, not least by the researchers themselves. There are numerous problems associated with self-selecting samples, in particular, ascertainment bias. In the case of twins, for example, 'the most likely way in which this would occur is that gay men whose twins are also gay would be more willing to volunteer than gay men with heterosexual twins'[28] perhaps because of the fear of conflict between twins with different orientations.

10.25 Thirdly, it is not clear whether researchers in behavioural genetics are able to define and measure sexual orientation adequately or comprehensively. One study has demonstrated that reported rates of familial homosexuality differ depending on the criteria used to define the trait.[29] As discussed, different scales are used in different projects. Some rely on simple questions, such as 'Have you ever had a fantasy about a member of the same sex?', which might be expected to generate higher rates of homosexual orientation than those scales which ask about life experiences and self-identification. The study by Kendler *et al* simply asked 'How would you describe your sexual orientation? Would you say you are heterosexual, homosexual or bisexual?' As the researchers note, 'the assessment of the complex phenotype of sexual orientation with a single item is far from ideal'.[30] However, it is not clear whether using multiple scales could circumvent this problem, nor is it clear

---

23 See, for example, Gotestam, K. O. *et al.* (1992). Handedness, dyslexia and twinning in homosexual men. *Int. J. Neurosci.* **63**, 179; McCormick, C. Witelson, S. & Kingstone, E. (1990). Left-handedness in homosexual men and women: neuroendocrine implications. *Psychoneuroendocrinology*. **15**, 69–76.

24 Gladue. B. A. & Beatty, W. W. (1990). Sexual orientation and spatial ability in men and women. *Psychobiology* **18**, 101–8.

25 McCormick, C. Witelson, S. & Kingstone, E. (1990). Left-handedness in homosexual men and women: neuroendocrine implications. *Psychoneuroendocrinology*. **15**, 69–76.

26 Ridley, M (1993). *The Red Queen*. London: Penguin.

27 Bailey, J. M., Pillard, R. C., Neale, M. C. & Agyei, Y. (1993). Heritable factors influence female sexual orientation. *Arch. Gen. Psychiat.* **50**, 217–23.

28 Bailey, J. M. & Pillard, R.C. (1995). Genetics of human sexual orientation. *An. Rev. Sex Res.* **6**, 126–50.

29 Bailey, J. M. & Benishay, D. (1993). Familial aggregation of female sexual orientation. *Am. J. Psychiat.* **150**, 272–7.

30 Kendler, K. S., Thornton, L. M., Gilman, S. E. & Kessler, R. C. (2000). Sexual orientation in a US national sample of twin and nontwin sibling pairs. *Am. J. Psychiat.* **157**, 1843–6.

whether attempts to integrate the different aspects of sexual orientation could ever accurately reflect the components of human sexual preferences. The implications of disagreement about what counts as homosexuality for research are important, as the category in which individuals are placed and the rate of sexual orientation estimated in the general population will both affect whether results appear significant. There is a tendency deliberately to conflate homosexuality and bisexuality in order to achieve more statistical power. Furthermore, researchers themselves are internally inconsistent with their classification. In the study by Bailey and Pillard described above, the researchers study both homosexual and bisexual males and calculate concordance rates accordingly, but their conclusions refer only to homosexuality.

10.26 A fundamental conceptual difficulty must be addressed by researchers in this field: is sexual orientation a dimorphic, trimorphic, or continuously distributed trait? That is to say, are there two or three distinct categories of sexual orientation or is there a spectrum of orientation? Many studies place homosexual and bisexual people in one category and contrast them with heterosexual people. This could suggest either that sexual orientation is viewed as a continuously distributed trait with easily defined points along it, or that the various orientations are entirely distinct. The former position is afflicted by the criticisms outlined regarding the measurement of the trait (paragraph 10.25). The latter position was taken by Hamer in his research into Xq28. He found that there was little overlap between individuals' self-reports on the Kinsey scale on four different aspects of sexuality: self-identification, attraction, fantasy and behaviour. Around 90% of individuals classed themselves as either 0 or 1, or 5 or 6 in all areas. Therefore, 'it was appropriate to treat sexual orientation as a dimorphic rather than as a continuously variable trait'. It is interesting to note that despite the use of measures such as the Kinsey scale, which was developed in order to reflect the spectrum of human sexual behaviour, some researchers nevertheless regard sexual orientation as dimorphic, and categorise the results of Kinsey questionnaires accordingly. A further problem is that there is no consensus about whether homosexuality in men and women is the same type of trait, or has the same origins in both sexes. It has been suggested that the specific genetic influences on sexual orientation will be different for males than for females.[31] All these uncertainties contribute to inconsistencies across research projects which make replication and comparison difficult, and allow great variation in the interpretation of results.

Evolutionary arguments against genetic influences on homosexuality

10.27 An argument often made against the possibility that homosexuality has a genetic origin is that such genes would not 'survive' in evolutionary terms, because gay couples generally do not have children. Various possible explanations for the survival of genes that influence homosexuality have been put forward. One is that the gene or genes in question have a beneficial effect on female fertility, meaning that women with the relevant genes are likely to have more children. Another possibility is that the genes are part of female mitochondrial DNA. If that were the case, they would be inherited by both male and female offspring, but only the female offspring would go on to reproduce. The resulting reduction of competition for resources among the extended family might have enhanced the reproductive success of the females.[32] Another suggestion is that homosexual family members contribute to the reproductive success of an extended family by assisting with

[31] Bailey, J. M., Pillard, R. C., Neale, M. C. & Agyei, Y. (1993). Heritable factors influence female sexual orientation. *Arch. Gen. Psychiat.* **50**, 217–23.

[32] Ridley, M (1993). *The Red Queen*. London: Penguin.

raising offspring. Finally, it has been proposed that homosexuality may be associated with another trait which is linked with improved reproductive success. All these hypotheses are no more than speculation: it is exceedingly difficult to guess how evolution may have worked with regard to a particular genetic variant. Such arguments are of very little value in answering the question of whether a genetic influence on a trait exists.

Future directions for research

10.28 Research into genetic influences on sexual orientation continues. Hamer and his colleagues are attempting to locate specific genes within the Xq28 region, although he has stated that 'There is no "gay gene" and I have never thought there was. Genes play a role, and there are probably more than one of them, and other factors as well.'[33] Other researchers are attempting to replicate Hamer's Xq28 research with larger samples, and to identify other regions of DNA that might be involved. Ongoing projects include the Australian Twin Study of Sexual Attitudes and Behaviour,[34] with data on almost 5,000 twins, and the Gay Brothers Study,[35] which has both molecular genetic and psychological components.

[33] Lehrman, S. (1995). 'Gay gene' study under scrutiny. *San Francisco Examiner* 7 July.

[34] Research on this project is led by Professor N Martin, Queensland Institute of Medical Research, Australia.

[35] Research on this project is led by Dr Khytam Dawood, Northwestern University and Professor Richard Pillard, Associate Professor of Psychiatry, Boston University.

Chapter 11

Central themes from the reviews of the evidence

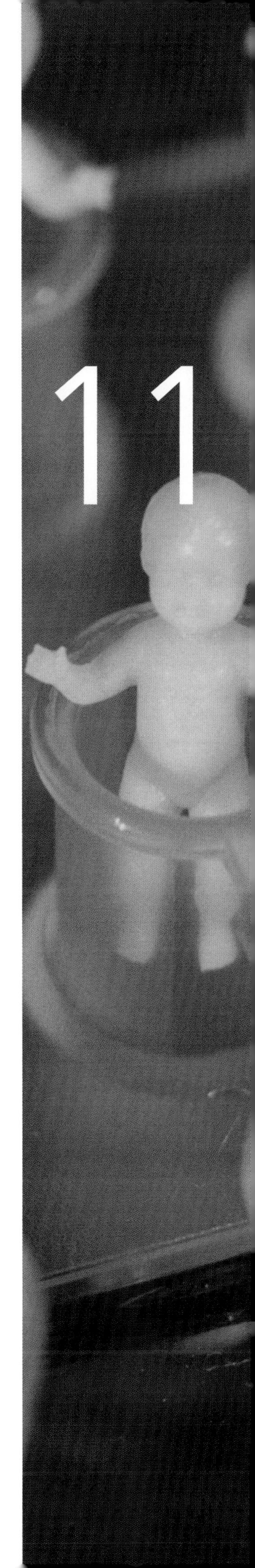

Central themes from the reviews of the evidence

Introduction

11.1 The four preceding chapters have set out some recent findings from research in behavioural genetics into intelligence, personality, antisocial behaviour and sexual orientation. These areas of research were selected to illustrate the breadth of topics which researchers in behavioural genetics are investigating and to include those areas in which practical applications of the research might be likely.

11.2 As the reviews of the evidence demonstrate, research is at different stages in different areas. For some traits, areas of the genome have been identified that might contain genes which have an effect on behaviour. For most traits, the route from such genetic factors to a particular behaviour is unclear. To date, most research in behavioural genetics has relied on quantitative methods (see Chapter 4) to assess the relative contributions of different types of factor. However, the use of molecular genetics (see Chapter 5) is increasing, a trend which is expected to continue. In this chapter, we draw some general conclusions about the research in the four selected areas and highlight some central themes that emerge. These will inform our consideration, in the next section of this Report, of the ethical, legal, social and policy issues to which the research gives rise.

The difficulty of defining and measuring traits

11.3 The traits on which research in behavioural genetics focuses are complex and multi-faceted. The difficulty of defining such traits in a rigorous and reproducible manner is a problem that equally affects psychologists and other researchers of human behaviour. Scores on scales of aggression, neuroticism or capacity for memory are useful tools for researchers and have applications in the realm of clinical psychology. However, broader claims from research in behavioural genetics about influences on human behaviour must be accompanied by a caveat about the necessarily artificial and limited context in which traits are considered.

Estimates of heritability

11.4 As noted in Chapter 4, the estimates of heritability derived from quantitative research methods apply only to particular groups of people, and represent the percentage of the variation in a trait that can be accounted for by genetic influences, among the members of that group, at the time of study. Thus, an estimate of the heritability of a trait does not provide any information about the number or identity of the genes that may be involved. Most calculations of heritability assume that the genetic influences in question work together in an additive fashion, so that if two hypothetical genetic factors contributed 5% of the variance each, together they would contribute 10% of the variance. However, it is likely that in many cases, the action of genes will depend on the presence of other genes and on particular environmental factors. Such effects can be overlooked by quantitative techniques. Furthermore, because heritability is a ratio of variation that has a genetic origin to the total variation, changes in the degree of variation that has an environmental origin will affect the estimate of heritability, even if the genetic contribution to the trait in question does not change.

11.5 Estimates of heritability refer only to the population sample on which they were calculated. If similar estimates are obtained across many studies that have different features, such as nationality, historical period and so on, this will show that the estimate can be generalised to some extent. It is commonly acknowledged by researchers in behavioural genetics that estimates of heritability for most human traits that have been measured are in the region of 0.40 to 0.60. Within this general range, some traits, for example intelligence (Chapter 7), appear to be more heritable than others, for example antisocial behaviour (Chapter 9). For the reasons given above, this information alone is of comparatively little value, except in so far as it only shows that there is some genetic influence, of whatever sort, on a particular trait, and thus makes the trait a potentially worthwhile candidate for molecular research. Such estimates are certainly not an appropriate basis for making claims about particular individuals, or for social policy.

The lack of replicated findings in molecular genetics

11.6 As we have seen, the task of finding genes that influence complex human behaviours is a difficult one. The reviews of the evidence have shown that there are very few confirmed and replicated findings in molecular genetics. No individual gene has been identified in humans that influences sexual orientation, antisocial behaviour or intelligence within the normal range. One gene variant, called monoamine oxidase A (MAOA), has been associated with low intelligence and aggression but so far, only in one family (paragraph 9.24). One study has indicated an effect of this genotype when combined with deleterious environmental conditions in male children, but this study awaits replication (paragraph 9.25). Another gene variant, called the dopamine receptor D4 gene (DRD4), has been associated with a handful of personality traits, psychiatric conditions and other behaviours, but the evidence remains inconclusive for its association with traits in the normal range (paragraphs 5.10 and 8.12). A gene that affects a chemical in the brain called serotonin has been associated with anxiety (paragraph 8.12). An alcohol-metabolising enzyme that protects against alcoholism has also been identified (Chapter 5, footnote 1), although this latter finding can be viewed as relating to a trait outside the normal range. Of course, when we consider that genetic influences on complex diseases such as diabetes and asthma are proving difficult to dissect, it is perhaps unsurprising that research on probably more complex behavioural traits should be even less advanced.

Applications of current research findings

11.7 In light of the lack of findings that have been replicated in research in behavioural genetics using molecular genetics techniques in this field, there are currently no practical applications of the research. There are no genetic tests for behavioural traits, nor are there pharmacological interventions that have been developed based on information about genetic influences on behavioural traits in the normal range.

11.8 With regard to intelligence, the only case where it seems plausible to see interventions based on genetic knowledge in the near future is that of serious mental retardation (see paragraph 7.14). However, future applications with regard to intelligence in the normal range cannot be ruled out, subject to the qualifications set out in this Report about the predictive accuracy of genetic tests for behavioural traits.

11.9 Scores on measures of personality can be moderately useful in predicting the likelihood of behavioural traits and disorders being exhibited in the future. For example, those who have a high score on the psychological scale of Neuroticism have an elevated chance of developing a neurotic disorder. Similarly, those with a high score who are affected by a disaster have a higher probability of developing post-traumatic stress disorder. These predictions are already made with the measures of personality used by psychologists. It is not clear whether, in the adult population, additional information about genetic factors will add to these abilities to make predictions. However, the ability to make predictions based on genetic information might, in principle, be used to devise interventions such as environmental manipulations that modify the genetic contribution. So, for example one might choose to provide an environment that would develop courage in a child with a genetic susceptibility to timidity.

11.10 In the context of antisocial behaviour, there are currently no practical applications of the research. One study suggests that a particular gene, MAOA, might have an effect on antisocial behaviour in males, depending on whether individuals are maltreated as children. If replicated, this finding could have implications for preventing antisocial behaviour (see paragraph 9.25).[1] The finding from other research in the field, that genetic variance influences behaviour, but is not necessarily associated with official efforts to control behaviour, may help add clarity to the controversy about whether or not offending is heritable. The status of juvenile delinquent and the conviction of adults in law courts are socio-political-legal constructions, and on the basis of this truism, scholars have questioned how such constructions could possibly be inherited. Research suggests that a distinction between antisocial traits which are heritable and delinquent/conviction status, particularly among juveniles, which is less heritable, is a crucial one. Information from research in behavioural genetics is unlikely to be relevant to individual cases in juvenile court proceedings. (See Chapters 14 and 15 for consideration of the use of information about genetic influences on behaviour with regard to legal practice and social policy.)

11.11 To date, no gene that affects sexual orientation in humans has been identified (see paragraphs 10.14–10.17). Thus, there are currently no practical applications of the research, in terms of the use of genetic tests for predictive purposes.

Reporting research in behavioural genetics

11.12 Research which claims to show an association between particular genetic variants and particular traits tends to receive considerable attention in the scientific and lay media. Research in genetics and research that aims to show why human beings behave as they do (for example psychological and sociological research) are both subjects of enormous interest to society, so it is perhaps unsurprising that, when combined in the form of research in behavioural genetics, any findings are widely reported and discussed.

11.13 However, we noted in Chapters 4–6 that the various methods of research in this field are not infallible, and the reviews of the evidence in Chapters 7–10 have shown that few findings have been replicated successfully to date. Thus, reports of such things as 'gay genes' or 'smart mice' convey a highly inaccurate impression of the state of the research. The lack of reporting of negative or contradictory findings exacerbates this problem. These difficulties are not unique to research in behavioural genetics. However, it does seem that such research is, at present, particularly susceptible to reporting which, whether strictly accurate or not, is misleading in the impression it gives to the reader. The potential for the abuse of findings in this area means that the reporting of this research ought to be conducted with particular care.

---

[1] Brunner, H. G., Nelen, M., Breakefield, X. O., Ropers, H. H & van Oost, B. A. (1993). Abnormal behaviour associated with a point mutation in the structural gene for monoamine oxidase A. *Science* **262**, 578–80.

11.14 **We consider that researchers and those who report research have a duty to communicate findings in a responsible manner. We welcome the Guidelines on Science and Health Communication published by the Social Issues Research Centre, the Royal Society and the Royal Institution of Great Britain and recommend that further initiatives in this area should be encouraged.**[2]

Funding research in behavioural genetics

11.15 It has proved difficult to gauge the precise extent of UK funding in this area. In response to our public consultation, the Medical Research Council (MRC) stated that 'funding for UK research in behavioural genetics is modest'. One problem with obtaining a more precise account is that, as we have repeatedly observed in this Report, there is no clear line between behaviour in the normal range and that which constitutes a disorder. Moreover, since it may be that the same genes that affect behaviour at the extremes of variation, which may be seen as disorders, also affect behaviour within the normal range, it will be difficult to distinguish research that focuses on the normal range from that which focuses on the extremes. It is possible that research which attempts to identify genes that affect extremes of behaviour may have implications for behaviour in the normal range, and conversely, that research that focuses on behaviour in the normal range may have implications for that at the extremes. For example, research suggests that the genetic factors which contribute to depression, which is a disorder, also contribute to the trait of negative emotionality, which is a trait that is continuously distributed throughout the population. This phenomenon also arises in research into diseases; for example, research into normal blood pressure may be useful in understanding hypertension.

11.16 Notwithstanding the difficulty in delineating research in behavioural genetics that focuses on behaviour in the normal range, the MRC stated in its response that it 'does not give grants for research into the genetics of what are seen as "normal" variations in behaviour or personality, but [does] fund work relevant to aspects of behaviour seen by society as significant medical, psychological or educational problems'. The MRC notes that research into genetic influences on traits in the normal range such as 'general intelligence' could have value, but that the MRC 'does not give grants for such work because we have a medical remit, and to us, the benefits do not clearly outweigh the risks'. In 1997, the MRC developed a policy on research in behavioural genetics and devised a list of criteria against which potential research projects should be assessed. This includes the possible misuse of the research findings. In its response to the consultation, the Wellcome Trust stated that 'some of the research we fund looks at "normal" (or milder) traits and other projects focus on "abnormal" variations'.

11.17 Our public consultation showed that many people consider that, compared to research on disease, research into genetic influences on behavioural traits in the normal range ought to receive low priority for funding. This was partly due to doubts about the likely success of the research, and partly due to concerns about the potential applications. **We take the view that research in behavioural genetics has the potential to advance our understanding of human behaviour and that the research can therefore be justified. However, we note that it is important that those who fund research in this area should continue to fund research of a high calibre,**

[2] Social Issues Research Centre, the Royal Society and the Royal Institution. Guidelines on Science and Health Communication. November 2001. http://www.sirc.org/publik/revised_guidelines.pdf (9 Aug 2002).

should be transparent about their funding practices and should be aware of the potential for the abuse and misinterpretation of results. In addition, we recommend that research sponsors who intend to focus strategic funding in this area should pay careful attention to public concerns about the research and its applications.

Conclusion

11.18 This section of the Report has summarised the current evidence for genetic influences on a selection of behavioural traits. It is clear that very little is yet known about particular genetic factors and their roles in influencing behaviour. However, a considerable amount of research is under way that aims to improve our understanding in this field. We note the need for careful and accurate reporting of research findings. In the following section of the Report, we move on to consider the possible implications for society if such programmes of research are successful.

Section 4

Ethical, legal, social and policy issues

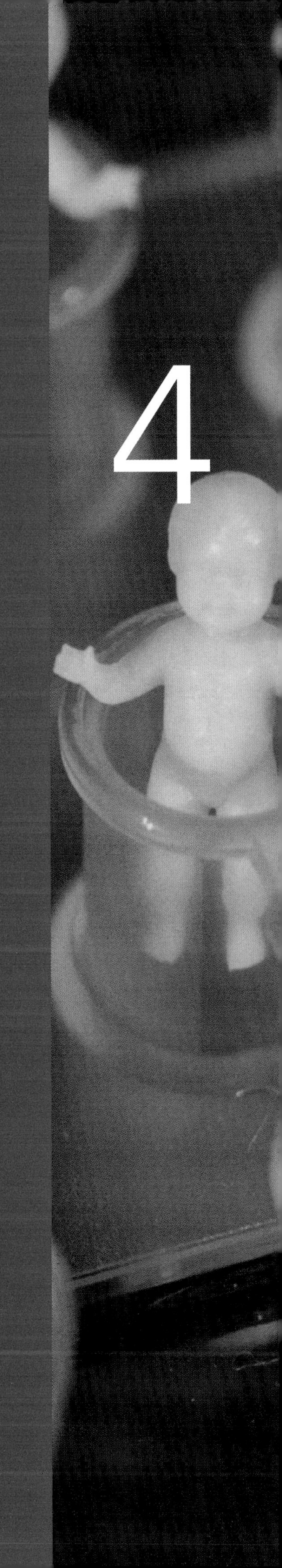

Chapter 12

Genetics, freedom and human dignity

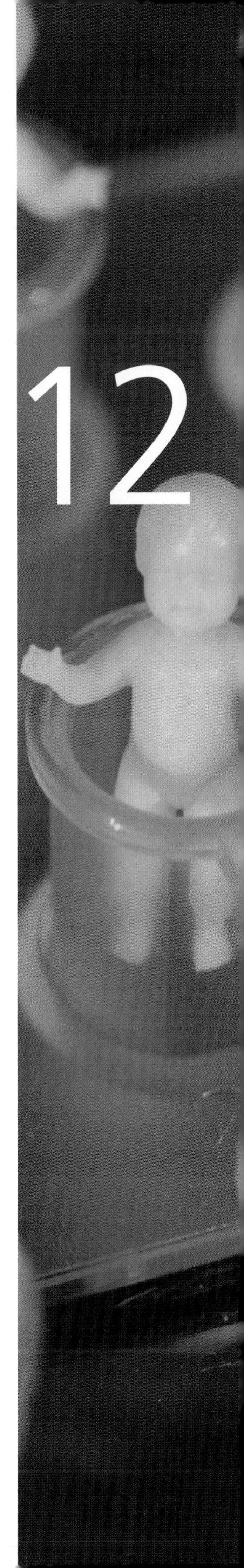

Genetics, freedom and human dignity

12.1 Although the reviews of the evidence in Chapters 7–10 indicate that very little is yet known about particular genetic factors that influence behaviour in the normal range, there can be no doubt that genes do make some contribution to behavioural traits, including fundamental aspects of human character. Since people do not choose their genes, and are therefore not responsible for them, it seems to follow that they are not responsible for these aspects of their character. But if this is so, then how far are they responsible for themselves at all? Does research in behavioural genetics undermine the normal sense of responsibility?

12.2 This sense of responsibility is not just a matter of legal concern. (This aspect of responsibility is discussed in Chapter 14.) Perhaps more importantly, it is an essential ingredient in the conception of human dignity, in the presumption that one is a person whose actions, thoughts and concerns are worthy of intrinsic respect, because they have been chosen, organised and guided in a way which makes sense from a distinctively individual point of view. If it turns out to be an illusion to suppose that people are responsible for themselves, then their actions and thoughts do not belong together as part of the meaningful life of an individual; a moral subject. In which case, one of the most fundamental reasons which people have for treating each other as worthy of respect would have been undermined.

12.3 This potential of research in behavioural genetics to undermine the way in which we think of ourselves can be contrasted with the implications of discoveries in genetic research as it relates to disease and disorder. In the latter case, research has established that, for example, some people may have a genetic predisposition to breast cancer. Finding out that one is affected in this way, however distressing, need not undermine one's sense of one's own identity. By contrast, what is suggested by research in behavioural genetics is that aspects of an individual's character, one's personal identity, may have a genetic basis. Thus, whereas in the case of disease and disorder, it is easy to differentiate oneself from that to which one is genetically predisposed, in the case of behaviour, it appears that one cannot do likewise; there is no deeper self which is unaffected by one's genes.

12.4 It is important, nonetheless, to understand from the start that such anxieties should not be occasioned simply by the recognition that people start out their lives with different abilities and weaknesses. If 'Tuesday's child is full of grace' whereas 'Wednesday's child is full of woe', woeful Wednesday is likely to have a harder start to life than graceful Tuesday; but this does not of itself imply that the children will not develop into adults who are capable of taking responsibility for their own character. Unless she is very unlucky, woeful Wednesday should be able to control her depression, and graceful Tuesday will need to take care of his charms.

12.5 Thus, if it can be shown that behavioural genetics, properly understood, does not threaten the conception of a person as a rational being capable of taking responsibility for himself or herself in free action, then it ought to be possible to welcome the deeper understanding of the springs of human motivation which behavioural genetics promises, without feeling that there is thereby a threat to the inherent dignity of humanity. Therefore, in this chapter, we consider whether behavioural genetics does undermine our conceptions of personal identity and responsibility.

The material self

12.6 Before one can identify and discuss this issue properly it is necessary to set aside one traditional way of thinking about ourselves. One view regarding the implications of behavioural genetics is that the research undermines the notion of responsibility simply because it reveals the fact that many important motivations have a physical basis in genes. The assumption here is that responsibility and thus free will depend upon the ability to transcend all such physical conditions. This traditional conception of free will stems from the conception of a person as comprising a material (physical) body that is associated with an immaterial self which is revealed in consciousness and is, for each person, what they 'really' are. The suggestion is that even if one's physical body is a part of the natural world, the actions of the immaterial self are no part of this system. Instead they constitute a domain of freedom in which a person controls the course of their life.

12.7 This conception of free will is threatened by behavioural genetics in so far as it implies that (material) genes affect the motivations of the (immaterial) self. But in any case, this conception of free will is implausible. If the immaterial self's exercise of its freedom is to make any difference to the course of life, in other words, if mental states are to be causally effective, the immaterial self's acts have to make a difference to the bodily movements which occur whenever one does anything. But the hypothesis that the actions of an immaterial self can produce effects upon a material body is intrinsically mysterious: there is no coherent way of understanding how this is possible. Instead, it seems inescapable that the causes of change in the material world must themselves be, in some respect, material. Hence the only tenable understanding of human freedom is one which does not postulate an immaterial self as the only really free agent.

12.8 It is worth observing that this hypothesis of a free immaterial self is not an essential ingredient of religious conceptions of human life. On the contrary, the doctrine of incarnation is a central feature of the Christian faith, including the thesis that the 'Word' (human thoughts, feelings, motivations and so on) really became 'flesh', that is, material. For this reason, orthodox Christianity has also always maintained that life after death requires the resurrection of a body.[1] Thus, there is no essential conflict at this point between a material view of the world and Christianity.[2]

12.9 It is difficult to characterise briefly the attitude of other religions concerning this issue of the immaterial self. Belief in the resurrection of the dead arose in late second-temple Judaism (see *Daniel* 12:2), but there have been many ways in which resurrection has been understood in Judaism, as in Christianity. One especially influential view was that of the medieval Jewish philosopher Maimonides.[3] In his *Guide to the Perplexed*, Maimonides treated material existence as a necessary stage in the soul's liberation from sin through suffering, so that immortality is achieved when the soul becomes purely rational and thereby immaterial. This transformational conception of human existence, from a material sinful life to an immaterial pure afterlife, is also to be found in Islam. It fits readily within a neo-Platonist conception of the self as essentially immaterial but 'imprisoned' in a

---

[1] Cullman, O. (1958). *Immortality of the Soul or Resurrection of the Dead?* London: Epworth; Polkinghorne, J. (1994). *The Faith of a Physicist: Reflections of a Bottom-up Thinker.* Princeton, NJ: Princeton University Press.

[2] The Christian tradition has also included thinkers with neo-Platonist views more sympathetic to an immaterialist position, but their positions have generally been regarded as heterodox (if not downright heretical).

[3] Kellner, M. (1990). *Maimonides on Human Perfection.* Atlanta, GA: Scholars Press.

material body during earthly life; but Islamic thought was also much influenced by Aristotle's thesis that the soul is the 'form' of the body, a thesis which cannot be readily combined with a conception of immaterial existence after death. Different Islamic thinkers resolve this tension in different ways: Ibn Sina (Avicenna) rejected the Aristotelian position in favour of a neo-Platonist conception of the soul. His position was then criticised by al-Ghazali, who insisted on the importance of physical resurrection, since only a physical being can be punished for sin. Finally Ibn Rushd (Averroes) returned to an Aristotelian position while allowing that we can gain a kind of immortality as we lose our individuality in universal knowledge.[4] These debates show the difficulty inherent in the conception of an immaterial personal existence, and similar tensions arise in Eastern religions in the context of doctrines of reincarnation, karma and nirvana. But although these doctrines imply the possibility of a form of immaterial existence, their theoretical context is not the same as that of Western religions and metaphysics, so the question of whether they also permit a materialist conception of the self is a complex one which cannot be pursued here.[5]

Determinism and fatalism

12.10 One common ground for the view that genetics undermines responsibility for oneself is the claim that genetics is a deterministic theory. This claim can be interpreted in many ways, but in the present context it can be taken as the hypothesis that the laws of genetics show that an individual's genotype determines an important range of facts concerning his or her life, including facts about a range of fundamental human abilities and dispositions.

12.11 In thinking about this position, it is useful to start from a thesis often associated with deterministic conceptions of human life, namely, fatalism. Fatalism is the thesis that that which is determined is 'fated': in other words, that it will take place whatever one chooses or attempts to do. Traditionally, fatalism was associated with myths concerning the power of gods over human life.[6] These myths are no longer believed, but fatalist language is still used to describe inescapable aspects of life, as when one says that everyone is 'fated' to die. In a similar way, fatalist language can be used to express the view that genetic discoveries imply that significant aspects of life are inescapably fixed by the identity of one's genes: as James Watson has put it, 'our fate is in our genes'.[7]

12.12 A distinct thesis is that of determinism, which, in this context, is the view that what we choose to do is determined by factors outside our control. Non-fatalist determinists allow that an individual's choice makes a difference to the course of his or her life, but hold that his choice has itself been determined. This is different from the fatalist thesis because it means that our choices do play a causal role, whereas the fatalist believes that future events will take place regardless of what we choose. Nonetheless, many determinists are also fatalists. This combination is particularly relevant here since, fatalism is clearly incompatible with the conception of ourselves as responsible moral agents.

---

4 Nasr, O. & Leaman, O., editors. (1996). *History of Islamic Philosophy*. London: Routledge.

5 See for example Collins, S. (1982). *Selfless Persons*. Cambridge: Cambridge University Press; Flaherty, W. D., editor. (1980). *Karma and Rebirth in Classical Indian Traditions*. Berkeley, CA: University of California Press.

6 For example, according to Greek myth, Apollo decreed that Oepidus, the son of Laius, would kill his father and marry his mother. Even though Laius, when told of this decree, attempted to avert his fate by arranging to have Oedipus killed as an infant, the myth recounts that Oedipus' life was saved and that he went on, unknowingly, to fulfil Apollo's decree.

7 Jaroff, L. (1989). The Gene Hunt. *Time Magazine* March 20.

12.13 If it were true that genes have inescapable implications concerning the later course of life, this fatalist language would be appropriate. But it is far from evident that these implications really are inescapable. In the case of some diseases, this is, in fact, the case. For example, those with the mutant allele responsible for Huntington's disease are indeed fated to develop this condition, although this is fortunately a rare condition. In the case of most diseases, however, genetic mutations lead only to a predisposition, or risk, of developing a condition. Moreover, there are generally also courses of action (such as a change of diet or lifestyle) which those diagnosed as being at risk can pursue in order to lessen the chance of their actually developing the condition in question. So these cases, which are overwhelmingly the most common, are not cases in which talk of fatalism is appropriate. Phenylketonuria (PKU) is a good case in point. This is caused by a recessive allele of the PAH gene[8] on chromosome 12 and is associated with serious mental retardation. It turns out that this association depends on following a normal diet. Once someone identified (soon after birth, through a blood test) as carrying the two recessive alleles adopts a diet low in the amino acid phenylalanine, this association is broken and the person concerned can develop relatively normally.

12.14 It is, then, plain that understanding the effects of our genes in the case of disease does not lead us to fatalism. In the case of behaviour, the reviews of the evidence in Chapters 7–10 demonstrate that in so far as there are genetic influences on behaviour, these do not follow the very rare pattern exemplified by Huntington's disease. Instead these genetic influences involve predispositions to aggression, anxiety, low or high intelligence and so on. They do not imply that the chances of these predispositions being realised are unalterable. On the contrary, when the outcome is undesirable, their discovery provides an incentive for intervening to enable those with the predispositions to learn how to control and overcome them. Equally, when the outcome is desirable, those found to have the relevant predisposition may be motivated to make the most of their genetically given qualities.

12.15 Thus, the effect of one's genes is not to fix the future structure of life as a fate from which one cannot escape. Equally, the effect is not to fix the structure of one's character, the kind of person one is. Genes certainly contribute to the initial make-up of one's abilities and motivations. But it does not follow that one cannot do things which develop these abilities and alter one's motivations.

Freedom, possibility and rationality

12.16 Even if behavioural genetics is not an inherently fatalist doctrine, there remain other ways in which it can appear to pose a threat to the notion of a sense of responsibility. One familiar argument starts from the thesis that someone who acts of their own free will, and is therefore responsible for their actions, is someone who 'could have done otherwise'. If theories in behavioural genetics imply that there are important respects in which one could not have acted otherwise, namely, where one's actions were determined by genetic dispositions, it seems to follow that there is a conflict between responsibility for oneself on the one hand and behavioural genetics on the other.

12.17 In this case, the type of genetic determinism involved does not have to be the fatalist type already discussed and rejected (paragraphs 12.10–12.15). Instead, the more insidious suggestion is that although one's choices do make a difference to the course of one's life, the

[8] Phenylalaninehydroxylase (PAH) gene.

fact that this capacity for choice, and the choices one makes, are themselves genetically determined in important respects shows that one is ultimately just a product of external forces, namely genes and the environment, and for this reason one lacks responsibility for oneself.

12.18 One obvious response to this argument is just to deny that behavioural genetics, and indeed genetics generally, support the deterministic hypothesis in question, since, as the earlier chapters show, genetic evidence is likely to generate only predictions of a statistical nature; for example, that A is twice as likely as B to behave in a particular way. But for two reasons this response is not satisfying by itself. First, as far as the implied threat to the notion of responsibility is concerned, it is not sufficient to dismiss the challenge to responsibility to say that genes are not entirely deterministic; for if the influence of early environment and other factors is taken into account, it may still be possible to get a considerably more robust, if not fully deterministic, connection between genetic and environmental factors, and one's behaviour. If this were true, genetics might turn out to be a major component in a deterministic science of behaviour. Secondly, it scarcely seems much of a defence of the notion of responsibility to rely on the presence of chance elements in the processes of human life. Responsible conduct seems even less like a merely chance occurrence than a determined course of events.

12.19 A much better response to the argument above is that it rests on an illusion: it invokes a conception of free will as being a capacity to act otherwise which is completely external to, and unconditioned by, one's natural constitution. Hence it is the argument's starting-point which should be rejected: that someone who acts of their own free will is someone who could have acted otherwise. Instead, the sensible position to take is that one acts of one's own free will when, first, one's action is the outcome of one's choice, and, secondly, this choice is itself the outcome of one's deliberations regarding what to do. What matters as far as acting of one's own free will is concerned is the involvement of one's rational deliberations in the causation of one's actions, and not the existence, or not, of an abstract possibility of acting otherwise.

12.20 Thus, freedom of action requires that one's reasons play a causal role in what one does. Once this is properly understood the threat of determinism falls away as irrelevant and it is not necessary to pursue further the question as to how far behavioural genetics implies determinism. Instead, there is a different question that needs to be faced, namely whether an understanding of human life that accepts that genetic factors contribute to behavioural predispositions undermines the involvement of the reasoning of people in an explanation of their behaviour. In the next section, we consider three philosophical approaches to this question: eliminativism, functionalism and rationalism. Box 12.1 provides a short summary of the distinguishing features of each approach.

Eliminating rationality

12.21 One influential contemporary view to the effect that behavioural genetics undermines this conception of free will rests on the thesis that the understanding of human life that is provided by genetics and the neurocognitive sciences is incompatible with our everyday understanding of a person as a rational being, capable of thinking and acting for reasons. The incompatibility is supposed to arise from the fact that our ordinary understanding of thought and action involves an inescapable element of subjective, personal interpretation which cannot be combined with the objective, impersonal explanatory schemes of the natural sciences. For this reason, some philosophers have argued that this ordinary self-understanding is only a preliminary 'folk-psychology', to be progressively 'eliminated' from descriptions of behaviour (and the rest of reality) as the neurocognitive sciences progress, in much the way in which 'folk-astronomical' references to sunrise and sunset linger on only as a harmless reminder of past belief, since we now know that the sun does not actually 'rise' or 'set'.[9]

12.22 This is not the place for a detailed critical appraisal of this eliminativist position; but two points can be made briefly concerning it. First, even if some element of subjectivity is essential for forming an initial understanding of others, it does not follow that the resulting understanding cannot be corrected and refined as further evidence is collected, until it becomes closer to the kind of objectivity that is characteristic of the natural sciences. Secondly, although there are areas of vagueness and imprecision in ordinary ways of understanding thought and action, it does not follow that behavioural genetics and other neurocognitive sciences provide ways of thinking which should displace this ordinary self-understanding. Instead, it is arguable that one should get used to the idea that human life just is vague and imprecise in some respects.

Accommodating rationality

12.23 The obvious alternative to the eliminativist position is the view that there is no incompatibility between the understanding of human life suggested by genetics and the neurocognitive sciences and the ordinary understanding of people as beings capable of thinking and acting for reasons. There are, however, two main ways in which this alternative has been developed; by supporters of functionalist and rationalist positions respectively. Supporters of a functionalist position argue that the ordinary psychological conceptions of free will and responsibility refer essentially to the roles of physical states of the brain. The detailed operations of these states are to be explained by the neurocognitive sciences in ways which largely tally with common sense beliefs. Thus, the functionalist argues that these scientific theories will eventually show how thoughts and motivations, the terms by which human life is normally understood, are 'realised', or implemented, within human beings.

12.24 Behavioural genetics fits into this functionalist position as a science which contributes to the difficult, but essential, task of characterising the basis, genetic and neural, of behavioural dispositions. Thus, for the functionalist, there is no incompatibility between the findings of behavioural genetics and the conception of oneself as a person capable of acting of one's own free will; on the contrary, the behavioural geneticist makes an essential contribution to understanding what it is about human beings that gives them this capacity.

12.25 A central feature of this functionalist position is that although the validity of rational explanations of thought and action is endorsed, any such explanation depends on the existence of connections at the level of the neural states which implement the thoughts and actions involved. Thus explanations of thought and action in which the agent's reasons play some part are themselves argued to be reducible to those branches of the neurosciences which do not recognise concepts such as 'reason', 'decision' and 'free will'. In other words, these ordinary concepts can be fully explained in terms of neuroscience.

12.26 It is this reductive thesis which is rejected by proponents of the rationalist position. According to the rationalist, the best ways of understanding those aspects of human life in

---

9 For a clear exposition of this position, see Stich, S. (1983). *From Folk Psychology to Cognitive Science*. Cambridge, MA: MIT.

which one is engaged as a rational subject and a free agent are to be found in explanations which are couched in terms of the implications of one's thoughts, feelings, decisions and so on. These explanations are connected to the explanations of such factors as limb movements, neural changes, and genetic predispositions, that are provided by sciences such as physiology, genetics and biochemistry. For the rationalist, behavioural genetics belongs here as a way of making some of these connections. But the rationalist denies that these connections bring with them the true explanation of behaviour; in other words, the suggestion that the exhaustive and exclusive explanation of what happens is to be found at the level of biochemistry.

12.27 In rejecting the functionalist position, rationalists agree with eliminativists that there is something distinctive about the ordinary understanding of thought and action. But rationalists disagree with eliminativists in thinking that the natural sciences alone provide a framework for understanding the world. Instead, rationalists argue that human life is normally best understood by reference to the thoughts and feelings of those involved in them, even if there is something inherently personal in this kind of understanding. Rationalists reject, however, the implication that this personal dimension in the ordinary understanding brings with it a 'subjective' dimension that is inherently defective when compared with the objectivity of the natural sciences. They argue that it is the characteristic mistake of those who are over-impressed by the natural sciences to think that a properly objective understanding can be arrived at only when it is framed in the impersonal concepts of the natural sciences.[10]

12.28 The resulting debate between functionalists and rationalists is a transformed, and much improved, version of the old debates about determinism and free will. In effect, the question of reductionism (which can be seen as a question of explanation) replaces the old misguided question of determinism (which is concerned with causation). Functionalists hold that reductionism, that is, an explanation of behaviour in physical terms, is compatible with our ordinary understanding of free will and responsibility. Rationalists reject this claim and affirm that rational explanations of human affairs cannot be reduced to explanations in terms of the natural sciences (see Box 12.1).

Box 12.1: Folk psychology and natural science

The central point at issue between *eliminativists* (paragraphs 12.21–12.22), *functionalists* (paragraphs 12.23–12.25) and *rationalists* (paragraphs 12.26–12.27) concerns the relationship between our familiar or common-sense understanding of human thoughts and actions, which draws on an individual's reasons, beliefs and desires (and which is termed, in these debates, *folk psychology*) and the kinds of explanation provided by the natural sciences. Eliminativists hold that these two approaches are incompatible, and that eventually, folk psychology will be eliminated as genetics and the neurocognitive sciences develop. For example, today, our folk psychology explanations of behaviour refer to the beliefs we have. Eliminativists maintain that as cognitive science progresses, reference to beliefs will be replaced by reference to mental representations identified purely as internal states of the brain, lacking any reference to the world. Functionalists deny that there is any incompatibility here: they argue that beliefs may well turn out to be states of the brain, but

[10] For a classic statement of a rationalist position of this kind, see Strawson, P. F. (1974). *Freedom and resentment.* In *Freedom and Resentment and Other Essays.* London: Methuen.

that does not show that our ordinary understanding of beliefs is incorrect. Thus, according to the functionalist, folk psychology needs to be supplemented in order that its explanations can be vindicated; but there is no reason to hold that this supplementation will lead to the radical undermining of folk psychology anticipated by the eliminativist. Finally, rationalists deny that folk psychology needs to be vindicated by being supplemented in this way. Like eliminativists, rationalists believe that folk psychology has distinctive features which imply that it cannot be reduced to the natural sciences. But, unlike eliminativists, rationalists hold that the distinctiveness of folk psychology is compatible with the natural sciences since they reject the assumption that everything can be explained within the framework of the natural sciences. One can summarise this debate as follows:

	Folk psychology provides a valid way of understanding human life	Folk psychology cannot be explained by, or reduced to, natural science	Everything about human life can be explained within the framework of the natural sciences
Eliminativists	Disagree	Agree	Agree
Functionalists	Agree	Disagree	Agree
Rationalists	Agree	Agree	Disagree

The implications of behavioural genetics

12.29 There is no denying that the scientific approach followed by most proponents of behavioural genetics fits more readily into a functionalist position than a rationalist one. Equally there is no denying that the ordinary sense of responsibility for oneself fits better with the rationalist position. Debate regarding the two positions continues, and it would be surprising if research in behavioural genetics alone yielded any decisive implications for this long-running debate between these two images of human beings.

12.30 It is nonetheless worth trying to clarify the significance, in other respects, of behavioural genetics for the understanding of human behaviour. Remarks such as that 'there is a significant genetic influence on divorce',[11] suggest that researchers in behavioural genetics see themselves as able to offer explanations of cultural phenomena such as divorce. But this is at best misleading: behavioural genetics is fundamentally a branch of biochemistry and biochemistry knows nothing of marriage and divorce. For this reason, sceptics argue that behavioural genetics can have little significant to say about human life, since most of what matters is culturally defined, and biochemistry says nothing directly about culture.[12]

[11] Muir, H. (2001). Divorce is written in the DNA. *New Scientist* 12 July. See also McGue, M. & Lykken, D. T. (1992). Genetic influence on divorce. *Psychol. Sci.* **3**, 368–73; Jockin, V. & McGue, M. (1996). Personality and the inheritance of divorce. *J. Pers. Soc. Psychol.* **71**, 288–99.

[12] See for example Rose, S. (1998). *Lifelines*. London: Penguin.

12.31 But this sceptical thesis is too strong. Here is a comparison: because physics says nothing directly about tables and chairs, there is nothing to be learnt from physics about how they are constructed. This inference is invalid. Physics has implications for the understanding of materials and structures, and these have obvious implications for the construction of tables and chairs. So if behavioural genetics can tell us about the 'materials' and 'structures' of human life, then it will have implications for the understanding of human life, including cultural phenomena about which it does not speak directly.

12.32 But what are the relevant 'materials' and 'structures'? One hypothesis, speculative but plausible, is that genes give rise to certain basic neural capacities which constitute an individual's 'intermediate phenotype' (see paragraph 3.15) and contribute (along with environmental conditions) to the formation of all the more specific abilities which constitute that individual's phenotype as characterised by reference to 'behaviour within the normal range'.

12.33 One area of special relevance to this hypothesis is the field of theories of personality. As the review of research on personality indicates (see Chapter 8), theories of personality postulate some basic traits: Eysenck's Three (Neuroticism, Introversion/ Extraversion, Psychoticism), or the Big Five (the first two of Eysenck's traits plus Conscientiousness, Openness and Agreeableness). The identity of these traits might well be thought to be too culturally-specific for their intended role (indeed, they sound like twentieth century versions of the old Four Humors), but it is not necessary here to assess how far a completely culturally neutral theory of personality is conceivable. For on any sensible view of the matter, both genes and the early environment play a part in fixing the parameters for personality traits; what is important in the present context is just that there is no inconsistency between this hypothesis and the thesis that social culture and individual rationality also shape one's life.

12.34 Indeed, the consistency of these two perspectives starts from the fact that rational thought and action presuppose abilities and capacities which are not themselves rationally grounded. Human action requires the capacity to appreciate reasons and the ability to act upon them, which are both antecedent to reason.[13] But the abilities and personality traits with which one is endowed, as a result of one's genes and one's environment, are not unalterable. They normally include a capacity for self-development and self-criticism through the very understanding of oneself and the world which they themselves make possible. It is only by unconsciously adhering to a fatalist myth that behavioural genetics and the psychology of personality can be regarded as inherently undermining one's responsibility for one's own character.

12.35 This rather abstract argument may appear excessively complacent. For there are of course people with personality disorders which make it practically impossible for them, even with psychiatric help, to take much control of their lives. But the fact that in some cases people suffer from these disorders does not show that behavioural genetics implies that the same inability to exercise control is true of everyone. Moreover, this can be true whether the causes of personality disorder are primarily genetic (as appears to be the case for schizophrenia) or environmental (as in the case of victims of abuse during childhood).

[13] One is, in Heidegger's phrase (Heidegger, M. (1927). *Sein und Zeit*. Verlag, Tubingen: M Niemayer), 'thrown' by one's genes and early environment into the space of reasons (Sellars, W. (1963). Empiricism and the philosophy of mind. In *Science, Perception and Reality*. London: Routledge and Kegan Paul. p. 169). One does not arrive there by one's own efforts.

Behavioural genetics, like medical science generally, implies that there are only differences of degree between 'illness' and 'health'. This implies that responsibility comes in degrees, but not that no one is truly responsible for their lives; differences in colour and taste are often, after all, 'only' differences of degree, but this does not show that differences of colour and taste are therefore unimportant.

12.36 It is impossible to read studies of identical twins without being impressed by the anecdotal tales of similarities and differences in the tastes and habits of those who were reared far apart.[14] But these tales do not describe people who are mere puppets; instead they describe people whose lives exemplify the unique synthesis that heredity, environment and opportunities help one make of oneself. A person's character is not the fabled 'tabula rasa' (or blank sheet of paper). The writing on the paper starts with one's genes and early environment. But, to varying degrees, these early influences also enable one to write more, and crucially, to erase, for oneself.

Conclusion

12.37 The aspect of human dignity that has been central to this chapter is the conception of oneself as a free responsible agent, capable of acting for reasons and directing the course of one's life in accordance with one's own values and understanding of the world. This does not exhaust the ethical content of the conception of human dignity, but it is a central component of it: to argue that the conception of oneself and others as responsible individuals is misplaced would be to reject one of the main reasons we have for holding that each person's life is intrinsically valuable in so far as it expresses that person's own, unique, perspective.

12.38 It has been argued that when the issues are correctly understood, there is no inherent conflict between a greater understanding of genetic contributions to behaviour and due regard for human dignity. A non-reductive, rationalist, understanding of human freedom can coexist with recognition of the genetic influences on our human abilities, capacities and motivations, even though a reductive, functionalist, account fits more readily alongside the scientific perspective employed by behaviour geneticists. It is not necessary here to take a stand on this debate. But any sensible understanding of human freedom and dignity must allow for some starting-point in the development of the abilities which are central to this freedom and dignity. Behavioural genetics promises to elucidate this starting-point, and thereby contribute to the understanding of humanity. But it no more offers a complete theory of human behaviour than does any other single scientific discipline. Thus, there is no reason for adherents of behavioural genetics, or critics, to regard it as offering a radically new way of understanding human life which threatens to undermine the dignity of humanity. It complements, and does not displace, the familiar social sciences, the humanities and indeed our ordinary understanding of behaviour.

---

[14] Segal, N. (2000). *Entwined Lives: Twins and What They Tell Us About Human Behavior*. New York: Plume.

Chapter 13

Selecting and changing behavioural traits

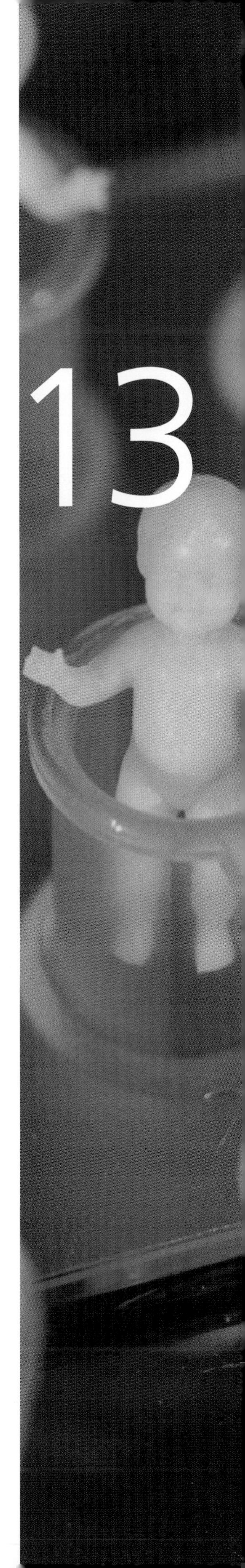

Selecting and changing behavioural traits

Introduction

13.1 In the next three chapters, we consider some of the questions that may arise if ways of identifying genetic influences on the traits or characteristics of an individual could be developed. In this chapter, we consider whether there are reasons for choosing certain types of intervention to select or change the traits and characteristics of individuals, both before and after birth. In Chapter 14 we assess whether research in behavioural genetics ought to change our conception of legal responsibility and the way in which we treat those who break the criminal law. In Chapter 15, we discuss the use of genetic testing for behavioural traits in the contexts of employment, education and insurance.

Will there be any practical applications of research in behavioural genetics?

13.2 Before we begin, however, we need to confront a sceptical challenge, to the effect that these reflections serve no useful purpose. The basis of this challenge is that, while everyone accepts that genes have an impact on behaviour, genetic tests will have a low predictive capacity because of the myriad other factors that influence our behaviour and the vastly complex interactions between genetic factors themselves. Hence, the challenge runs, if the workings of the many genes involved in behaviour are so complex that it is impossible to make any robust predictions based on genetic tests, or to design any effective interventions as a result of them, there is no point in discussing the ethics of their application.

13.3 One response to this challenge is that it does not exempt us from considering anxieties aroused by popular beliefs in this area, even if these beliefs turn out to be misconceptions. In the past, social policies, for example eugenic policies, have been built on minimal, or erroneous, scientific foundations. More recently, misunderstandings about genetics have led to unwarranted discrimination: the US National Sickle Cell Anemia Control Act of 1972 led to the unjustified discrimination and stigmatisation of African Americans in education, employment, insurance and the granting of licences to adopt and marry.[1]

13.4 A second response is to consider the available evidence in the field of research in behavioural genetics and to try to make realistic predictions about whether it will lead to practical applications. As we noted in Chapter 11, it is clear that, currently, very few individual genes that influence human behavioural traits in the normal range have been identified. Despite this, we need to keep in mind that in the future it may become possible to make predictions, albeit limited ones, about behaviour, based on genetic information and to design useful applications of this knowledge.

13.5 Hence, while it is certainly too early to discuss detailed applications of behavioural genetics, we need to confront anxieties based on current beliefs about this subject. As Barbara Katz Rothman has argued, there is reason to consider these possibilities now:

> 'The scientists quickly speak up: that isn't possible, they reassure us, you don't understand the genetics involved. Five years later, of course, that *is* possible, and then it is too late to decide whether or not to do it: we wake up to find it done.'[2]

---

1 Serjeant, G.R. (1985). *Sickle Cell Disease*. Oxford: Oxford University Press.

2 Katz Rothman, B. (1998). *Genetic Maps and Human Imaginations*. New York: WW Norton. p. 37.

13.6 As information about genetic influences on behaviour in the normal range is acquired, ways of changing the traits in question may also be developed. Such interventions could take one of three different forms: genetic manipulation; the use of medicines; or changes to the individual's environment. In this chapter, we will refer to these three categories as 'genetic interventions', 'medical interventions' and 'environmental interventions'. In discussing these, we also distinguish interventions which take place before birth from those which occur later in life. We consider the issues raised by prenatal selection in paragraphs 13.57 – 13.78 below.

Genetic interventions

13.7 Genetic interventions can be of two types, depending on the cells in the body to which they are applied. Somatic gene therapy is the process of changing the genotype of an individual by modifying the DNA in the cells of their body. This type of therapy is currently being studied as a potential cure for genetic disorders such as haemophilia and cystic fibrosis. The aim is to replace, in the relevant parts of the body, the mutated DNA that causes the disease. For example, a person with cystic fibrosis might receive gene therapy that was targeted at the lungs. An individual who has received this type of gene therapy would, however, be unlikely to pass on the genetic changes to his or her children, because the therapy would not affect the cells that are important in reproduction, namely the egg and sperm cells.

13.8 The second type of gene therapy is called germline gene therapy (it is also referred to as germline genetic engineering). This involves modifying the germline cells, those cells that are transmitted to children by their parents. Thus, germline gene therapy would change not only the characteristics of the individual who received the therapy, but also the characteristics of their children and future generations. There is a general consensus that, at present, the consequences are not well enough understood for this procedure to be attempted safely, and thus that germline gene therapy should not currently be attempted.[3] Indeed, the Council of Europe (1997) *Convention for the Protection of Human Rights and Dignity of the Human Being with Regard to the Application of Biology and Medicine: Convention on Human Rights and Biomedicine* states in Article 13 that 'an intervention seeking to modify the human genome may only be undertaken for preventive, diagnostic or therapeutic purposes and only if its aim is not to introduce any modification in the genome of any descendants'.[4]

13.9 Genetic interventions are still at a preliminary stage even in the comparatively less complex case of single-gene disorders. The possibility of their use in altering complex traits is still far off, but as the *Report of the Committee on the Ethics of Gene Therapy*, presented to Parliament in 1992, observed: 'We are alert to the profound ethical issues that would arise were the aim of genetic modification ever to be directed to the enhancement of normal human traits'.[5] (We consider the possibility of somatic and germline gene therapy for traits in the normal range in paragraphs 13.31 – 13.32).

---

[3] See 'Changing the World' in Harris, J. (1992). *Wonderwoman and Superman*. Oxford: OUP for an interesting analysis of the ethical arguments against germline gene therapy.

[4] Council of Europe (1997) *Convention for the Protection of Human Rights and Dignity of the Human Being with Regard to the Application of Biology and Medicine: Convention on Human Rights and Biomedicine*. ETS No: 164.

[5] Committee on the Ethics of Gene Therapy (Chairman: Clothier, C.). (1992). *Report of the Committee on the Ethics of Gene Therapy*. London: HMSO; Cm 1788. p. 7, paragraph 2.16.

Medical interventions

13.10 It seems more likely that if new interventions aimed at changing behavioural traits in the normal range are developed as a result of research in behavioural genetics, they will take the form of drugs, or of environmental interventions such as changes in diet or in social policies. Medical interventions such as anti-depressant drugs and drugs that claim to alleviate shyness are already in use, and it may be that additional drugs will be developed that can alter normal behaviour. Predictions that there will be drugs to enhance our memories, improve our cognitive function, or change our personalities are often made when scientists, journalists and other commentators speculate on future advances. Research in behavioural genetics might lead in this direction by suggesting which genes might be the best targets for new drugs.

Environmental interventions

13.11 The third type of intervention involves environmental strategies for changing behaviour. We already have some clear examples of such interventions. For example, it seems likely that improving the diet and standard of living of children also improves their IQ.[6] There is also good evidence that exposure to chemicals such as lead can adversely affect behavioural traits.[7] Other social policies such as the provision of free education and schemes such as Sure Start[8] are specifically premised on the capacity to change or enhance various traits in the population.

13.12 In paragraphs 13.26 – 13.48, we consider whether there are good reasons to prefer a particular type of intervention to change behavioural traits, both at an individual level and with regard to the wider community. Before that, we discuss two general concerns about the consequences of applying findings from research in behavioural genetics – medicalisation and stigma – that apply more generally to the research itself and the use of tests, as well as to potential interventions to change traits.

'Medicalising' human behaviour

13.13 Traits such as sexuality, aggression and intelligence have in the past been thought of as outcomes of inheritance, family background, socio-economic environment, individual choice and even divine intervention. If research in behavioural genetics identifies the influence of genes on such traits, they may mistakenly come to be thought of as being fundamentally determined by genetic factors and even as aspects of life which belong to one's 'fate' (see paragraphs 12.10 – 12.15). Indeed, being diagnosed as at risk of disease may have a tendency to make healthy people feel ill, or feel fatalistic about their chances of survival, despite the existence of diets, life-styles or treatments to avoid the development of disease. It is possible that information about genetic factors that indicate susceptibility to a disease may make people think that the unwanted outcome is

[6] See for example Center on Hunger, Poverty and Nutrition Policy. (1995). *Statement on the Link between Nutrition and Cognitive Development in Children*. Medford, MA: Tufts University School of Nutrition and Meyers; A. F. *et al.* (1989). School Breakfast Program and school performance, *Am. J. Dis. Child.* **143**, 1234–9. Also, Ivanovic, D. M. I (2000). Long-term effects of severe undernutrition during the first year of life on brain development and learning in Chilean high-school graduates. *Nutrition* **16**, 1056–63.

[7] See for example Stein, J. *et al.* (2002). In harm's way: toxic threats to child development. *J. Dev. Behav. Pediatr.* **23**, S13–22 and Dietrich, K. N. I. (1993). The developmental consequences of low to moderate prenatal and postnatal lead exposure: intellectual attainment in the Cincinnati Lead Study Cohort following school entry. *Neurotoxicol. Teratol.* **15**, 37–44.

[8] Sure Start is a programme run by the UK Government that aims to improve the physical, social and intellectual development of babies and young children so that they can flourish at home and at school. It focuses on encouraging good health in families with young children in deprived areas and on making available other facilities such as early learning.

inevitable.[9] It has been suggested, that the word 'genetic' is interpreted as synonymous with something fixed or unchanging in Western culture, when it is used in relation to disease.[10] With regard to behavioural traits, therefore, information about genetic susceptibility might engender similarly fatalist beliefs.

13.14 As the reviews of the evidence indicate, fatalism about genetics is a misconception. Even when behavioural traits are influenced by genes, there are always other influences, and the existence of genetic influences does not show that we are powerless to change or modify our character: 'scientists may well identify an allele that causes a genetic predisposition to shyness, but such a discovery does not mean that shyness cannot be overcome.'[11] Nonetheless, this misconception is pervasive and gives rise to the anxiety that behavioural genetics will lead to the 'medicalisation' of those who are found to be genetically predisposed to certain behavioural traits.

13.15 At the root of concerns about medicalisation is the idea that behavioural traits that have previously been regarded as 'normal' will come to be viewed as 'abnormal' or pathological. In addition, behavioural traits within the normal range may turn out to be amenable to influence by pharmacological interventions as a result of knowledge about the biological factors that affect them. Concerns about medicalisation have been expressed for many decades, for example in relation to the increasing number of psychiatric conditions that are recognised, and in the increasing use of medicines. In the era of genetic research, the fear is that the identification of the influences of genes will exacerbate this trend, encouraging the re-classification of behavioural traits as within the realm of medicine.

13.16 In some cases genetic research may indicate that a behavioural trait is one for which medical interventions are appropriate and welcome. Findings from research concerning the biological basis of addiction to alcohol, and of autism, helped to liberate individuals and parents from the charges previously laid against them of moral weakness and of neglecting their children respectively. In such cases, it should be acknowledged that this 'medicalising' tendency is beneficial: the research helps to confirm the view that the individuals concerned should be perceived as ill, rather than bad, and in need of medical help, rather than discipline and punishment.[12]

13.17 However, in other cases, medicalisation may have adverse effects. One such problem is that of diagnostic spread, or the tendency for disorders to be broadly defined so that more and more individuals are caught in the diagnostic net. This tendency may arise as a result of an erroneous assumption that once a biological influence on a trait has been identified, the trait becomes the proper subject of medical intervention. Or, it may be that if medicines are developed that have an effect on a trait, that trait will come to be seen as a disorder, or something to be treated and altered.

---

9 Senior, V., Marteau, T. M. & Weinman, J. (1999). Impact of genetic testing on causal models of heart disease and arthritis: an analogue study, *Psychol. Health* **14**, 1077–88.

10 Marteau, T. M. & Senior, V. (1997). Illness representations after the human genome project: the perceived role of genes in causing illness. In Petrie, K. J. & Weinman, J. A., editors. *Perceptions of Health and Illness: Current Research and Applications.* Reading, UK: Harwood Academic Publishers. pp. 241–66.

11 Rothstein, M. A. (2000). Genetics and the work force of the next hundred years. *Columbia Bus. Law Rev.* **2000** (3), 371–401 at p. 383.

12 See for example Conrad, P. & Schneider, J. W. (1992). *Deviance and Medicalisation: From Badness to Sickness.* Philadelphia: Temple University Press.

13.18 An example of this latter phenomenon is the prescription of methylphenidate (Ritalin) to children with Attention Deficit Hyperactivity Disorder (ADHD). This example is controversial because there are undoubtedly some children who have serious behavioural problems and who benefit greatly from the drug. It would be wrong to suggest that ADHD has been invented; indeed, the condition has been recognised for many decades. However, the advent of medicines that are effective in improving concentration and reducing hyperactivity is a fairly recent development. In 1999, the US National Association of State Boards of Education estimated the number of children taking Ritalin on a daily basis at between 1.3 and 2 million. The National Institutes of Health in the US has recently undertaken a study to examine prescribing practices.

13.19 Similarly, the producers of new 'anti-shyness' drugs, such as Paxil and Luvox, have been accused of applying to normal behaviour, interventions developed for pathological traits.[13] Paxil is licensed in the US for the treatment of depression, Social Anxiety Disorder (SAD), Generalised Anxiety Disorder (GAD),[14] Obsessive Compulsive Disorder, Panic Disorder and Post-traumatic Stress Disorder. The Paxil website notes that approximately 10 million adults are diagnosed with GAD each year in the US.[15] The website encourages individuals to take an online 'self-test' for GAD, which involves answering three questions:

1. Do you worry excessively or are you anxious a lot of the time?

2. Are you often bothered by the following:

   - Feeling restless, keyed-up, or on edge?
   - Feeling tense?
   - Feeling tired, weak, or easily exhausted?
   - Having difficulty concentrating?
   - Feeling irritable?
   - Having difficulty sleeping?

3. Would you say your anxiety or worry interferes with your work, family or social life?

Answering 'yes' to more than 1 of the complaints listed in question 2, even if the answers to questions 1 and 3 are negative, is sufficient to generate a response that says the results are inconclusive and suggests discussing them further with a health professional.

13.20 A similar self-test can also be undertaken for SAD, the key symptoms of which are a persistent fear of and an associated avoidance of social situations involving strangers. In an article in the *New York Times Magazine* about SAD, one commentator observed:

> 'until recently, it was thought to be a rare disorder ... Then in 1999, buoyed by the success of the new psychotropic drugs, the pharmaceutical company SmithKline Beecham began marketing its antidepressant Paxil as a treatment for social phobia ...

[13] See for example Koerner, B. I. (2002). First, you market the disease...then you push the pills to treat it. *The Guardian*, (30 July). taken from Koerner, B. I. Disorders made to order. *Mother Jones* magazine. July/August (2002).

[14] GAD is psychiatric disorder which features in the two main classification systems for mental illness, the *Diagnostic and Statistical Manual of Mental Disorders, Fourth Edition* (DSM-IV) and the ICD-10 *Classification of Mental and Behaviour Disorders*.

[15] http://www.paxil.com (17 July 2002).

Experts cited alarming new statistics – around 13% of us were socially phobic, for example – and magazines dished up the requisite alarmist trend stories. A set of traits and behaviours, at least some of which were once regarded as neutral, or even desirable, re-emerged as a pathology – a function of brain chemistry, amenable to and indeed demanding pharmacological manipulation.'[16]

13.21 These examples can be viewed as illustrations of diagnostic spread, the re-classification of behavioural traits, and the possibility of commercial and social pressure to make use of medical interventions. While these examples are not the result of findings in genetic research, they demonstrate the existence of a tendency towards medicalisation, and corresponding problems, to which findings in genetics may contribute.

13.22 A further potential problem related to medicalisation is the tendency to focus excessively on the biological factors that influence particular traits, rather than the social or economic factors. In paragraph 3.17, we observed that those factors that are described as the 'cause' of a particular trait are often those by which one hopes to control or alter that trait. Thus, there is a risk that the role of genetic factors will be over-estimated, so that genetic and medical interventions can be provided, rather than focusing on the social and economic environments which are also likely to play a vital role. This may be so even though there is no scientific reason for assuming that if genetic influences on a trait are identified that trait will be easier to alter using medical or genetic interventions rather than other forms. Examples of this phenomenon include the risk that medicines may be prescribed for children who are disruptive but do not have a clinical diagnosis of hyperactivity, rather than investigating other approaches such as reducing class sizes, and that medication may be used rather than diet and exercise as strategies for dealing with hypertension or obesity.

13.23 Medicalisation is an issue that affects many areas of life, not just behavioural genetics. In the case of behavioural traits, since research into genetic influences is at an early stage, it is not possible to say whether medicalisation will be likely, or whether it will have, on balance, positive or negative implications. However, examples of the deleterious effects of medicalisation in other areas suggest the need for awareness of potential problems. **We conclude that research in behavioural genetics has the potential to contribute to the existing phenomenon of medicalisation. Deleterious effects that should be borne in mind include shifting the boundary between normal variation and disorder further away from the extremes of variation; reducing social tolerance of previously 'normal' behavioural traits; and the routine selection of genetic or medical interventions without adequate consideration being given to environmental interventions and other options.**

13.24 Any discovery of biological mechanisms that influence behaviour, including genes, may aid in the development of drugs which modify behaviour. We consider that there is potential for the unhelpful widening of diagnostic categories, to encourage the use of medication by people who would not necessarily be thought of as exhibiting behavioural traits outside the normal range. In addition to the potentially harmful effects already listed, this could lead to unnecessary increased expenditure by the health service. **We recommend that**

[16] Talbot, M. (2001). The shyness syndrome: bashfulness is the latest trait to become a pathology. *New York Times Magazine* 24 June.

health service providers, and in particular the Department of Health, specifically charge a named agency with monitoring and, if necessary, controlling, this means of the deliberate medicalising of normal populations.

Stigma

13.25 A rather different anxiety arises from the perception that the use of genetic tests might increase social stigma and tendencies towards the labelling of people who display the traits being tested. For example, claims that a genetic predisposition to homosexuality has been identified may give credence to the view that homosexuality is pathological, thereby increasing the stigmatisation of homosexuals, and leading to pressure for gay people to be 'cured', and for prenatal selection against 'gay' fetuses. This is illustrated in Box 13.1 below, which illustrates the public response to genetic research into sexual orientation that was summarised in Chapter 10. As Box 13.1 indicates, knowledge of a genetic predisposition may also help to reduce the stigma associated with a trait by leading to acceptance of it as 'natural'.

Box 13.1: Public responses to genetic research into sexual orientation

Responses to research into genetic influences on sexual orientation, in particular the widely-publicised findings of Hamer and Le Vay, varied greatly even within the lesbian and gay community.[*] Many gay and lesbian groups seemed keen to capitalise on the trend, demonstrated in numerous opinion polls, towards increased acceptance of homosexuality if it is conceptualised as a biologically determined trait, regardless of whether or not this was shown to be accurate. However, others were more sceptical:

> 'Does your response to someone you know is gay depend on knowing why he or she is gay? Should the right to live free of discrimination depend on a biological explanation of difference? Most importantly, would finding a biological explanation make any difference in the way we perceive ourselves and each other?'[†]

Outside the gay community, most publicity was obtained by those who viewed the research as leading to the possibility of curing or eliminating homosexuality. The Chief Rabbi at the time spoke in favour of using the research in this way, saying that we may practise medical ingenuity to relieve suffering or a human disability.[‡] (Other Jewish groups, including the Union of Jewish Students in Britain, vehemently rejected the use of genetic engineering or termination of pregnancy to eliminate homosexuality.) In 1997, James Watson published an article in a national newspaper in which he proposed that women should be allowed to abort fetuses predisposed towards homosexuality which drew similar opposition from gay and lesbian groups, journalists and other commentators.[ʃ]

[*] See Chapter 10 for a discussion of these findings.

[†] PFLAG (Parents, Families and Friends of Lesbians and Gays). (1995). *Why ask Why? Addressing the Research on Homosexuality and Biology*. (pamphlet).

[‡] Chief Rabbi Lord Jakobovits, quoted in Rose, H. Gay brains, gay genes and feminist science theory. In Weeks, J. & Holland, J., editors. (1996). *Sexual Cultures*. Houndmills, Basingstoke: MacMillan.

[ʃ] Langton, J. (1997). The genie of the gene. *Sunday Telegraph*. 16 February.

Evaluating different ways of changing ourselves

13.26 Despite these concerns about medicalisation and stigma, we consider that there is, *prima facie*, no reason for preferring one type of intervention over another as a matter of principle. For any given trait and any given individual, the factors influencing the development and expression of that trait are likely to be many and varied. In different cases, there may be reasons for thinking that different forms of intervention are appropriate. In the next section, we consider five features of any intervention that may provide moral reasons for accepting or rejecting their use, namely the effectiveness, safety and reversibility of the intervention, the extent to which one can make choices about its use, and its implications for individuality.

(i) Effectiveness

13.27 The effectiveness of genetic interventions, which would be most likely to take the form of gene therapy, is difficult to predict. As we noted in Chapter 3, and as the reviews of the evidence reflect, genes that influence behavioural traits in the normal range are likely to exert small individual effects, which are likely to depend on the presence of other genes, as well as environmental factors. This means that, even if one could alter the expression of one or a few genes successfully, it would by no means be certain that the desired change in the phenotype would occur.

13.28 This is also likely to be true of medical and environmental interventions. Research in behavioural genetics does not suggest that pharmacological interventions are likely to be universally successful any more than environmental interventions, such as changes in parental care, diet, methods of education, social pressures, economic conditions and so on. The fact is that predicting the likely effectiveness of different types of intervention is a difficult task. For example, many commentators have argued that if we wish to enhance children's IQ scores, it is their environment rather than their genotypes that we should be seeking to affect. But our ignorance of the ways in which genes affect IQ is matched only by our ignorance of how the environment affects IQ. It is clear that environmental changes must have contributed to the 20–30 point rise in scores on standard IQ tests that occurred in the twentieth century (see Chapter 7, footnote 3). But we do not know which environmental changes. It seems probable that there were a large number, each with a small effect (changes in nutrition and general health, different styles of education, more emphasis on problem solving and more exposure to sophisticated visual messages, have all been suggested). Furthermore, the belief that it will be a simple matter to alter the environment in such a way as to increase children's IQ scores is just as fallacious as the converse belief that genetic effects are immutable. One intervention that has been shown to produce a substantial increase in the IQ scores of children living in poverty and neglect is to have them adopted.[17] But this can hardly be translated into social policy.

(ii) Safety

13.29 At first glance, it might be thought that environmental interventions are the safest form of intervention, in the sense that they seem least likely to have unpredicted or undesirable consequences. However, it should be noted that changes in an individual's psychosocial environment can have adverse results that persist throughout his or her life.

[17] Duyme M. *et al.* (1999). How can we boost IQs of 'dull children'?: a late adoption study. *Proc. Natl. Acad. Sci. USA* **96**, 8790–4.

13.30 Medical interventions raise issues of safety because of the potential side-effects and adverse events that may be related to the use of a particular drug. The regulatory system for licensing medicines and the systems for warning individuals about potential risks will, of course, also apply to new drugs developed as a result of research in behavioural genetics. Nonetheless, it is important to note that adverse reactions to drugs are one of the leading causes of death in the developed world. One serious concern is that, once medical interventions are provided 'over the counter', without prescription, and perhaps fall outside the statutory regulations of medicinal products, in the way that some complementary therapies currently do, there may be risks of mis-selling and misleading marketing. We discuss this further in paragraphs 13.49 – 13.56 below.

13.31 Genetic interventions currently bring with them serious concerns about safety. The United Nations Educational, Scientific and Cultural Organization (UNESCO) *Universal Declaration on the Human Genome and Human Rights* states in Article 5 that 'Research, treatment or diagnosis affecting an individual's genome shall be undertaken only after rigorous and prior assessment of the potential risks and benefits pertaining thereto and in accordance with any other requirement of national law'.[18] The Clothier Report on the ethics of gene therapy identified a number of ways in which gene therapy might pose a risk to safety.[19] These included mistakes in inserting the correcting gene, the possibility that the gene would be expressed in the wrong place or at the wrong time, the possibility that insertion of the gene might cause a new mutation or genetic disease, and the possibility that the correcting gene might move from its target location in the body and affect other cells. As a result, all applications to carry out trials of gene therapy in humans in the UK are monitored by the Gene Therapy Advisory Committee (GTAC). **We consider that in view of the risks inherent in gene therapy, considerable caution should be exercised before contemplating its application to traits that do not have serious implications for health. We note that if somatic gene therapy for traits in the normal range were to become a possibility, any research would fall under the remit of the GTAC.**[20] **We recommend, therefore, that the GTAC and other relevant bodies should develop guidelines for research into gene therapy for normal behavioural traits before such research takes place**.

13.32 Germline gene therapy raises particular issues concerning safety because the effects of the therapy reach far into the future and cannot be easily predicted. **The Clothier Report concluded that 'there is insufficient knowledge to evaluate the risks [of germline gene therapy] to future generations' and that therefore 'gene modification of the germ line should not yet be attempted'. In the context of behavioural variation within the normal range, which by definition is not life-threatening, we cannot envisage any circumstances in which the modification of the human germline would be justifiable**.

---

[18] United Nations Educational, Scientific and Cultural Organisation. (November 1997). *Universal Declaration on the Human Genome and Human Rights.*

[19] Committee on the Ethics of Gene Therapy (Chairman: Clothier, C.). (1992). *Report of the Committee on the Ethics of Gene Therapy*. London: HMSO; Cm 1788.

[20] GTAC's remit is 'the deliberate introduction of genetic material into human somatic cells for therapeutic, prophylactic or diagnostic purposes'. An analogous role is performed in the US by the Food and Drug Administration (FDA). In July 2002, it was reported that the FDA is to create a new department to oversee gene therapy, within the Center for Biologics Evaluation and Research (New FDA Office for Gene Therapy. (2002). *Nat. Med.* **8**, 646).

(iii) Reversibility

13.33 An important question concerning any intervention is whether or not it is reversible, since there may be unwanted side effects or other undesirable consequences, and because individuals affected by an intervention may themselves change their minds about the desirability of its effects as social trends and practical circumstances change. Genetic interventions may be difficult to reverse, even when they are not targeted at stem cells, and as such, their use in the context of traits that are not regarded as diseases, and which might be influenced by other forms of intervention, ought to be viewed with caution. The effects of medical interventions are often more easily reversible because the effect of a drug will usually wear off once it is no longer being ingested. The reversibility of environmental interventions is difficult to assess. It seems plausible that some interventions that take place early in a person's development may not be reversible in later life. The degree of reversibility of the effects of an intervention will be particularly important in considering whether an intervention is appropriate for a child, or someone unable to give consent.

(iv) Choice

13.34 There are three ways in which the idea of individual choice is relevant here. The first, as we have just noted, is that individuals should be able to exert their autonomy with regard to the use of an intervention. This has implications for the use of interventions in infancy and childhood, and for interventions that may be applied to society at large, rather than to an individual. On the one hand, environmental interventions often benefit all the individuals in a particular population, whereas medical interventions would only benefit those identified as requiring the intervention, and such targeted interventions risk stigmatising the individuals receiving them. But, on the other hand, it may be harder for individuals to avoid an environmental intervention if they do not wish to make use of it. Examples of this problem can be seen in the debates about fluoridation of the water system or the systematic addition of folic acid to bread.

13.35 The second way in which the notion of choice is engaged is the possibility that there will be reduced tolerance for differences and increased pressure towards the cultivation or acquisition of traits that are perceived to be desirable within society. Familiar examples of this tendency (not based on the results of genetic research) include social pressures on individuals to make use of cosmetic surgery, cosmetic orthopaedics (the use of orthopaedic surgery to lengthen the bones in the legs), skin lightening and other processes to make individuals more beautiful, taller or Caucasian-looking. One can readily envisage similar pressure to use genetic tests, were they to become available, to help design medical interventions to eliminate 'unattractive' personality traits. In this way, individuals may feel obliged to make use of particular interventions. This seems a potential hazard in the case of any type of intervention.

13.36 The third aspect of choice that is important relates to the effect of genetic tests on an individual's self-perception. Genetic tests for intelligence or sporting ability might increase pressure on a person to develop an aspect of their personality for which the test is positive, or close off the possibility of enjoying an activity for which they are led to believe they are 'biologically unsuited'. In such cases, the tests could in fact only suggest malleable predispositions; but given the likelihood of their misinterpretation by parents as indications of their children's talents, any use of such tests would need to be very carefully introduced, controlled and monitored. Indeed, even now, in the case of disease or disorder, medical geneticists are usually reluctant to test children for genetic conditions for which they may be pre-symptomatic and for which no early interventions exist.[21] If this is the case with non-behavioural or personality-relevant conditions, then there are even stronger reasons for caution when it comes to intelligence and personality where a diagnosis of predispositions might be misunderstood by parents or children themselves.

(v) Intervention and individuality

13.37 It has always been acknowledged that achievement is related partly to factors outside an individual's control, such as accident of genetic endowment, privilege of birth and opportunity. But these factors alone are not sufficient to guarantee success in most fields. In order to be a first-class athlete, or to win a first-class degree, the individual has to work hard, to train the body or brain, and to master complex techniques and memorise information, among other skills. One anxiety concerning the future is that genetic and medical interventions might substantially replace the effort of an individual in achieving such goals. At present, of course, the possibility of such interventions is the stuff of science fiction and it is therefore difficult to assess and evaluate these hypothetical products. But what one can say is that if almost anyone might be helped by these techniques to achieve what are now regarded as remarkable results, the techniques would undermine the significance of these results as individual achievements.[22] As Parens has observed, 'in many valued human activities, the means of acquiring the capacities required for the activity are a part of the very definition of the activity, and transforming them transforms, and can devalue, the activity itself.'[23] This is one of the concerns that underlies disapproval of the use of drugs in sport.[24] It is of course also possible that even greater achievements might become possible through a combination of these interventions and individual effort and skill. But commercial pressures to exploit these possibilities would need to be resisted so that the value of these achievements could be judged carefully in each case.

13.38 Similarly, in the case of psychiatric disorders, it is sometimes argued that the use of medicines rather than other forms of therapy reinforces the tendency to think of ourselves in mechanistic terms, undermining our conception of ourselves as responsible agents. But this case is much less convincing than that envisaged above. Drugs do form an important and effective part of the treatment of psychiatric disorders, and if genetic tests indicate a predisposition to such disorders which might be prevented from having an effect by taking suitable drugs, it is hard to see what is wrong with such a course of action. There is little merit in the argument that a human life must involve suffering or lack of fulfilment where this could be averted by some intervention, only because this intervention is quicker or easier than some alternative.

13.39 How does this argument translate in the case of behavioural traits in the normal range? One might argue that it would not only be wrong to inhibit people making use of such interventions, but that there are reasons to encourage their use. It is not immediately obvious why it would be a bad thing if people were generally less likely to exhibit antisocial

---

[21] Clarke, A. The genetic testing of children. In Marteau, T. M. & Richards, M., editors. (1996). *The Troubled Helix*. Cambridge: Cambridge University Press. The Nuffield Council on Bioethics has recommended in earlier publications that predictive genetic testing of children in such circumstances should not be permitted. (Nuffield Council on Bioethics (1993) *Genetic screening: ethical issues* and (1998) *Genetics and mental disorders: the ethical context*).

[22] In addition, if everyone has the capacity to achieve certain goals, the advantage of attaining those goals may be lost. If everyone becomes more intelligent, then one individual's increased IQ score will not advantage him with respect to others.

[23] Parens, E. (1998). *Enhancing Human Traits: Ethical and Social Implications*. Washington, DC: Georgetown University Press. p. 52.

[24] See, for example, Radick, G. Discovering and patenting human genes. In Bainham, A., Day Sclater, S. & Richards, M., editors. (2002). *Body Lore and Laws*. Oxford: Hart. pp. 289–307.

behaviour, or more likely to be of high intelligence. As they get older, most people would welcome a way of maintaining their ordinary capacity for memory.[25] Assuming such traits could be enhanced in existing people without undesirable side effects or implications for genetic diversity, would it be wrong to aim at such goals? It could be argued that a general increase in intelligence would not, in fact, increase happiness or provide social benefits. But this gloomy prediction does not accord with our current social practices that aim to provide more education for individuals, to develop their cognitive abilities and so forth.

13.40 One way to think about the difference between interventions targeted at disorders, such as depression, and those interventions speculatively envisaged in this section, is that the former are primarily intended to help people overcome handicaps which prevent them from making the most of themselves, whereas the speculative interventions are supposed to make it easy for people to achieve results that are now only available to a few especially talented individuals. This difference is a case of a general distinction between therapy and enhancement; and, just as in the case of the interventions discussed here, there is a widespread view that whereas therapeutic interventions are generally valuable, the possibility of enhancement is more problematic, giving rise to, for example, questions of fairness where it is of limited availability. So we turn now to discuss this distinction and its significance.

Therapy versus enhancement

13.41 The way to distinguish between those interventions which count as 'therapies' and those which count as 'enhancements' is by reference to the condition that is to be altered: therapies aim to treat, cure or prevent diseases and to alleviate pathological conditions which place someone outside the normal range, whereas enhancements aim to improve already healthy systems and to advance capacities which already fall within the normal range. The distinction between health and disease is of course evaluative. Nonetheless, we largely agree on what counts as a disease and on the idea of an illness resulting from a failure to function properly. So, most medical care is therapy, concerned with the prevention, treatment or cure of disease. By contrast, for example, cosmetic surgery which simply aims to alleviate some of the manifest effects of ageing is enhancement.[26]

13.42 The distinction between therapy and enhancement is often used to justify a distinction between interventions which merit public support and those which do not. The suggestion is that there is a duty to ensure that our fellow citizens receive therapies, but no duty to ensure that they receive enhancements. In some respects, this principle needs qualification. Where resources are scarce, it may well be impossible to provide effective public support for therapies; equally, as later discussion will show (paragraphs 13.44 – 13.48), there may be enhancements which are such that, if they are permissible at all, they should be available to all. Nonetheless, the principle which associates the distinction between therapy and enhancement with that between public and private provision is a useful starting-point in this area.

---

[25] There is some evidence that the anti-Alzheimer drug Aricept can be used to enhance memory, though it has disagreeable side-effects. Yesavage, J. A. *et al.* (2002). Donepezil and flight simulator performance: effects on retention of complex skills. *Neurology* **59**, 123–5 (and see BBC News. 8 July 2002. *'Smart drugs' boost pilot memory*. http://news.bbc.co.uk/hi/english/health/newsid_2116000/2116476.stm. (9 August 2002)).

[26] There is an extensive literature on the definitions of and differences between health, disease, disorder and illness. An interesting analysis in the area of psychiatric disorders is provided in Fulford, K. W. M. (1989). *Moral Theory and Medical Practice*. Cambridge: Cambridge University Press.

13.43 Although therapy is usually thought of as the treatment of diseases with an identifiable biochemical basis, there can be cases in which someone suffers from a pathological condition which places them outside the normal range in some respect, without there being any such identified basis for it. In such cases, interventions to overcome the resulting impairment are also to be regarded as therapies; hence the basic principle affirmed in the previous paragraph implies that such interventions merit public support to make them available to all. The important issue is the severity of the handicap, not its cause. We take the view that this conclusion should be applied to interventions which become available in the field of behavioural genetics. Any decision to provide public support through the National Health Service (NHS) for interventions to enable individuals to overcome disabilities which obstruct their capacity for behaviour in the normal range should not be dependent on the underlying cause of the disability.

Access to interventions

13.44 Genetic tests and interventions which lack any therapeutic application and are designed to enable individuals to enhance their capacities within the normal range provide the context for the issue raised in paragraph 13.42: who should be able to make use of tests and interventions? And who should bear the cost of the tests and interventions? A standard view is that since the state does not have an obligation to provide techniques for improving intelligence or athleticism, these interventions should not normally be provided as part of a public healthcare system. Nonetheless, it may also be argued, within a free society and a free market, these techniques should be available for purchase.

13.45 The anxiety, however, is that if such tests and interventions were available for private purchase, the result could be that only the more affluent members of society would have access to them. Because these techniques would enhance capabilities, this could lead to even greater inequalities and increase social and economic polarisation. In particular, where not everyone has access to these interventions, equality of opportunity is threatened. One theory about the likely effects of such polarisation was postulated by Lee Silver in his book *Remaking Eden*.[27] In Silver's futuristic scenario, advances in diagnosis and reproductive technology enable those who can afford such services to produce children who have greater skills and talents. He postulates that over time, society will segregate into the 'GenRich' who control the economy, the media, and the knowledge industry, and the 'Naturals,' who work as low paid service providers or as labourers. (It may be observed that this scenario is not dependent on genetic enhancement; arguably, it has always happened, as a result of inequitable distribution of other inherited resources such as wealth, except in so far as the modern state has intervened to promote equality of opportunity).[28]

13.46 The implication of these considerations is that a society which values equality of opportunity will ensure that genetic tests and interventions to enhance important behavioural traits, such as intelligence, should either be made freely available to all or limited to special cases not dependent on private wealth. In both cases, as a history of the NHS in the UK shows, it may well be that financial barriers to access are not the only ones; there may be geographical, institutional and cultural barriers that need to be given active consideration. For without some active engagement to break down these barriers, it could

[27] Silver, L. (1998) *Remaking Eden*. London: Weidenfeld.

[28] Martin Richards has identified other problems with Silver's theory. See Richards, M. Future bodies: some history and future prospects for human genetic selection. In Bainham, A., Day Sclater, S. & Richards, M., editors. (2002). *Body Lore and Laws*. Oxford: Hart. pp. 289–307.

be that a society divides, not into Silver's 'GenRich' elite and a 'Natural' majority, but into a talented majority and a 'Natural' (or 'GenPoor') minority underclass.

13.47 Public provision of new tests and interventions, especially when accompanied by further efforts to prevent the formation of an underclass, would, of course, require considerable resources. For the egalitarian, if these resources are not available, then the tests and interventions should not be introduced at all. But there is a powerful libertarian counter-argument which draws on the existing patterns of investment in the future of children by those who pay for private schooling, tennis coaching or French lessons. Libertarians argue that there is no moral basis for a distinction between interventions based on genetic variants and the familiar use of extra resources in the fields of education and sport. In particular, in the context of what might be termed 'desirable' traits such as increased intelligence, it is simply wrong to 'equalise downwards' by banning a particular intervention. If a trait is desirable and there is an intervention that will increase the likelihood of it occurring, the correct response is to ensure that it is available as widely as possible. While this may entail that, for at least a limited period of time, there will be some who do not have access, the overall goal should be to raise everyone to the highest level. As Ronald Dworkin argues:

> 'We should not ... seek to improve equality by levelling down, and, as in the case of more orthodox medicine, techniques available for a time only to the very rich often produce discoveries of more general value for everyone. The remedy for injustice is redistribution, not denial of benefits to some with no corresponding benefits to others.'[29]

13.48 It is difficult to adjudicate in the abstract between these egalitarian and libertarian positions. It is only once some effective intervention is under consideration that the costs and benefits of full public availability versus limited private availability for a privileged few can be assessed seriously. **We believe that equality of opportunity is a fundamental social value which is especially damaged where a society is divided into groups that are likely to perpetuate inequalities across generations. We recommend, therefore, that any genetic interventions to enhance traits in the normal range should be evaluated with this consideration in mind.**

Monitoring the provision of genetic tests and interventions

13.49 If genetic tests and corresponding genetic, medical or environmental interventions relevant to traits in the normal range are developed, it is important to consider how such tests and interventions may be made available. Genetic tests for variants that influence behaviour in the normal range might be thought of as comparable to personality or IQ tests, rather than genetic tests that are used to diagnose or predict the onset of a serious disease such as cancer. Similarly, interventions might be seen as comparable to vitamin supplements or cosmetic surgery. In both cases, therefore, if the comparisons are a guide, it may turn out that individuals are left to make decisions about whether to make use of tests or interventions without the involvement of health professionals.

[29] Dworkin, R. (2000). *Sovereign Virtue: The Theory and Practice of Equality*. Cambridge, MA: Harvard University Press. p. 440.

13.50 This has important implications for the regulation and monitoring of tests and interventions. Without appropriate safeguards, consumers may be at risk of exploitation through misleading marketing practices. This is particularly likely in novel areas of science, where most people will not be well placed to make informed judgements. In the case of genetic tests, there is currently no specific legislation in place that would provide a regulatory mechanism for assessing the efficacy or reliability of a test. This applies even to genetic tests for diseases, as well as to the hypothetical tests for genetic influences on behavioural traits that are the focus of this Report. In 1997, the Advisory Committee on Genetic Testing (ACGT), a non-statutory committee that reported to the Department of Health, produced a *Code of Practice and Guidance on Human Genetic Testing Services Supplied Direct to the Public.*[30] The code of practice was a voluntary one, and suppliers of genetic tests were expected to submit their proposed tests to the ACGT for consideration before introducing them to the public. The ACGT noted that it would be necessary to review how successful the voluntary system proved to be, and to consider recommending 'a more rigorous statutory regime' if necessary.

13.51 The remit of this code of practice was restricted to tests for genetic disorders, and did not include tests for traits in the normal range. Some of the code's requirements are pertinent, including the need for verifiable external quality assurance and control of laboratories conducting the tests and the importance of protecting the confidentiality of the data obtained. However, we consider that the issues raised by tests for behavioural traits and other traits that exhibit normal variation require specific attention. The questions addressed by these tests include very sensitive areas of personal and family vulnerability, and there is considerable potential for exploitation of the anxieties and aspirations of members of the public in an area where the science is not well understood. This danger is particularly important since both tests and interventions might be applied to children without their consent. Thus, we take the view that it is not adequate in this area to rely on the same mechanisms that apply to non-genetic or non-medical enhancements, such as recourse to the Advertising Standard Authority or the Office of Fair Trading, to prevent misleading claims being made and ineffective tests from being sold.

13.52 The ACGT was subsumed in 2001 by the Human Genetics Commission (HGC), which currently has responsibility for administering the code of practice. The HGC issued a public consultation document on the supply of genetic tests direct to the public in July 2002.[31] This summarises the current situation and poses a number of specific questions covering issues such as consent to testing, storage and use of samples, and confidentiality of data. It notes that tests in the field of behavioural genetics are likely to be particularly controversial.

13.53 **On the presumption that tests for genetic influences on behavioural traits in the normal range, of varying quality and predictive power, will become available, we welcome the consideration by the HGC of genetic tests supplied directly to the public. We encourage the HGC to give thorough consideration to the issues raised by genetic tests for behavioural and personality traits. We recommend that both the public and private provision of such tests, if they are developed, should be stringently monitored and regulated as necessary.**

---

[30] Advisory Committee on Genetic Testing. (September 1997). *Code of Practice and Guidance on Human Genetic Testing Services Supplied Direct to the Public.* London: Health Departments of the United Kingdom.

[31] Human Genetics Commission. Consultation on Genetic Testing Services supplied Direct to the Public. http://www.hgc.gov.uk/testingconsultation/index.htm (16 Jul 2002).

13.54 In addition to genetic tests, interventions may be developed, whether medical, genetic or environmental, on the basis of information about genetic variants. The HGC consultation document recognises that some genetic tests may be accompanied by a corresponding intervention that is recommended, depending on the test results. How should such interventions be regulated? It is useful here to consider the types of intervention separately. In the case of genetic interventions, we have already noted (paragraph 13.31) that the use of gene therapy will be regulated by the GTAC.

13.55 Medical interventions such as pharmacological substances will not necessarily be classified as medicines. While some would be subject to the existing regulation in place for medicines, others might be classified as foodstuffs or herbal remedies. Those which are not classified as medicines are unlikely to be harmful, but there is a risk that they will be promoted on the basis of unreliable, or even non-existent scientific evidence, and that consumers will be misled. Similarly, environmental interventions, such as changes in lifestyle or surroundings, may be promoted on the basis of genetic information about an individual. As noted above, we do not consider that there are currently any public bodies constituted in such a way as to monitor the provision of such interventions effectively and ensure that they are appropriate and of sufficiently high quality. **We recommend, therefore, that those charged with the monitoring and regulation of genetic tests for behavioural traits in the normal range should also be responsible for ensuring appropriate monitoring of the provision of interventions based on such genetic information, which fall outside the scope of other regulatory bodies**.

13.56 We note the difficulties for monitoring and regulation raised by the sale of existing tests and interventions on the internet, and encourage the efforts of the Office of Fair Trading and consumer protection agencies such as the National Consumer Council and the Consumers' Association in developing codes of practice and strategies, such as kite-marks for assisting consumers.

Prenatal selection

Technologies for prenatal testing and selection

13.57 The speculative interventions discussed so far are generally applied to those already born (although many environmental and medical interventions can affect fetuses, and it is possible that gene therapy could be carried out *in utero*). In the last section of this chapter we consider a different type of intervention that affects the traits of an individual, not by altering them but by selecting them in advance. One such intervention is prenatal testing, which has been practised on clinical grounds for thirty years in the UK. Techniques such as serum screening, ultrasound scanning and amniocentesis are in widespread use to detect pregnancies affected by Down's syndrome, spina bifida or other abnormalities, in order to offer couples early information on the pregnancy. Many couples opt for termination of pregnancy if abnormalities are detected. These techniques are known as prenatal diagnosis (PND).

13.58 A second intervention has been developed over the last 15–20 years, in which the process of *in vitro* fertilisation (IVF) has been coupled with embryo biopsy. Fertilisation of eggs by sperm takes place in the laboratory. Embryos are allowed to grow to the eight-cell stage, at which point one or two cells are removed for genetic testing. The remaining cells of the embryo still have the potential for normal development. Having tested each embryo, doctors can offer prospective parents the choice of which embryo is reintroduced. This technique is known as pre-implantation genetic diagnosis (PGD). In the UK, stringent regulation of this technology by the Human Fertilisation and Embryology Authority (HFEA) means that it is only currently offered to families affected by inherited disorders such as Duchenne's muscular dystrophy and cystic fibrosis.[32] PGD means that parents can ensure that their child does not have these serious diseases, but avoid the termination of pregnancy, a process which is emotionally or morally unacceptable to many people.[33] The benefits of PGD over PND are that the outcome is a healthy pregnancy, rather than termination of an established pregnancy accompanied by the need to start again at conception. The disadvantage is that IVF is an intrusive procedure, which may have to be carried out on numerous occasions before a successful pregnancy is achieved. There are, however, difficulties in obtaining funds from health authorities for IVF, so in practice it is provided largely by the private sector in the UK.

13.59 Another, largely theoretical, approach would move selection further back in time, by allowing choice between different gametes. Experimental techniques now allow sperm to be sorted, enabling parents to choose the sex of their embryo. This technique remains somewhat unreliable: there are reports of an 8% error rate for females and 28% in males. It is not clear that this type of technique will ever be applicable to traits other than sex, and it is particularly difficult to envisage its applications to the complex traits considered in this Report.[34] The use of PGD and sperm sorting are just two technologies that have generated concerns about so-called 'designer babies' (see Box 13.2).

Box 13.2: 'Designer babies'

'Designer baby' is one of those terms, like 'Frankenstein foods' and 'slippery slope', which is central to public discourse on genetics, but which can be misleading. The word 'design' can connote a *purpose*, a *plan* or the idea of *fashion design*. The use of the phrase 'designer babies' in the media and public debate confuses these three aspects of the term. Understood in the third sense listed, that of fashion, the phrase 'designer baby' could refer to a general process in which babies are valued for what might be thought trivial reasons, such as hair or eye colour. This would be a 'designer baby' in the sense that it exemplifies the values of a

---

[32] Recently, this was extended to allow the parents of a child with a serious blood disease to select an embryo that did not have the same condition and which had been tissue-typed to ensure that it could be a matched donor of bone marrow cells to its sibling. The HFEA announced on 13 December 2001 that PGD and embryo selection would be allowed in order to ensure the birth of a child without a genetic disorder who would be a matched donor for a sibling. The way in which this decision was reached was criticised by the House of Commons Select Committee on Science and Technology. (House of Commons Science and Technology Committee. (18 July 2002). *Developments in Human Genetics and Embryology*. Fourth Report of Session 2001–02. London: HMSO). The HFEA subsequently rejected an apparently similar request from a family whose child suffered from a rare condition called Diamond Blackfan anaemia. Their application was turned down on the grounds that the embryos were at no increased risk of having the condition: the use of PGD and tissue typing would be purely for the benefit of the existing child, and was not necessary to ensure the health of the implanted embryo. This ruling contradicted the advice of the HFEA's own Ethics Committee which took the view that there was no moral distinction between the two types of case (Ethics Committee of the HFEA. (November 2001). *Ethical Issues in the Creation and Selection of Preimplantation Embryos to Produce Tissue Donors*).

[33] PND, which can lead to the selective termination of pregnancy, can be distinguished from PGD, which involves the selective implantation of embryos. Because abortion is an invasive procedure often associated with distress, it might be suggested that PND on non-clinical grounds is less likely to become widespread than the less traumatic process of PGD.

[34] It is possible to take selection back yet another stage: there is a phenomenon important in research in genetics called 'assortative mating', which refers to the fact that people often choose partners who have similar traits (see paragraph 9.12). For example, there is a positive correlation as high as 0.47 between husbands and wives on IQ scores (eg. DeFries, J. C. *et al*. (1979). Familial resemblance for specific cognitive abilities. *Behav. Genet.* **9**, 23–43), though correlations for other personality traits are much lower. Whatever the precise correlations, the fact remains that people do choose who to have children with, and these decisions may in part be based on characteristics such as appearance, intelligence and personality. Thus, the philosopher John Harris has argued that all decisions to have a child involve selection: natural conception is not a random exercise.

consumer society and an unhealthy focus on unimportant, frivolous characteristics. An alternative use of the term 'designer baby' has been to refer to a child whose characteristics have been deliberately chosen, rather than left to chance, such as the recent cases of embryos being selected in such a way that their cord cells can be used to provide donor cells for a sibling.* This use of the term misleadingly implies that particular characteristics of a child are being manipulated or engineered. In reality, the only techniques currently available are the selection of gametes before fertilisation, of embryos before implantation or selective termination of pregnancy. These techniques are all examples of the selection or choice of alternative options rather than the actual manipulation or design of babies. There is a third potential use of the phrase 'designer baby', which refers to the possibility of truly designing a child, by choosing characteristics from a menu of possibilities to create a child, for example using gene therapy, but this notion is still in the realms of science fiction.

* For example: *The Sun* (11 April 2002). A designer baby would end our heart ache; *Guardian* (23 February 2002). Designer baby gets the go ahead; *The Times* (25 February 2002). British couples queue up to have 'designer' babies; *Independent* (24 February 2002). Five more designer babies on way in UK.

13.60 Before discussing the ethical arguments surrounding use of prenatal selection by PND or PGD, it is important to emphasise points made earlier regarding the practical difficulty of selecting for behavioural traits using these technologies. Because of the multiplicity of genes involved, a very large number of embryos would need to be screened before the desired 'chance' combination of genes was obtained. Indeed, given that the available genes will depend on the genotype of the parents, it may not be possible to find the 'ideal' combination. Currently, IVF tends to produce, on average, only about four to five embryos for each couple undergoing treatment.

Selection on non-clinical grounds: ethical arguments

13.61 The forms of selection outlined above are currently only practised on clinical grounds in the UK. However, the start of a trend towards selection on other grounds can be identified. The recent decision by the HFEA to allow the selection of embryos free from genetic conditions that can also act as donors to existing siblings is an important move in this direction.[35] Another relevant example is sex selection. In the UK, PND and PGD can be used for sex selection if it is necessary for clinical reasons, for example to avoid the birth of a child with an X-linked genetic disease. However, there is a policy of not offering sex selection on non-clinical grounds using PGD or PND. In the US, the Ethics Committee of the American Society of Reproductive Medicine concluded that PGD should not be initiated for purposes of sex selection, and that PGD for sex selection during IVF treatment should not be encouraged.[36] A complex set of concerns underlies such policies, involving the ethics of terminating healthy pregnancies, the need to accept offspring for themselves and not their particular characteristics, tendencies in some societies to favour male rather than female offspring, and the limited availability of genetic services.

[35] See footnote 32 above.

[36] Ethics Committee of the American Society of Reproductive Medicine. (1999). Sex selection and preimplantation genetic diagnosis. *Fertility and Sterility* **72**, 595–8.

13.62 Recently, some commentators in the US have called for this policy to be reassessed and for the possibility of sex selection of gametes to be reconsidered in certain circumstances.[37] In the UK, the Government has requested that the HFEA examines the advances in techniques of gamete selection on the basis of sex, something which is already possible and unregulated in the private sector. The HFEA intends to launch a public consultation on sex selection in late 2002.

13.63 There are numerous companies in the US that offer infertile couples the opportunity to purchase donor sperm or eggs. Donors with a few common genetic or infectious diseases are excluded, although some genetic risk remains nevertheless. Some information about various characteristics of donors is made available to prospective parents, including eye, hair and skin colour, so that parents can aim to have children who bear some physical resemblance to them. In the UK, couples requiring donated sperm are able to make use of similar information to provide a means of matching the characteristics of the donor to that of the husband. However, it has been suggested that private fertility clinics in the UK may allow couples to 'select sperm donors who bear little resemblance to themselves', in particular, donors who have 'desirable' characteristics.[38] The *5th Code of Practice* of the HFEA does not explicitly state that parents may not select 'desirable' traits when choosing a gamete donor.[39] It only states, in section 3.18, that 'centres should take into account each prospective parent's preferences in relation to the general physical characteristics of the person providing gametes for donation.' Preventing the selection of gametes based on non-clinical features, whether physical characteristics or behavioural traits such as intelligence or personality would therefore require new guidance.

13.64 In the US, most companies also provide information about the educational qualifications of donors and even their grades on school and college examinations. Some individuals who regard themselves as 'high achievers' have subsequently sold or given away their sperm on the internet. The most famous sperm bank of this kind was the Repository for Germinal Choice, which operated from 1980 to 1999. It collected sperm from people of high intelligence, including a number of winners of the Nobel Prize and the Field medal, a prestigious award in mathematics. Men of high intelligence who had family histories of serious genetic disease or disorders such as schizophrenia were excluded. Women purchasing the sperm were excluded if they were unmarried, unhealthy, over the age of 40 or had criminal records. Another group that received considerable publicity is Ron's Angels, which offers donor eggs and sperm from attractive men and women. The company's website asks, 'If you could increase the chance of reproducing beautiful children and thus giving them an advantage in society, would you?'[40]

13.65 Law and clinical practice support the use of genetic information to provide informed choice for prospective parents. But professional and public opposition has been voiced, for a variety of reasons, to the use of non-clinical attributes such as the traits considered in this Report in testing and selection. There seems to be a consensus in clinical genetics and in public opinion against use of PGD or PND in order to select babies on the basis of non-

---

[37] Robertson, J. A. (2001) Preconception gender selection, *Am. J. Bioethics* **1**, 2–9.

[38] Calvert, J. & O'Reilly, J. (2002). Babies-to-order raise 'eugenic' fears. *The Sunday Times*. 21 July.

[39] Human Fertilisation and Embryology Authority. (2001). *Code of Practice*. 5th Edition.

[40] Ron's Angels. Egg Auction. 2000. http://www.ronsangels.com/auction.html (16 Jul 2002). The website states that the company has generated an income of $3.2 million in sales since 1999.

Box 13.3: Views about prenatal selection expressed by respondents to the public consultation

'We have grave concerns regarding prenatal testing for any trait other than in untreatable genetic disorders that normally result in death.'

Royal College of Psychiatrists

'We need a wide variety of behaviours, personalities and temperaments if human society is to adapt to the changing circumstances we find ourselves in. Variety is the spice of life, and it is also essential for evolution.'

Grant Vallance, PhD student, Open University

'in an increasingly autonomy-oriented climate, it may be impossible to draw firm lines against such selection ... Use of law to prevent such selection is the worst possible alternative, because it opens the door to other restrictions on people's decisions about reproduction.'

Professor Dorothy C Wertz, University of Massachusetts

clinical characteristics (Box 13.3 contains examples of responses to the Working Party's public consultation that address this issue). **In the case of PND, we share this view. Setting aside the contested issue of the ethics of abortion on social grounds, which is outside the scope of this Report, we take the view that the use of selective termination following PND to abort a fetus merely on the basis of information about behavioural traits in the normal range is morally unacceptable.**

13.66 But the issues raised by the use of PGD are different. Whereas selective termination following PND is applied to a fetus that has already implanted and is developing in the womb, PGD is used to select which embryos to implant. Thus, PGD does not precede the termination of a potential human life, but precedes instead the choice as to which embryo, among those created by IVF, is to be given a chance of developing into a human being. And in this context, it is not so clear that it is morally unacceptable to make this choice on the basis of genetic information about the traits that are the focus of this Report. Whereas PND would be used to end a life, PGD is, in effect, used to choose which life to start. Hence, the moral prohibitions which apply in the case of PND, do not apply in the same way in the use of PGD. Nonetheless, the potential use of PGD to select embryos that are more or less likely to exhibit particular behavioural traits is widely thought unacceptable. In the final part of this chapter, we attempt to evaluate this position.

For selection

(i) The right to proceative autonomy

13.67 The main argument in favour of the permissibility of selection is that this is a legitimate exercise of individual liberty. There is, quite generally, a strong presumption in favour of the exercise of individual liberty wherever its exercise does not conflict, directly or indirectly, with the legitimate interests of others. This presumption is especially powerful when the activity in question lies within what is normally the sphere of private life, as the conception of children clearly does. For, on the one hand, within this sphere it is hard to see how others are harmed by what is done; and, on the other hand, intimate matters of this kind matter greatly to those directly concerned, so that it is all the more important and difficult to justify any interference in them. Hence, the liberal position is sometimes described in terms of the existence of a 'right to procreative autonomy', which would include a right to employ safe and reliable methods for the selection of children with a genetic predisposition for enhanced abilities within the normal range.[41]

Against selection

(i) The 'expressivist' argument

13.68 One argument opposes selection for traits in the normal range because of the signals it might send about the value of different types of people and different forms of life. Many advocates of disability rights use this 'expressivist' objection to oppose selection on clinical grounds, arguing that termination of pregnancies affected by disability signals that disability is unacceptable or that disabled people are inferior.[42] In the case of behavioural genetics, if parents used selection to avoid the birth of babies carrying alleles associated with homosexuality, for example, this might reflect and reinforce prejudices such as homophobia. Selection for higher intelligence or sporting prowess might be thought to similarly devalue others who did not possess these traits, or whose parents could not afford to invest in selection techniques. However, this argument does not seem particularly strong in the case of non-disease traits. By definition, most of the traits in question are possessed in some degree by everyone and many of them, such as higher intelligence, are already valued widely in society and aimed at through educational programmes and other social policies. So it is hard to see why permitting selection on the basis of genetic predispositions in favour of enhanced abilities within the normal range, if it were possible, should be thought to 'express' a specially worrying evaluation of these abilities which is not already manifest in social practices.

(ii) Equality

13.69 We have noted previously (paragraphs 13.44 – 13.48) that the introduction of interventions based on genetic tests which aim to enhance abilities within the normal range poses a threat to the equality of opportunity. Does the same anxiety apply here? Since prenatal selection is the issue, it is not clear that it does: for a child who is conceived and born without any method of selection is not someone who has been deprived of an opportunity for enhancement that has been made available to a child whose conception has made use of methods of selection such as PGD. In this context, the method involved is one that selects for different people, rather than enhancing the abilities of a given person. Nonetheless, egalitarian anxieties do have a genuine basis: a society divided between those possessing enhanced abilities as a result of prenatal selection and those conceived naturally with the ordinary range of abilities might well develop consequential divisions which make life more difficult for ordinary people. But much depends here on the rest of the assumed social and political context. If we assume a democratic context whose political institutions and culture are organised in such a way that the public as a whole, and in particular those who are less talented, benefit from the exceptional abilities of a few, especially talented individuals, then there seems no good reason for thinking that things will get worse, in ways that are unfair, if such people are created. By contrast, if the society is one in which a talented elite enjoy their good fortune without any commensurate benefits for the rest of society, then

[41] Dworkin, R. (1993). *Life's Dominion*. London: Harper Collins.

[42] This concern can be seen as arising from the eugenic programmes we discussed in Chapter 2, in which people without desirable traits were devalued and abused.

there is no reason why the latter should welcome the creation of a larger and correspondingly more powerful elite.

13.70 The conclusion to be drawn, therefore, is that the introduction of PGD as a method of prenatal selection does provide grounds for egalitarian anxieties; but also that if one assumes a background social and political system in which anti-elitist egalitarian values are already well entrenched, it should be possible to accommodate prenatal selection without any great resulting unfairness. Hence, the judgement in any particular case as to whether there is a significant egalitarian objection to prenatal selection depends on whether egalitarian values are already well established in the social and political context in question.

(iii) Natural humility

13.71 The intuitive objection to prenatal selection is that it is 'interfering with nature'. By itself this is no argument, since all medical interventions involve some such interference. But the 'conservative' opponent of prenatal selection will argue that the kind of interference involved in prenatal selection undermines the proper relationship between parents and their children. For by inviting parents to exercise their preferences in making a selection it introduces an element of control over the result of conception which makes the experience of parenthood very different from the present situation in which, in the majority of cases, parents are happy just to take their children as they find them. One might compare the present situation to that of eating at the kind of family restaurant which used to be common, where there is no menu and one simply takes what is given; and then compare the envisaged use of prenatal selection to eating at a restaurant where there is a menu from which one can make a selection (and send back a dish if it was not what one ordered). Just to make this comparison, of course, is not to provide an argument; and the challenge for conservative opponents of prenatal selection is to convert this kind of intuitive reaction against prenatal selection into arguments that are robust enough to defeat the liberal proponents of a 'right to procreative autonomy' (see paragraph 13.67 above).

13.72 One attempt to do so has been made by Deena Davis, who deploys Joel Feinberg's argument that children have a right to an open future.[43] This concept was developed by Feinberg in relation to existing children, to explain that they had rights which they were not capable of exercising but which should be 'held in trust' for them until they were fully autonomous individuals. Until that point, anything that reduced the child's available options and eliminated opportunities for it to make its own choices could be said to infringe its right to an open future. If this argument is transferred to prenatal selection, it might suggest that choosing traits – from sex to enhanced abilities – narrows the options for that child. The obvious difficulty with this argument, however, is that it mischaracterises the parental choice: for it is a choice between different possible children and not one concerning different abilities which one and the same child might have possessed. So it is not true in a straightforward sense that prenatal selection 'narrows the options' for a child.

13.73 Nonetheless, it can be argued that what is wrong with prenatal selection is that it restricts a child's freedom by the pressure it places upon a child to fulfil the hopes and wishes of the parents which guided their decision to select that child for implantation rather than the other embryos that were available. People who want a male child so strongly that they resort to prenatal selection techniques may well seek to bring up their

---

[43] Davis, D. S. (2001). *Genetic Dilemmas*. New York: Routledge.

son to conform to a stereotyped gender role. It can be objected that one should distinguish the selection of an embryo from what parents do to the resulting child once he or she exists. There is no reason to assume that parents, having selected a child, would necessarily place pressure on the child or treat him or her in an undesirable way. However, if people care so strongly about a trait that they are willing to select for it, it is perhaps to be expected that they will rear the child in a stereotypical way or place pressure on the child and be upset if he or she does not fulfil the aspirations for which they have selected.

13.74 The conservative opponent of prenatal selection holds that this kind of parental pressure is a symptom of the changed relationship between parents and children which prenatal selection will motivate. At present, parents accept their children as they find them in an attitude of 'natural humility' to the unchosen, or chance results of procreation. This attitude is an important feature of parental love, the love that parents owe to their children as individuals in their own right; for this is a love that does not have to be earned and is not dependent on a child having characteristics that the parents hoped for. When we fall in love as adults we exercise some degree of choice in selecting our partner, the person we love. But parental love for children does not include a similar element of choice and it would be very destructive of it if it were to do so.

13.75 Natural humility is entirely compatible with the familiar parental aspiration, which is indeed another element of parental love, that one should do what one can to enable one's children to make the best of themselves by overcoming natural weaknesses and developing natural abilities by means of education, encouragement and so on. Involvements of this kind, however, are not attempts to ensure a specific future for a child. Not only are such attempts likely to fail, thereby leading to resentment or a sense of failure or both; more importantly, they manifest a failure by parents to understand that parental love requires the respect which gives children the opportunity to frame their lives for themselves in accordance with their own abilities and aspirations.

13.76 For the conservative, parental love which includes this element of natural humility is, therefore, incompatible with the will to control. It is not compatible with attempts to interfere in the life of a child except where the interference is in the child's own interest. Equally, it is not compatible with the practice of prenatal selection which seeks to identify, as a basis for choice, genetic predispositions for enhanced abilities or special traits. For this is an attempt to determine the kind of child one will have, which is precisely not the unconditional, loving acceptance of whatever child one turns out to have.

13.77 For the conservative, therefore, the advocates of prenatal selection in the name of the right to procreative autonomy fail to take account of the value inherent in our present attitude of natural humility, which informs the loving relationship between parents and children. They urge that in this most intimate area of personal life we should seek to curb our will to control.

13.78 Given that we are dealing here with only speculative possibilities, and since the likely small effects of individual genes may make accurate predictions of future behaviour very difficult, it is hard to evaluate the disagreement between the conservatives and the liberals. In particular, it may be that the contrast between the liberal's affirmation of a right to procreative autonomy and the conservative's defence of natural humility is too simple. It might turn out that there are possibilities for modest applications of PGD in relation to the traits considered in this Report which would not seriously undermine the present relationship between parents and their children. **While not entirely persuaded by this conservative line of argument, we do accept that, at present, the case for permitting prenatal selection based on the identification of genetic predispositions for enhanced abilities remains to be made. We recommend, therefore, that the technique of preimplantation genetic diagnosis, which is currently restricted to serious diseases and disorders, should not be extended to include behavioural traits in the normal range such as intelligence, sexual orientation and personality traits**.

Chapter 14

Legal responsibility

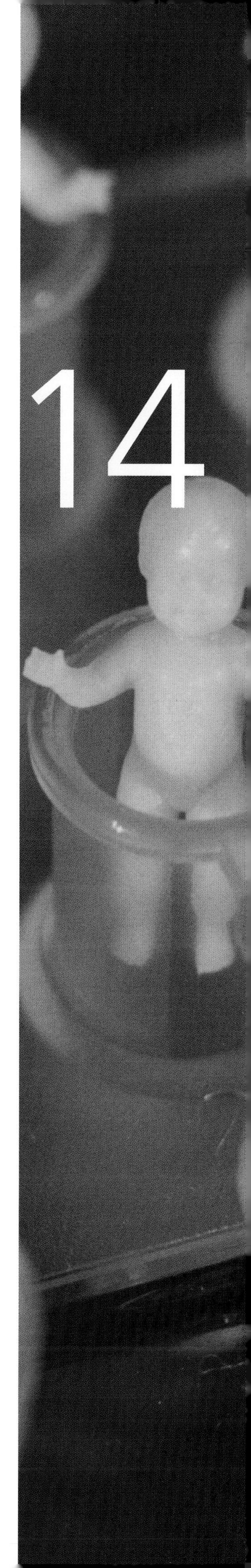

Legal responsibility

14.1 We concluded in Chapter 12 that the results of research in behavioural genetics do not warrant a substantial revision of our current conceptions of human action and moral responsibility. However, one area in which the research may have more immediate and more persuasive implications is in the attribution of legal responsibility and the role of punishment. In this chapter, we consider the status of biological explanations of behaviour in the context of criminal law and the possible impact of behavioural genetics on the legal system. In the following chapter we consider issues that also concern the law, namely employment and insurance, but this chapter focuses on criminal law and responsibility for criminal behaviour.

The history of biological explanations of human behaviour in law

14.2 Interest in biological explanations of criminal behaviour is by no means new. In the nineteenth century the Italian criminologist, Cesare Lombroso, wrote extensively on the association between crime and physiognomy, drawing attention to what he saw as the typical facial and cranial features of the criminal.[1] Interest in Lombrosan criminology waned, but this movement expressed a widespread and persistent enthusiasm for identifying a physical explanation of crime. It is this same interest which prompted research in the mid-twentieth century into the distribution of body types amongst juvenile offenders, and, arguably, which prompts contemporary interest in scientific explanations of antisocial behaviour, whether the preferred theory be neurological, dietary or genetic. Although such interest is understandable, it is important that a desire for a simple, intelligible cause of a serious social problem should not obscure the need for scientific rigour in scrutinising the claims of such theories. Crime is a complex phenomenon, and interpretations of crime that focus on one aetiological factor are likely to be misleading. Such approaches are also open to the criticism that they represent the 'quick fix' response, thereby obscuring the need to address other, potentially more expensive and uncomfortable solutions.

14.3 Some commentators have suggested that the search for genes that influence crime or antisocial behaviour is fundamentally misconceived, since crime is a socially constructed phenomenon. This criticism has also been levelled at research in behavioural genetics into other traits, including intelligence and personality characteristics, but it is particularly pertinent in the case of crime and antisocial behaviour. Nikolas Rose has noted that biological criminologists are:

> 'quick to acknowledge that crime as such does not exist; that lawbreaking acts are heterogenous; that crime is culturally and historically variable; that infraction of law is common; that those arrested, charged and convicted are not representative of those who break the law but a skewed sample produced through all sorts of social processes.'[2]

Consequently, it makes little sense to talk of genes for crime, or even genes for particular types of antisocial conduct, such as robbery or physical assault. Researchers in behavioural genetics do not deny this. Their research tends to focus on more narrowly defined and

---

[1] Lombroso, C. (1876). *L'Uomo Delinquente*. Milan: Horpli.

[2] Rose, N. (2000). The biology of culpability: pathological identity and crime control in a biological culture. *Theoretical Criminology* **4**, 5–34.

measurable traits such as impulsivity, aggressiveness and psychiatric disorders, such as conduct disorder and Attention Deficit Hyperactivity Disorder (ADHD). Nonetheless, it may be the case that our concepts of crime and antisocial behaviour are so complex and socially and culturally influenced that they will simply not be amenable to scientific investigation.

14.4 In this chapter, we review biological explanations of crime and antisocial behaviour that have been offered in recent history and consider the implications of research in behavioural genetics for our legal system. In particular, we consider three separate areas of criminal justice which may be affected by advances in research in behavioural genetics:

- *Exculpation*: Whether genetic information about a behavioural trait should affect our attributions of legal responsibility, that is, as an exculpatory factor.
- *Sentencing*: Whether genetic information about a behavioural trait should affect the way in which we sentence and treat convicted offenders.
- *Prediction*: Whether genetic information should be used to predict the future occurrence of antisocial behaviour.

Previous genetic and physiological explanations of crime

XYY males

14.5 In 1965 a paper was published based on research involving almost 200 males who had been committed to the State Hospital at Carstairs in Scotland.[3] Seven of the men were found to have an extra Y chromosome, a much higher rate than was thought to be the case in the general population. The research raised the possibility that this genetic abnormality could be related to the aggressive behaviour of the inmates. Further research showed that XYY males were more likely to be taller than average and of low intelligence, but failed to provide conclusive evidence about a link to aggressive or violent behaviour.[4] In 1976 a paper was published which concluded that XYY males were more likely to be imprisoned, but that this was due to their low intelligence and low socioeconomic status which placed them at higher risk of being caught.[5] The current state of opinion on the XYY issue is that there is insufficient evidence to establish any firm link between the particular genotype and an increased risk of aggressive behaviour, although there does appear to be an increased risk of offending.

14.6 There are no legal cases in the UK in which a genetic diagnosis of XYY has been used to establish a defence. At least five major US cases attempted to use the fact that the accused was XYY in defence but none was successful. In one, *State* v *Roberts* (1976), the judge stated that 'presently available medical evidence is unable to establish a reasonably certain causal connection between the XYY defect and criminal conduct'.[6] We discuss the issue of the quality of scientific evidence that is admissible in the legal system in paragraph 14.23.

---

[3] Jacobs, P.A. , Brunton, M. , Melville, M. M., Brittain, R. P. & McClermont, W. F. (1965). Aggressive behaviour, mental subnormality and the XYY male. *Nature* **208**, 1351–2.

[4] Baker, D., Telfer M. A., Richardson, C. E. & Clark, G. R. (1970). Chromosome errors in men with antisocial behavior: comparison of selected men with 'Klinefelter's syndrome' and XYY chromosome pattern. *JAMA* **214**, 869–78; Jacobs, P. A., Price, W. H., Richmond, S. & Ratcliff, B. A. W. (1971). Chromosome surveys in penal institutions and approved schools. *J. Med. Genet.* **8**, 49–58; Schiavo, R. *et al.* (1984), Sex, chromosome anomalies, hormones and aggressivity. *Arch. Gen. Psychiatry* **4**, 93–9.

[5] Witkin, H. A. *et al.* (1976). XYY and XXY men: criminality and aggression. *Science* **193**, 547–55.

[6] *State* v *Roberts* (1976). 14 Wash. App. 727, 544 P.2d 754.

In the case of XYY males, it is highly unlikely that the syndrome will acquire legal significance because of the difficulty in showing that it is directly linked to forms of antisocial behaviour.

14.7 It is perhaps worth making the observation here that having just a single Y chromosome is highly correlated with criminal behaviour: the vast majority of the prison population in the UK are men. This correlation does not seem to generate the same concerns, in that 'being male' is not suggested as something that absolves individuals from responsibility for criminal acts, nor is it taken into account as a mitigating factor in sentencing. We consider the relevance of the frequency of a genetic trait or predisposition in the population with regard to predicting behaviour in paragraph 14.38.

Syndromes

14.8 Numerous syndromes have been claimed to weaken or eliminate moral responsibility in cases where the accused person pleads not guilty by reason of insanity. These include syndromes thought to arise as the result of an environmental trauma, for example battered spouse syndrome, battered child syndrome and post-traumatic stress disorder, and those thought to arise as the result of a biological condition, such as premenstrual syndrome and postnatal depression. In these 'biological syndromes', the argument is that chemical or hormonal changes in the body affected the individual's capacity to control their actions to such a degree that they cannot truly be said to be responsible for them. The defence of premenstrual syndrome has been successful in Britain but is now rarely used because there has been a subsequent increase in measures to improve early detection and prevention of the condition.

Genetics: Huntington's disease

14.9 Huntington's disease, a single gene disorder that may be associated in some cases with aggressive behaviour, has obvious implications for criminal law. A person with this disorder may behave irrationally and may carry out assaults with no apparent motive.[7] Such behaviour is, of course, more easily seen as a concomitant of illness than is the case with asymptomatic genetic conditions, and is therefore more likely to be treated by the courts as an exculpatory factor. Prosecutorial discretion often prevents the bringing of charges against a person suffering from a diagnosed and obvious condition, such as dementia, and it is for this reason that legal precedents do not articulate the implications for criminal guilt of such conditions. The important point to note, however, is that it is not the genetic mutation which is regarded as exculpatory here but its impact on the brain. If a person suffering from Huntington's disease were to be acquitted of a criminal charge relating to aggressive behaviour produced by the condition, then this would be on psychiatric rather than on genetic grounds.

Genetics: Monoamine oxidase A (MAOA) deficiency

14.10 As noted in Chapter 9, there has been very little research on individual genes that might influence antisocial behaviour or criminal activity, with the exception of the family whose

[7] Mild psychotic and behavioural problems can appear some years before the onset of the disease. A study by Danish researchers in 1998 found increased prevalence of criminal behaviour in men with the genetic mutation that causes Huntington's disease and concluded that this was linked to the personality changes that are often seen in people with the condition (Jensen, P., Fenger, K., Bolwig, T. G. & Sorensen, S.A. (1998). Crime in Huntington's disease: a study of registered offences among patients, relatives and controls. *J. Neurol. Neurosurg. Psychiatry*. **65**, 467–71).

male members were deficient in a protein called MAOA. These males were found to be more likely to have been convicted of aggressive crimes such as rape and arson. Since this finding is currently confined to members of one family, it seems unlikely that it will have an impact in the legal system.[8] However, as we noted in paragraph 9.25, one recent study has suggested that the MAOA genotype may be a relatively effective predictor of antisocial behaviour in children who are also maltreated.

Genetic information as an exculpatory factor

14.11 If an association were to be established between the possession of a particular genetic variant and antisocial behaviour of some sort, for example, aggressive acts, it might be suggested that this information could be used not only in an attempt to explain crime, but also to excuse, or absolve from responsibility, those charged with criminal offences. This possibility raises a challenge to the notions of legal responsibility which underlie our system of criminal justice. As we observed in Chapter 12, if it were the case that responsibility for our acts is a matter of 'genetic luck', antisocial behaviour would cease to be a matter of personal responsibility as it would depend on factors beyond the control of the individual.

14.12 While it is unlikely that genetic explanations of behaviour will change the fundamental assumptions on which criminal justice relies, they could nonetheless have some effect. We should recall that, in the past, new scientific insights have been resisted by the courts, only to be fully acknowledged with the passage of time. One example here is the technique of DNA fingerprinting. Another is the readier acceptance of psychiatric defences in a number of West European countries, which accompanied the birth and development of modern psychiatry in the second half of the nineteenth century. This latter example, however, can also serve to highlight the difficulties that may arise when evidence from a new discipline is incorporated into the legal system. The disinclination of the courts to accept particular medical or scientific explanations should not be assumed. Equally, nor should their capacity for assessing the validity of novel scientific claims be overestimated.

14.13 Traditionally, the criminal law bases its notions of responsibility on the assumption that every adult is answerable for his or her acts, and is hostile to ideas which challenge the existence of free will and individual responsibility. The law endorses the idea of personal responsibility that lies behind the way in which we conduct our everyday lives in society, since the very idea of punishment and retribution makes little sense unless free will is assumed. 'Very simply, the law treats man's conduct as autonomous and willed, not because it is, but because it is desirable to proceed as if it were.'[9]

14.14 At the core of criminal responsibility is the notion that human action consists of an act and an accompanying mental state, usually an intention on the part of the individual. With the exception of offences of strict liability (regulatory offences in which the state of mind of the accused has no bearing on liability), the mental element behind action is of great importance in the law. The criminal law is not usually concerned with motive, at least for the purposes of allocating responsibility. What matters is the attitude of the individual towards the act itself. If an act is intentional, or performed recklessly or with

[8] In *Mobley* v *State* (1995). 265 Ga. 292, 455 S.E. 2d 81 the defence lawyers of a man accused of murder attempted to have their client tested for MAOA deficiency. However, the court refused to allow such a test, saying that 'the theory of genetic connection ... is not at a level of scientific acceptance that would justify its admission'. The request was made as a potential mitigating factor, not an exculpatory factor, in an attempt to avoid the death penalty.

[9] Packer, H. (1968). *The Limits of the Criminal Sanction.* Stanford: Stanford University Press.

culpable negligence, then the individual may be held responsible for it unless a valid defence is identified and accepted. In most cases, then, the law is concerned with choice. We make free choices with regard to our actions, and we then answer for these choices as free individuals.

14.15 Not all actions which infringe the criminal law will attract liability. Actions performed without a relevant accompanying mental state, such as acts performed in a state of unconsciousness, for example (automatic acts), will not result in liability. Defences are also available to those who are affected by a mental disorder or syndrome. It is this latter category of defences that is relevant to the debate regarding behavioural genetics.

14.16 An exponent of a 'genetic defence' might argue that the reason why a person has committed the criminal offence in question is that a genetic variant has either caused the behaviour in an immediate sense (in the same way as an electrical stimulus may produce a muscular reaction), or because the genetic variant has contributed to the development of a personality, or, in moral terms, a character (or set of dispositions) which are manifested in certain forms of action. These are distinct claims, and it is the second, more common line of argument which we shall address here. This claim maintains that because genes play a role in the emergence of dispositions, and these dispositions in due course play a role in the performance of acts, our acts are not just the product of whatever choices we have made, but are produced by factors which we did not choose and for which we are not therefore responsible. We have already discussed this issue in its philosophical context in Chapter 12; our concern here is to consider how such an argument might be integrated with existing theories of criminal defence.

14.17 An obvious analogy can be made to personality disorder, since a personality disorder and the possession of a genetic variant predisposing to antisocial conduct (if such characteristics were to be identifiable) might be viewed as similar conditions. However, it must be remembered that personality disorders are psychiatric conditions which cannot be said to fall within the range of normal variation. A predisposition to behave aggressively or impulsively does not necessarily entail that an individual has a disorder. We recall the normal distribution curve explained in Chapter 3 (Figure 3.3): it is axiomatic that with such a distribution half the population will have an above-average score for a particular trait. Moreover, the point at which the normal range becomes an extreme score or a disorder is never clear. Thus, genetic influences on traits such as aggression or impulsivity may have implications not just for those with psychiatric disorders, but for other individuals accused of antisocial behaviour.

14.18 With regard to individuals with personality disorders and those thought to have an increased risk of antisocial behaviour as a result of a genetic variant, there is no question of individual responsibility for the occurrence of the condition or disposition. In both cases, the condition is a background against which a decision to act in a particular way is made. The decision to ignore the condition as a possible exculpatory factor might therefore be reached on the same basis. A person who has a psychopathic personality disorder may claim that his or her antisocial actions are the product of a condition for which he or she is not responsible. The psychopath does not choose to be a psychopath. Whatever view is taken of the aetiology of this condition, the psychopathic personality is probably shaped at an early age and it is generally not regarded as something which the individual is able to change. The psychopath cannot therefore be blamed for being a psychopath, even if there is room for blame in respect of his or her conduct. However, in practice, we do generally regard persons with a psychopathic personality disorder as being responsible for their actions, even if we may accept that it is more difficult for them to comply with social and moral restraints. Certainly, as far as the law is concerned, in spite of some cases in which psychopathic personality disorder has been admitted as grounds for a plea of diminished responsibility, the preferred approach of the courts is to treat such individuals as ordinary offenders.

14.19 The psychopath is considered to be responsible for legal purposes, because to hold otherwise would undermine the assumptions about responsibility which need to be made in society. We have noted above that whatever the claims of determinism may be in the moral domain, we order our social and moral lives on an assumption that individual responsibility for actions does exist. Quite apart from these grounds, pragmatic considerations point to a need to limit exculpatory conditions. If the scope of available excuses, whether genetic or environmental, is too broad, then it would be only too easy for a defendant in a criminal trial to claim that the behaviour was not his or her own but was determined by past experiences and influences. The impracticality of such an approach is self-evident, and would seriously compromise our social arrangements. It would remove, in effect, the need to make any moral effort to comply with society's rules; everything would be potentially excusable. This potential weakening of the justice system is a vital consideration in examining whether genetic influences on behaviour in the normal range ought to be taken into account in attributing responsibility.

14.20 Regardless of whether a predisposition is derived from genetic or non-genetic influences, the crucial question is what is the status of that predisposition in the legal context? One response might be that the relevant question to ask of a person with an alleged genetic disposition to a trait is 'was the predisposition so strong he or she could not resist it?' This raises immediate problems concerning what constitutes an irresistible predisposition and how such a thing could be measured. More fundamentally, it does not seem plausible that genetic influences on antisocial behavioural traits will generate irresistible predispositions. Rather, genetic and other factors may contribute to our characters in ways that make certain behaviours more or less likely, rather than certain. If this is so, what should we say about a genetic predisposition to impulsivity which makes it more difficult for a particular individual to avoid acting aggressively than it is for other people? In such a case, resistance to the predisposition would not be impossible, just considerably more difficult than average. Should this be taken into account when blaming an individual for their behaviour? It has been argued by various philosophers that those to whom virtuous behaviour comes naturally are less deserving of praise than those for whom such behaviour requires great self-restraint and effort. Might a similar argument be made to take account of the greater effort required by the 'less naturally virtuous' individual's struggle against his or her character traits? The question of how difficult it is for us to control our behaviour as a result of genetic influences will be important in the context of the sentencing and treatment of offenders, which we discuss in paragraphs 14.26-14.33 below.

14.21 Characteristics that are influenced by genetic variation and are within the range of normal variation cannot be considered to amount to an illness or, indeed, an abnormality. This would suggest that they are outside the scope of the existing legal excuses of insanity or diminished responsibility. This is quite consistent with the notion that criminal law does not pay attention to the range of abilities or characteristics which defendants may have, outside the very limited defence of provocation. Irascibility or inability to resist temptation are not characteristics which the courts would take into account in determining responsibility. This is because the criminal law relies on a single standard of conduct which is expected of all. To allow individual characteristics and capacities to affect responsibility would destabilise the criminal justice system and would be regarded as unacceptable and unfair by the public. This therefore precludes a role in responsibility for any genetically-associated characteristic within the normal range.

14.22 Could it be argued that a genetic predisposition to antisocial behaviour ought to be defined as a disorder, and therefore, that it should act to lessen responsibility in the same way that some psychiatric disorders are recognised as entailing diminished responsibility? This would be an example of medicalisation, which we discussed in paragraphs 13.13–13.24. If a particular genotype has not manifested itself in symptoms of illness, then in ordinary language we would probably not describe the person as being ill, even if we were to say that they were affected by a particular condition. This would therefore act against any attempt to bring the possession of a particular genotype into the category of an exculpatory illness. To say that a person is ill because he or she has a particular genetic make-up which may be associated with antisocial behaviour is counter-intuitive. Only when the genotype has manifested itself symptomatically and given rise to identifiable physical pathology or psychiatric illness will we say that the person is ill and therefore potentially not responsible for his or her conduct. For this reason, genetic factors will only currently be relevant in so far as they are productive of other identifiable conditions: in themselves they do not amount to the excusing condition. For example, if the responsibility of a schizophrenic person were to be at issue, it would make no difference whether the illness were to be attributed to a genetic factor or to an environmental factor. The individual would be excused on the grounds of the illness, not its cause.

14.23 A further problem with the use of information about genetic variants that influence behaviour, at least for the foreseeable future, is the degree to which a causal link can be established between a particular genetic trait and a particular criminal act. In the US, it was previously the case that scientific, medical or psychiatric evidence had to be generally accepted within the relevant academic community. Following a landmark case in 1993, the position in the US is now that evidence must be relevant and reliable, but does not have to be generally accepted. Of course in practice it seems likely that relevant and reliable evidence will often also be generally accepted.[10] In Britain, the position is similar, in that relevance and reliability are the key criteria by which evidence is assessed for admissibility.[11] It seems likely that behavioural genetics, if it identifies genetic influences on behaviour, will be able to do no more than offer evidence of correlations of varying strengths between particular genetic variants and broad categories of antisocial behaviour. It is unlikely that such correlations would be viewed by the legal system as sufficiently reliable to warrant excusing an offender.

14.24 **We conclude that research in behavioural genetics does not pose a fundamental challenge to our notions of responsibility as they are applied in the legal context. We consider that genetic variants in the normal range are unlikely to be considered an excuse for legal purposes, at least for the foreseeable future. They fall outside the scope of the defences of insanity and diminished responsibility and cannot be said to absolve individuals from responsibility for their actions.**

---

[10] *Daubert* v *Merrell Dow Pharmaceuticals Inc.* (1993). 509 US 579.

[11] See, for example, *R* v *Robb*. (1991). 93 Cr App Rep 161 at 166; *R* v *Mohan*. (1994).2 SCR 9.

14.25 If progress in behavioural genetics were to be such that close and clearly identifiable associations between particular genetic variants and particular forms of antisocial acts were to be demonstrated, there would be a case for a re-examination of the legal implications. It might be that the concept of diminished responsibility, for example, could be expanded to embrace such conditions, perhaps by redefining views of illness. If this possibility were to be considered, thought would have to be given to the potential dangers of unwarranted over-reliance on genetic information and the consequences of reducing responsibility for our actions.

Sentencing and treatment of offenders

14.26 Responsibility is one thing; the question of what to do with the convicted offender is another. Future insights of behavioural genetics might play a greater role in the punishment of offenders. At this stage of the criminal process it is possible to take a much broader view of the background of an offence and the person who commits it. Currently, defence lawyers submit a wide range of information about the offender and his or her background and circumstances to the judge, who can choose whether or not to take it into account in determining the appropriate sentence (within the existing constraints on sentencing). Other factors, such as public safety, are also important considerations. There are all sorts of features of individuals for which a correlation with antisocial and criminal behaviour has been suggested. For example, in the context of juvenile delinquency, reported risk factors include poverty, being born to a teenage mother, being reared in a family with at least four children, being adopted, having divorced parents and having an aggressive father.[12]

14.27 The mechanisms by which such environmental factors influence susceptibility to antisocial behaviour are not well understood, but evidence of such correlations exists, and may influence a judge's sentencing decision (although there is an increasing number of crimes for which sentencing constraints exist, such as mandatory life sentences for murder, automatic life sentences for serious repeat crimes and minimum sentences in other areas such as burglary and drug trafficking). Judges are permitted to take into account, when sentencing, information about the circumstances of an offence and any aggravating and mitigating factors that may be relevant. Relevant circumstances can include information about the age and vulnerability of the victim, the offender's previous criminal record, the extent to which the crime was premeditated, and the offender's motive. Mitigating factors can be taken into account to reflect an individual's enhanced or diminished culpability for a crime, or because the judge believes that a milder sentence may be sufficient to discourage the offender from committing further crimes. An offender may be judged to have diminished culpability because of provocation or temptation, mental disorder, stress or the effect of medicines, narcotics or alcohol. Judges can also take into account evidence that an offender is of good character, which is usually determined on the basis of a lack of previous convictions.[13] It is less clear to what extent judges acknowledge the influence of environmental factors that are statistically correlated with an increased likelihood of antisocial behaviour, such as poverty, family size and so on (see paragraph 14.26).

---

[12] See Rutter, M., Giller, H. & Hagell, A. (1998). *Antisocial Behaviour by Young People*. Cambridge: Cambridge University Press, for a comprehensive summary of those risk factors relating to juvenile delinquency.

[13] There are numerous other factors that can be considered in mitigation. For further detail of those mentioned and additional factors, see Walker, N. & Padfield, N. (1996). *Sentencing: Theory, Law and Practice*. 2nd ed. London: Butterworths. See also the work of the Sentencing Advisory Panel which provides advice to the Court of Appeal http://www.sentencing-advisory-panel.gov.uk/ (8 July 2002).

14.28 Should information about genetic factors that are correlated to a similar degree with antisocial behaviour also be admissible? Jonathan Glover has observed that it is 'unclear that there is anything radically different about explanations where the causal story goes back to the genes and explanations where the causal story goes back to early environment.'[14] But what might be the implications of widening admissible factors to include genetic information?

14.29 The idea that facts about an individual's environment can affect the extent to which they should be punished for criminal acts contains an implicit assumption that individuals have essentially sound characters, but that unavoidable external influences they did not choose can have a negative effect on them. In contrast, if genetic information about an individual's susceptibility to antisocial behaviour is accepted, it seems to imply that the individual has essentially an unsound, or at least, a less sound character. We noted earlier (paragraph 14.20) that, given a particular background or environmental context, a genetic predisposition to impulsive behaviour, for example, might mean that an individual finds it harder than others do to control his/her actions.

14.30 If a genetic predisposition is identified in an offender, how might this information be interpreted in the context of sentencing? One possibility is that the offender will be seen as less accountable for his/her acts and therefore less deserving of punishment. But another possibility is that the offender will be seen as more likely to offend and less likely to be successfully rehabilitated. Nikolas Rose has suggested that:

> 'if antisocial conduct is inscribed in the body of the offender, it seems that it is not mitigation of punishment that is required but the long-term pacification of the irredeemable individual in the name of public protection, even if this means the rejection of many rule of law considerations, such as those concerning the proportionality of crime and punishment.'[15]

Such a concern would be misguided in the case of behavioural genetics, because, as we have stressed throughout this Report, the effects of genes are not immutable. Genetic influences on traits such as impulsivity and aggression cannot make us an 'irredeemable individual' because the effects of our genes are not inevitable.

14.31 In the case of antisocial behaviour, various ways of reducing their influence may be available. Potential interventions might include cognitive therapy and programmes in self-control and anger management. Other potential interventions such as gene therapy or medical treatments might also be possible. We took the view in Chapter 13 that, *prima facie*, the application of each of the three categories of intervention might be justified. However, we also noted that the use of genetic and medical interventions may be less desirable for a number of reasons. First, regarding genetic interventions, the safety of techniques such as gene therapy is liable to be lower. Secondly, if an individual has a genetic predisposition to aggression or impulsivity, it is likely that this will be manifested in response to certain environmental situations. The unwanted conduct will

---

[14] Glover, J. The implications for responsibility of possible genetic factors in the explanation of violence. In Bock, G. R. & Goode, J. A., editors. (1996). *Symposium on Genetics of Criminal and Antisocial Behaviour, Ciba Foundation* 194. Chichester, UK: Wiley.

[15] Rose, N. (2000). The biology of culpability: pathological identity and crime control in a biological culture. *Theoretical Criminology* **4**, 5–34.

tend to occur at isolated intervals and might therefore be amenable to interventions that target the behaviour as it occurs, rather than those that attempt to alter the individual's underlying character. Such interventions might be more effective, but it is likely that cases would have to be assessed individually, with reference to the factors identified in Chapter 13 (see paragraph 13.26) before a judgement could be made about the most suitable course of action.

14.32 **We conclude that, with regard to the sentencing of convicted offenders, the criminal law should be receptive to whatever valid psychiatric and behavioural evidence is available. The taking into account of genetic factors would depend on the degree to which such evidence is convincing and relevant. Credible evidence of influence and a robust test for the genetic factor in question would be essential: the weight to be accorded to such information would be determined by the judge**. Currently, environmental, social and psychiatric assessments may be taken into account by judges in determining appropriate sentences. These must also be supported by valid, accurate and reliable evidence. It would be unwise to assume that genetics will not be able to assist in determining degrees of blame, even if the 'all-or-nothing' question of responsibility is not affected by genetic factors themselves. Such a role would not compromise basic assumptions as to responsibility.

14.33 Exchanges between genetics and the criminal law are at present not very productive given the uncertain nature of the evidence. This is likely to change. **We recommend that the criminal justice system should be open to new insights from disciplines that it has not necessarily considered in the past. The regular exchange of ideas in this area between researchers in behavioural genetics, criminologists and lawyers could be an effective means of ensuring that legal concepts of responsibility are assessed against current evidence from the behavioural and medical sciences**.

Predictive use of genetic information

14.34 Criminal justice adheres to the notion that liability and resulting punishment should always be based on specific and proven instances of misconduct. In the future, however, it is possible that genetic information could be used, either on its own, or in conjunction with information about environmental influences, in an attempt to show that an individual is likely to exhibit antisocial behaviour, even if he or she has not yet committed a crime and indeed may never do so.

14.35 Currently, attempts to predict future behaviour can play a role in the criminal justice system, but only in respect of decisions as to the future treatment of a person who has already committed an offence. Even in this limited context, it is important that claims as to ability to predict future behaviour are subjected to close scrutiny. At present the accuracy of such predictions – usually made on a psychiatric basis – is a matter of controversy. Where these are used as the basis of decisions to detain individuals on mental health grounds, they raise major issues of civil liberty and of the potential abuse of psychiatric disposal as a means of control.

14.36 In cases where the individual in question has not exhibited antisocial behaviour or been convicted of a crime, attempts to predict the likelihood of such behaviour in the future raise even greater concerns. In 1999, the UK government initiated consultation on the treatment of individuals with severe personality disorder. One option set out was the introduction of 'powers for the indeterminate detention of dangerous severely personality disordered people in both criminal and civil proceedings. Those detained under the new orders would be managed in facilities run separately from prison and health service provision. The location for detention would be based on the risk that the person represented and their therapeutic needs rather than whether they had been convicted of an offence.'[16] Concern was widely expressed at the suggestion that individuals might be detained without having committed a crime, and furthermore, that this decision might be based on the diagnosis of a controversial psychiatric disorder.[17] In this Report, we have often drawn attention to the blurred line between behaviour in the normal range and that which is considered a disorder. The case of 'severe personality disorder' is an important illustration of the risks of basing public policy on classifications and diagnoses which are not clearly defined and are not the subject of consensus among medical professionals.[18]

14.37 Despite the controversy over whether there is such a disease as 'severe personality disorder', it is fair to say that the estimated 2000 individuals in Britain thought to have the condition are those who display the extremes of behaviour, and would be most unlikely to fall within the range of normal variation. Could the use of genetic information to predict the behaviour of those who do lie within the normal range be justified? Further, could the use of genetic information in conjunction with other information, such as that concerning environmental influences on behaviour, for the prediction of antisocial behaviour be justified?

14.38 As far as the use of genetic information as a sole predictor of antisocial behaviour is concerned, it is unlikely that such information will be of sufficient accuracy to justify its use. Consider a hypothetical genetic variant that is present in 30% of the population and confers a five-fold increase in the probability of an individual committing a criminal act. If that act were common – say 5% of the total population was expected to commit the act in the future – then of those in the population with the 'at risk' genotype only 11% could be expected to commit the criminal act. Nearly nine out of ten individuals 'at risk' could be expected not to offend. Moreover, nearly one third of the individuals who subsequently commit the crime would have the 'low-risk' genotype.[19]

14.39 However, it may be that by combining information about environmental and genetic influences on antisocial behaviour with regard to a particular individual, a more accurate prediction is possible. Although, as we have repeatedly stressed in this Report, the effects of genes are not inevitable, information about genetic and environmental influences may generate statistical information relating to the chance of a particular individual exhibiting antisocial behaviour that may be thought sufficient to warrant intervention. In the case of children, attempts are already made to predict whether an individual who has not already done so is likely to exhibit antisocial or criminal behaviour in the future. In the UK, early

16 Home Office, Managing dangerous people with severe personality disorder: proposals for policy development. http://www.homeoffice.gov.uk/cpd/persdis.pdf (8 July 2002).

17 For example, in an article in the Guardian newspaper, the president of the Royal College of Psychiatrists, Dr Mike Shooter, said that dangerous severe personality disorder was 'a diagnosis which does not exist anywhere in the world' (Boseley, S. (2002). Psychiatrists to join protest over bill. *The Guardian* 29 July). The editor of the *Journal of Forensic Psychiatry* has observed that dangerous severe personality disorder 'is not a recognised term in psychiatry or psychology' (Buchanan, A. & Leese, M. (2001). Detention of people with dangerous severe personality disorders: a systematic review. *Lancet* **358**, 1955–9).

18 Specific reference to 'severe personality disorder' is not included in the draft Mental Health Bill which is being considered by the UK government in 2002. However, this Bill does allow for the detention of an individual with a serious mental health problem which is not amenable to treatment (in other words, a serious personality disorder) and who is judged to be a significant risk to others, even in the absence of a criminal conviction.

19 One study concerning dangerous severe personality disorder has suggested that in order to prevent one person with dangerous severe personality disorder from committing a violent act, six people would have to be detained, because of the difficulty in making accurate predictions of behaviour. The authors note that 'the decision as to what rate of error should be deemed acceptable from the point of view of preventive detention is ultimately a moral one.' (Buchanan, A. & Leese, M. (2001). Detention of people with dangerous severe personality disorders: a systematic review. *Lancet* **358**, 1955–9).

intervention programmes target 'at risk' groups in order to provide environmental interventions.[20] These interventions are aimed at benefiting the individual concerned, and thereby indirectly benefiting society. This is a very different situation from one in which an individual is detained against his or her will in the interests of society. What arguments can be made against including the use of genetic information in current practice?

14.40 As a starting point, it must be firmly acknowledged that attempts to identify classes of potential offenders would offend the presumption of innocence which we make of our fellow citizens and which underlies principles of equality. This applies both to predictions based on genetic information and on information about environmental factors. However, this presumption of innocence must also be balanced against the need to ensure a safe society. Since no prediction using either genetic or environmental factors will be infallible, there must be very good reasons for encroaching on the presumption of innocence. One such reason might be the possibility of an intervention that would reduce the likelihood that antisocial behaviour would be displayed.

14.41 A strong argument against the use of such genetic information without the consent of the individual in question is that conducting a genetic test might be seen as an unjustified invasion of privacy.[21] With regard to the testing of adults, it is permissible in extreme circumstances to subject people to compulsory diagnostic procedures, but these are strictly limited by law. It is unlikely that genetic testing of people who have not been convicted of any crime would fall within the boundaries of any currently permissible category. With regard to the predictive testing of children, it is firmly enshrined in law and practice that medical interventions in children must be for their benefit, that is, in their best interests. For this reason, predictive genetic testing of children for late-onset diseases is not undertaken unless it is required to enable early intervention.[22]

14.42 Despite current attitudes towards the predictive testing of children, it might be suggested that children should be tested to discover whether they are likely to exhibit antisocial behaviour, perhaps as part of a strategy for reducing juvenile antisocial behaviour. We noted that one study has suggested that children with a particular genotype may be at higher risk of exhibiting antisocial behaviour if they are exposed to abusive parenting (paragraph 9.25 and paragraph 14.10). If this result were found to be reliable, it might be suggested that children should be tested for the relevant genotype in order that particular attention could be directed at their family environment if required.

14.43 Medical tests on children not competent to give consent require the consent of the parent or other adult legally entitled to give consent on behalf of the child. Such consent is only valid if it is in the best interests of the child. It is possible that testing linked to environmental interventions, and indeed medical interventions, could be described as being in the best interests of the child. However, a case could be made against this

---

[20] One interesting programme is the charity Communities that Care, which is funded by the Joseph Rowntree Charitable Trust and aims to build safer neighbourhoods by targeting risk factors in the lives of children (www.communitiesthatcare.org.uk (11 July 2002)). The programme is based on a US scheme that aims to reduce antisocial behaviour among children by reducing risk factors and increasing preventive factors. Risk factors are identified at the level of the community, school, family and individual. While medical or genetic factors are not considered, it is possible to imagine a similar rationale being put forward for their use.

[21] There is a growing body of international bioethical norms which specifically prohibit non-consensual genetic testing, on the grounds that it constitutes an invasion of the right to private life. These international conventions are outlined in Box 15.1.

[22] Older children who are found competent to consent may be tested predictively for late-onset diseases or for carrier status on their request.

argument on the grounds of privacy and of stigma. It can be argued that children have the same right to genetic privacy as do adults and that there are therefore limitations to the circumstances in which general diagnostic testing of children should be authorised. If stigmatisation based on knowledge about genetic influences on behaviour is greater than that which may arise in response to knowledge about environmental influences, this could provide a reason for allowing prediction based on environmental information only. Additionally, it might be argued that interventions aimed at those who are more likely to exhibit antisocial or criminal behaviour, which rely on information about environmental factors, tend to target groups, such as classrooms, schools or communities, rather than singling out individuals, and are thus less problematic than those that would also make use of genetic information to target interventions at specific individuals. However, in both cases, it is ultimately the case that interventions are aimed at individuals.

14.44 We take the view that while the reduction of antisocial behaviour and crime are important goals, any attempt to predict the behaviour of an individual who has not exhibited antisocial behaviour, and to intervene accordingly, poses a significant threat to civil liberties and should be treated with great caution. The use of predictive genetic tests to anticipate antisocial behaviour for the purposes of preventive action in the case of individuals who have not already exhibited such behaviour raises ethical questions about balancing the interests of individuals against those of society. **We consider that the predictive use of genetic information about behaviour in the normal range, used in isolation in the case of individuals who have not exhibited antisocial behaviour, is unlikely to be warranted because the predictive power of such information is likely to be weak and there is a risk of false predictions. However, we take the view that the use of such information in conjunction with information about other, non-genetic influences on behaviour may be justified if the aim is to benefit the individual, and in doing so, to benefit society also. We recommend that the prediction of behaviour with a view to detaining an individual who has not committed a crime is not justified, whether such predictions are based on information about genetic or non-genetic influences on behaviour.**

Conclusion

14.45 In this chapter, we have considered three different ways in which information about genetic influences on behaviour may be used in the criminal justice system: to absolve an individual from responsibility; as a mitigating factor in sentencing an individual who has been convicted of a crime; and to predict the likelihood that an individual will exhibit antisocial behaviour in the future, when he or she has not already done so. In the first case, we concluded that genetic influences on behaviour in the normal range should not absolve an individual from responsibility for their behaviour. In the second, we concluded that, in the same way that environmental factors may be taken into account in mitigation, genetic factors could play a similar role, depending on the reliability and accuracy of the information. With regard to predictive testing, we concluded that neither genetic nor non-genetic information should be used to predict future behaviour with a view to detaining an individual who has not been convicted of a crime. However, we suggested that, if such information could be used for the benefit of the individual, for example, as a reason for improving particular environmental conditions, this may be justified. We also recommended that genetic information should not be used in isolation in such cases.

Chapter 15

Testing and selection in employment, education and insurance

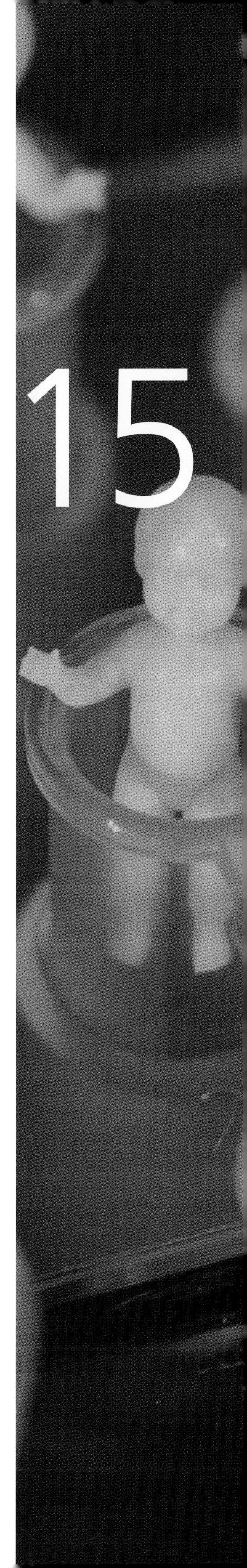

Testing and selection in employment, education and insurance

15.1 As noted in Chapters 13 and 14, the selection of individuals on the basis of a genetic predisposition to behavioural traits may have potential applications in several different settings. These include the streaming of children in schools, aptitude testing for university entrance or employment, and the screening of potential or existing employees on the basis of genetic susceptibility to behavioural traits such as aggression, anxiety, novelty-seeking or sexual orientation. Insurers might also wish to make use of knowledge about genetic predispositions to certain behaviours, such as risk-taking, for some types of personal and life insurance and employer's liability and medical insurance. These possible uses of genetic information are discussed in this chapter, following an account of some relevant general principles.

15.2 One series of questions relevant to all these contexts is those relating to privacy, consent and confidentiality. These were investigated in relation to inherited disease and disability in the earlier Report of the Nuffield Council on Bioethics on *Genetic Screening: Ethical Issues* (1993), and in the report of the Human Genetic Commission (HGC), *Inside Information: Balancing Interests in the Use of Personal Genetic Data* (May 2002). Although issues regarding privacy, consent and confidentiality which are specific to behavioural genetics are discussed in this chapter, the reader is referred to those reports for consideration of the broader aspects.[1]

15.3 Another general question concerns the accuracy and predictive capacity of genetic tests. Earlier chapters of this Report have indicated that our behaviour is complex, influenced both by genetic and environmental factors, and by our own decisions. At present, accurate and reliable tests of the genetic components of behaviour in the normal range simply do not exist. If a screening device is not accurate and reliable, it cannot be the basis for fair and efficient decisions in relation to education, employment or insurance. In addition, if a behavioural trait is wrongly assumed to be immutable, then many personal achievements, which are the product of learning, individual initiative, determination and hard work, may be neglected. This is not a problem peculiar to genetic testing for behavioural traits. There is considerable use of IQ and aptitude tests for entrance to schools and universities. In the context of employment, interviewing is by far the most commonly used technique for the recruitment for managerial, professional and skilled manual jobs. However, a recent survey by the Chartered Institute for Personnel and Development (CIPD) revealed that questionnaires to evaluate personality traits are increasingly used.[2] These methods profess to assess cognitive ability, personality, propensity for dishonesty or other deviant behaviour and traits such as anger, aggression, anxiety, obsession and low self-esteem. There is much scepticism about the predictive validity of these tests.[3] The major risk is that of wrongly attributing to the individual the characteristics of the group. It is difficult to know how accurately the test will identify those who will act on a particular propensity.

---

[1] The Reports are available at the websites of the Nuffield Council on Bioethics and the Human Genetics Commission, http://www.nuffieldbioethics.org/publications/index.asp and http://www.hgc.gov.uk/insideinformation/index.htm respectively (17 June 2002).

[2] CIPD. (2001). *Fifth Annual Report on UK Recruitment Practices.* Personality questionnaires were used by 40.7% of respondents; 54.5% used general ability tests; 60.1% used tests of specific skills and 44.6% literacy/numeracy tests.

[3] See Finkin, M. W. (2000). From anonymity to transparency: screening the workforce in the information age. *Colum. Bus. L. Rev.* **2000**, 403–51, at pages 417–26 and 447–51 for a review.

Box 15.1: Guiding legal principles

The general legal principles relevant to policy and regulation of the use of genetic information can be derived in the main from three instruments:

- The Convention For the Protection of Human Rights and Dignity Of The Human Being with Regard To The Application of Biology and Medicine (Council of Europe, Oviedo, 4 April 1997) ('the Convention')
- The Universal Declaration on the Human Genome and Human Rights (UNESCO, 11 November 1997) ('the Declaration')
- Charter of Fundamental Rights of the European Union (EU, Nice, 7 December 2000) ('the Charter').

The relevant provisions of these instruments may be summarised as follows:

The Convention
The Convention expressly prohibits any form of discrimination on grounds of genetic heritage. Further, it provides that tests which are predictive of genetic diseases or which serve to identify a person as a carrier of a gene responsible for disease or to detect a genetic predisposition or susceptibility to a disease may be performed only for health purposes* or for scientific research linked to health purposes and subject to appropriate genetic counselling. Interventions on the human genome are prohibited unless undertaken for preventive, diagnostic or therapeutic purposes and only if the aim is not to introduce any modification to the genome of any descendants. The Convention has not yet been ratified by the UK and has no legal force in this country.

The Declaration
The Declaration provides that everyone has the right to respect for their dignity and their rights regardless of their genetic characteristics and that such dignity 'makes it imperative not to reduce individuals to their genetic characteristics and to respect their uniqueness and diversity' (Article 3). Research, treatment and diagnosis affecting an individual's genome shall only be undertaken after rigorous and prior assessment of the risks and benefits pertaining thereto. Like the Convention, the Declaration includes an express prohibition on discrimination based on genetic characteristics that is intended to or has the effect of infringing human rights. Genetic data must be held in conditions of confidence, and no research or applications of research concerning the human genome (in particular in the fields of biology, genetics and medicine) should prevail over respect of human rights and the dignity of individuals. The Declaration has no legal force and is intended only as a statement of principles which states are asked to promote.

The Charter
In common with the Convention and the Declaration, the Charter contains an express and free-standing provision which prohibits any discrimination based on genetic features. As part of the right to respect for physical and mental integrity, Article 2 provides that, in the fields of medicine and biology, particular respect must be given to prohibition of eugenic practices,† in particular those aimed at the selection of persons. The UK, as a Member of the European

Union, is a party to the Charter. The Charter is a non-binding instrument which is likely to have only indirect legal force through resort to it by the European Court of Justice as a source of legal principle.

* The Explanatory Report to the Convention (paragraphs 84 to 86) makes clear that genetic testing for employment or insurance purposes or other commercial purposes falls outside the legitimate testing for health care purposes, and is a disproportionate interference with the rights of the individual to privacy. Paragraph 86 provides: 'An insurance company will not be entitled to the holding of a predictive genetic test. Nor will it be able to refuse the conclusion of modification of such a policy on the ground that the applicant has not submitted to a test as the conclusion of a policy cannot reasonably be made conditional on the performance of an illegal act'. The Convention does, however, provide (in Article 26) that the restriction on predictive genetic tests may be overridden where prescribed by law and necessary in a democratic society in the interest of public safety, for the prevention of crime, for the protection of public health or for the protection of the rights and freedoms of others.

† It is to be noted that the European Group on Ethics in Science and New Technologies, when reporting on the draft Charter insisted (by a majority) that a specific additional provision dealing with eugenic practices be included. The minority considered that there was a difficulty in defining eugenics and the group as a whole recognised that certain current practices might be properly termed as eugenics. The majority, however, insisted on inclusion of a specific prohibition because otherwise 'the Charter would be missing the point if it did not refer to one of the main challenges of human genetics.' See European Group on Ethics in Science and New Technologies. Citizens Rights and New Technologies: A European Challenge (Brussels, 23 May, 2000). http://www.europarl.eu.int/charter/civil/pdf/con233_en.pdf (18 Jul 2002).

Employment

The current legal framework

15.4 In this section we set out how the law currently deals with the use of genetic information in the context of employment. It is important to note that, to date, most discussion in this area has focused on clinical disorders. The potential use of genetic information that concerns behavioural traits in the normal range of variation has not been widely considered.

15.5 At present there is no legislation in the UK that directly regulates genetic testing or the use of genetic information in employment. At common law, an employer may lawfully require an applicant to undertake genetic testing in order to be appointed to a particular job. Whether an existing employee can be required to submit to a genetic test depends on the express or implied terms of the individual's contract of employment. Employers have no general power to require employees to submit to medical examination (this would include a genetic test). However, it may be implied that the employee could be required to do so if the employer had reasonable grounds for believing that the employee might be suffering from a mental or physical disability likely to cause harm to the employee or to other people. This is an aspect of the so-called duty of mutual trust and confidence between employer and employee, which is an obligation of uncertain scope that depends upon judicial interpretation.[4] Similarly, at common law the right to use genetic information about an employee depends upon the express or implied terms of the employment contract. In some circumstances, discrimination law, the law on unfair dismissal and the developing law of privacy and confidentiality for employees might give rise to rights for jobseekers and employees (see paragraphs 15.11 – 15.15).

[4] See, for example, *Bliss* v *South East Thames Regional Health Authority*. (1985). Industrial Relations Law Reports 308. The Court of Appeal found that a medical examination had been imposed without reasonable cause because what the employer did (according to Lord Justice Dillon) was 'by any objective standard outrageous'.

15.6 By contrast, about half the states in the US have enacted laws prohibiting genetic discrimination in employment. President Clinton signed a similar Executive Order applicable to federal employees, excluding the Armed Forces, on 8 February 2000. The main reasons for this legislation in the US are, first, that employers responsible for the medical costs of employees and their dependants have a strong incentive to exclude those genetically predisposed to certain illnesses and, secondly, that individuals who are at a genetic risk of illness may be discouraged from taking genetic tests if they believe that their employers will have access to this information. Both of these reasons are significant in the US because of the employer's role in financing health care. The existence of the National Health Service (NHS) means that these motivations are of less significance in the UK.

Discrimination laws

15.7 In both the US and the EU, genetic screening and the practice of using genetic information may run foul of employment discrimination laws, if the test or practice has a disproportionately adverse impact on a protected class such as women or ethnic minorities which cannot be objectively justified for reasons other than the gender, race and so on of the affected group. In the landmark case of *Griggs* v *Duke Power Co.*,[5] the US Supreme Court held that under Title VII of the Civil Rights Act, facially neutral standardised tests and high school graduation requirements had a disparate impact on black applicants and employees, and accordingly, the employer had to prove that the qualification requirements were job-related and consistent with business necessity.[6] Genetic testing would offend Title VII only if the effect of the test were to discriminate on the basis of race, colour, religion, sex or national origin. So far as is known, Title VII has not yet been invoked in respect of genetic testing. This may be due to the availability of the Americans with Disabilities Act 1990 (ADA) which can be used to challenge mandatory medical examinations that are not related to employment. However, even this is of limited significance because a genetic test that revealed the susceptibility of an employee to stress or other traits in certain working environments would be job-related and hence lawful.[7]

15.8 In the EU, a similar approach is taken to that in the US, under Article 141 (ex 119) of the European Community (EC) Treaty and the Equal Treatment Directive 76/207/EEC, in respect of what is termed 'indirect' sex discrimination. UK law has recently been amended, in line with the Burden of Proof Directive 97/80/EC, to define indirect sex discrimination as existing where 'an apparently neutral provision, criterion or practice disadvantages a substantially higher proportion of the members of one sex unless that provision criterion or practice is appropriate and necessary and can be justified by objective factors unrelated to sex.' For example, a factor which favours spatial ability may tend to be biased against women and the use of this criterion will have to be objectively justified. The Race Relations Act 1976, in section 1(1)(b), contains a slightly differently worded definition but the effect is also to make unlawful a requirement or condition which has an unjustifiable adverse impact on a particular racial group. On 29 June 2000, the EC adopted a directive on discrimination on grounds of race or ethnic origin, which must be implemented by the

---

5 *Griggs* v *Duke Power Co.* (1971). 401 US 424 .

6 A test is facially neutral if it does not appear to be discriminatory. As illustrated, facially neutral practices may be found in violation of law if they result in significant differences in the distribution of benefits or services to persons based on race, national origin, sex or disability without a substantial legitimate justification, or, if there are equally or comparably effective alternative practices available that meet the same goals with less disparate impact.

7 Rothstein, M. A. (2000). Genetics and the work force of the next hundred years. *Colum. Bus. L. Rev.* **2000**, 371–401. See p. 388.

UK by 19 July 2003. This defines 'indirect discrimination' as occurring where a provision, criterion or practice 'puts persons of a racial or ethnic origin at a particular disadvantage' without objective justification. On 28 November 2000, the EC adopted Directive 2000/78/EC for combating direct and indirect discrimination in employment on the grounds of religion or belief, disability, age or sexual orientation.[8] This contains a definition of indirect discrimination similar to that in the UK Race Relations Act. The provisions in the EC Directive on sexual orientation must be implemented by the UK by 2 December 2003. They will effectively prevent the use of genetic information relating to sexual orientation in the field of employment. Those relating to disability must be implemented by 2 December 2006, but are unlikely to involve any significant change in existing UK law.

15.9 Although these prohibitions in indirect discrimination do provide a potential barrier to the use of genetic testing and information, their limitations are obvious. The employer can justify its actions on the grounds that the specific test is accurate and reliable and that the use of the information is 'appropriate and necessary' to the requirements of the job. Effectively, discrimination law leaves the control of genetic testing in the employer's hands and is not primarily concerned with its effect on the dignity or autonomy of the employee.

15.10 The Disability Discrimination Act 1995 (DDA) in the UK aims to protect disabled persons from discrimination. A disability is defined as 'a physical or mental impairment which has a substantial and long-term adverse effect on a person's ability to carry out normal day to day activities.' 'Impairment' is not defined but Regulations provide that addiction to alcohol, nicotine or any other substance is to be treated as not amounting to an impairment for purposes of the Act.[9] Similarly, the following conditions do not amount to impairments: a tendency to set fires, a tendency to steal, a tendency to physical or sexual abuse of other persons, exhibitionism and voyeurism. Although mental illness is covered by the Act, the illness must be 'clinically well-recognised'.[10] Moreover, a person is disabled only if their 'ability to carry out normal day-to-day activities is impaired' and the impairment must have a 'substantial and long-term adverse effect' on the ability to carry out those activities.[11] While some 'progressive conditions' are covered, this does not include those who merely have a genetic or other predisposition to (or risk of) a progressive condition in the future. In the US, on the other hand, the Equal Employment Opportunity Commission has issued an interpretation of the ADA that an employer who discriminates against an individual on the basis of the results of a predictive genetic test would be 'regarding' the individual as having a disability and so violating the ADA. The view of at least one leading legal expert is that this interpretation will not withstand judicial scrutiny.[12] In any event, the UK legislation does not at present include those who are simply 'regarded' as having a disability. The DDA, therefore, at present has little relevance to genetic predisposition to behavioural traits in the normal range.

[8] The Sex Discrimination Act and the EC Equal Treatment Directive do not apply to discrimination on grounds of sexual orientation: *Secretary of State for Defence* v *MacDonald*. (2001). *Industrial Relations Law Reports* 431.

[9] Disability Discrimination (Meaning of Disability) Regulations. (1996). SI 1996 No.1455.

[10] Disability Discrimination Act. (1995). Schedule 1, paragraph 1(1).

[11] Disability Discrimination Act. (1995). Schedule 1, paragraph 1(1).

[12] Rothstein, M. A. (2000). Genetics and the work force of the next hundred years. *Colum. Bus. L. Rev.* **2000**, 371–401. See p. 388.

Unfair dismissal

15.11 An employee who is already working for an employer may have a remedy under the Employment Rights Act 1996 (ERA).[13] The weakness of this protection, from the employee's viewpoint, is that in determining this question, the tribunals give employers a broad margin of discretion (the so-called 'band of reasonable responses') in deciding whether or not to dismiss the employee. An employer would, however, be bound to follow a fair procedure, including a reasonable investigation and an opportunity for the employee to contest the facts or show why he or she should not be dismissed.

Privacy and confidentiality

15.12 Article 8 of the European Convention on Human Rights and Fundamental Freedoms (ECHR) provides that everyone has the right to respect for their 'private or family life'. The ECHR was incorporated into domestic law by the Human Rights Act 1998 (HRA), giving individuals the right to claim compensation against public authorities (including public employers) who violate this right. Courts and tribunals are bound to give effect to the ECHR, so that when interpreting the duty of mutual trust and confidence or the law on unfair dismissal (paragraph 15.11) they must have regard to Article 8.

15.13 It seems likely that aspects of biometric and genetic testing and the use of genetic information about an individual fall under the concept of 'private and family life'. This can be deduced from the case law of the European Court on Human Rights which has afforded a high degree of protection under Article 8 to personal health and bodily integrity. The right is not, however, absolute. The infringement may be justified if it is shown to be 'necessary in a democratic society in the interests of national security, public safety or the economic well-being of the country, for the prevention of crime or disorder, for the protection of health or morals, or for the protection of the rights and freedoms of others.'[14] In the employment field, it is likely that courts and tribunals will require the employer to show both that the use of genetic information was necessary in relation to a specific job, and that its use was proportionate to a legitimate aim such as protecting the health and safety of others. It seems that a contractual restriction on the right to privacy will also have to pass this strict test of justifiability.

15.14 Another possible form of protection for genetic information is the common law on breach of confidence. An obligation of confidence arises in an employment relationship, but it is by no means clear what kinds of personal information would be protected since nearly all the decided cases involve breach of commercial confidences. Accordingly, the Data Protection Act 1998 (DPA) is much more significant than the common law. Under the DPA 'sensitive personal data' is given special protection. This includes personal data of a person's 'physical or mental health or condition'. Most genetic information would appear to fall under this protection, as would genetic information about a person's 'sexual life'.

---

[13] For example, an employee who is dismissed for refusing to submit to a genetic test or for not allowing the use of genetic information, where this is not provided for in the contract of employment and amounts to a breach of the duty of mutual trust and confidence may complain that the dismissal is unfair. Even short of actual dismissal, there may be a 'constructive' dismissal entitling the employee to resign and claim compensation. The employer will have to show that it genuinely believed that the dismissal related to the employee's 'capability' or 'conduct' or 'some other substantial reason' justifying dismissal. The employment tribunal will then assess whether the dismissal is fair or unfair 'having regard to equity and the substantial merits of the case'.

[14] European Convention on Human Rights and Fundamental Freedoms. Article 8(2).

15.15 The handling of genetic test results is required to meet the DPA's principles of fairness and lawfulness. In particular, the explicit consent of the individual is required (unless there is a legal obligation to process the data). The EC Data Protection Directive 95/46/EC, on which the DPA is based, specifies that consent must be 'freely given, specific and informed'. The UK Information Commissioner has given guidance interpreting this as meaning that there must be some active communication between the parties.[15] An individual or organisation who uses data cannot infer consent simply from non-response to a communication. The Information Commissioner has issued a draft code of practice on the use of personal data within employer/employee relationships, under section 53 of the DPA. This contains a section dealing with the use of genetic testing in employment which is based on the recommendations of the 1999 report of the Human Genetics Advisory Commission's (HGAC) on *Implications of Genetic Testing for Employment*.[16] The final version of the Code relating to medical and genetic testing is due to be published by the end of 2002.

Earlier reform proposals

15.16 The potential uses of personal genetic information in employment have been the subject of several earlier reports. However, all of these focus on information that is predictive of inherited disease or information about particular genetic variations that might indicate that a person is susceptible to a specific occupational disease or workplace chemical. None of these reports has considered the use of personal genetic information relevant to particular traits within the normal range of behaviour. Our focus is on whether the conclusions in those earlier reports relating to inherited disease and occupational hazards are also applicable to normal behavioural traits.

15.17 The report of the HGC concluded that at present there is no evidence in this country of any systematic use of predictive personal genetic information in employment.[17] This confirms the findings of the earlier reports of the Nuffield Council and the HGAC.[18,19] Indeed, since the latter reports were published, the only employer that had been known to use such tests (the Ministry of Defence, to screen aircrew recruits for sickle cell disease) has ceased the practice. The HGAC concluded that 'it will take major developments both in our understanding of common diseases and in genetic testing itself before genetic testing becomes a serious issue for employment practice' and this conclusion applies equally strongly to behavioural traits and non-clinical characteristics.

15.18 The report of the HGAC proposed a common set of principles for policy, aimed at providing appropriate protection to the public if and when genetic testing for diseases in employment becomes a real possibility. We consider that these principles form a useful basis for policy-making and apply equally to behavioural traits as to diseases. They are:

---

15 The Information Commissioner enforces and oversees the Data Protection Act 1998 and the Freedom of Information Act 2000. The Commissioner is an independent supervisory authority reporting directly to the UK Parliament.

16 Human Genetics Advisory Commission. (July 1999). *Implications of Genetic Testing for Employment.*

17 Human Genetics Commission. (2002). *Inside Information: Balancing Interests in the Use of Genetic Data*. paragraph 8.9.

18 Nuffield Council on Bioethics. (1993). *Genetic Screening: Ethical Issues*. Chapter 6.

19 Human Genetics Advisory Commission. (1999). *The Implications of Genetic Testing for Employment*, para.3.5; Trade Union Congress. (1998). *Genetic Testing by Employers.* 2nd ed., reported that 'genetic testing by employers is still rare in this country'. The Health and Safety Commission. (1996). *Report of the Working Group on Genetic Screening and Monitoring,* p.7, made a similar finding.

(i) An individual should not be required to take a genetic test for employment purposes – an individual's 'right not to know' their genetic constitution ought to be upheld.

(ii) An individual should not be required to disclose the results of a previous genetic test unless there is clear evidence that the information it provides is needed to assess either current ability to perform a job safely or susceptibility to harm from doing a certain job.

(iii) Employers should offer a genetic test (where available) if it is known that a specific working environment or practice, while meeting health and safety requirements, might pose specific risks to individuals with particular genetic variations. For certain jobs where issues of public safety arise, an employer should be able to refuse to employ a person who refuses to take a relevant genetic test.

(iv) Any genetic test used for employment purposes must be subject to assured levels of accuracy and reliability, reflecting best practice in accordance with the principles established by the Advisory Committee on Genetic Testing: '[A]ny use of genetic testing should be evidence-based and consensual. Results of any test undertaken should always be communicated to the person tested and professional advice should be available. Information about and resulting from the taking of any test should be treated in accordance with Data Protection principles ... Furthermore, test results should be carefully interpreted, taking account of how they might be affected by working conditions.'

(v) If multiple genetic tests were to be performed simultaneously, then each test should meet the standards set out in (ii), (iii) and (iv).

15.19 The Report of the HGC concluded that genetic testing is unlikely to provide any information that cannot be gathered by means of existing medical and screening procedures. Given the current uncertainties about interpreting genetic information, the HGC considered that it would be more appropriate to monitor the health of a person by other more direct means.[20] It recommended a voluntary undertaking by employers to inform the HGC of any proposals to use genetic testing for health and safety purposes.[21] The HGC also recommended that genetic tests should not be a condition of employment.[22]

Testing for behavioural traits

15.20 As already noted, the recommendations in earlier reports are concerned with the occupational health and safety of employees and jobseekers. They apply a model of the autonomy of the individual patient in the medical sphere to the employment relationship. In the case of behavioural traits within the normal range, which are the subject of this Report, we are not concerned with patients. Moreover, the employment relationship is less receptive to the application of the medical model. The inherent inequality of bargaining position and power between the employer and the individual employee means that the employer is likely to initiate the tests and to decide how they are to be administered and used. A 'right to refuse' to take a test to disclose genetic information or a 'right to know'

---

[20] Human Genetics Commission. (2002). *Inside Information: Balancing Interests in the Use of Genetic Data*. paragraph 8.18.

[21] Ibid. paragraph 8.19.

[22] Ibid. paragraph 8.15.

the outcome, is likely to be of little practical value where the employee has to choose between exercising the right or waiving it in order to secure a livelihood. The public interest or paternalistic justifications for overriding the individual's wishes where there is a serious danger to the health or safety of the employee or third parties do not exist in the case of non-clinical behavioural traits.

15.21 This leads us to the following conclusions and recommendations in the context of the use by employers of genetic testing for behavioural traits:

- **The primary duty of employers is to provide a safe environment for their employees and others. The aim should be to remove hazards from the workplace, not to remove employees on the basis of inherited characteristics or susceptibility to particular forms of behaviour within the normal range.**

- **Employees should be selected and promoted on the basis of their ability to meet the requirements of the job, and they should be monitored to ensure that their performance meets those requirements.**

- **Employers should not demand that an individual take a genetic test for a behavioural trait as a condition of employment. The proper approach would be to monitor employees for early warning signs of behaviour (such as violence) that would make them incapable of performing the job satisfactorily.**

- **Any inquiry into the potential use of genetic testing of behavioural traits in the workplace should include an investigation of the use of other purportedly predictive scientific methods, such as psychometric tests, for similar purposes.**

15.22 There is a question whether the Disability Discrimination Act (DDA) should be extended to cover (i) genetic predispositions in general, and (ii) non-clinical behavioural traits in particular. On the first question, the Disability Rights Commission (DRC) has recommended that the DDA should be extended to people who have a genetic predisposition and that legislation should prohibit employers from viewing the results of genetic tests save in very limited circumstances.[23] The DRC has not dealt specifically with the second question. In our view, there is a danger that singling out genetic predispositions to behavioural traits within the normal range for special treatment or labelling them as 'disabilities' will aggravate the stigma attached to certain behavioural traits. This danger might be overcome by including discrimination on grounds of 'genetic features' in a single general statute covering all forms of unlawful discrimination.[24] Such legislation should specifically cover asymptomatic employees.

Education

15.23 Some of the traits that are studied in behavioural genetics are of particular relevance to education. The most obvious link is with intelligence, but research into traits such as antisocial behaviour may also have implications for the education system. Educationalists have already developed a range of tests with which children can be assessed, such as

[23] Disability Rights Commission (2002). *First Review of the Disability Discrimination Act.*

[24] This would be in accordance with Article 25 of the EU Charter of Fundamental Rights.

reading ability, verbal ability, IQ scores and so on. The classification of children based on such skills and the provision of particular types of educational programme accordingly is also an established part of our educational system. It is not clear how findings in behavioural genetics and the potential development of genetic tests might or should impinge upon current practices. Some researchers in behavioural genetics have highlighted the potential importance of the research in informing practices in education but as yet the issue has not received substantial attention.[25]

15.24 The development of tests that provide information about genetic influences on traits such as intelligence and antisocial behaviour would raise a number of questions:

- Should genetic tests be used to identify children who may be susceptible to traits that could affect their own educational achievement, such as lower than average IQ?
- Should genetic information be used to determine which type of educational programme a particular child, or group of children, receives?
- Should genetic tests be used to identify children who may be susceptible to traits that could affect the educational achievement and wellbeing of other children, for example antisocial behaviour?

15.25 The use of such tests in the educational context may lead to stigmatisation or a tendency towards 'genetic self-fulfilling prophecies' that constrain a child's self-image. We noted in paragraphs 14.41 – 14.43 that carrying out a genetic test on a child unable to consent to the procedure would have to be in the best interests of the child. It may be argued that in relation to education, the predictive use of genetic information could be justified, if the aim of such an approach was to provide better and more appropriate schooling for children. Whether genetic information could be used in this way to positive effect is currently unclear. It may be that, when used in conjunction with other information about children, including evidence from previous educational performance, such information could play a useful role. However, wider arguments about the advantages and disadvantages of tailoring educational programmes to groups of children, in whatever way such groups are defined, will also be relevant.

15.26 We note, with some concern, that the implications for education of research in behavioural genetics have not yet received significant critical attention. **In the light of the issues that may arise if genetic information about behavioural traits is applied in the context of education, we recommend that further investigation of the ways in which such research might be applied, and the resulting ethical and social issues, be undertaken. We recommend that dialogue between those involved in education and researchers in behavioural genetics be promoted. We recommend, further, that until such dialogue and research is undertaken, genetic information about behavioural traits in the normal range should not be used in the context of the provision of education.**

[25] For example, see suggestions made regarding the constructive use of genetic information in education by Professor Robert Plomin in the following article: *Genius of genes*. 8 August 2000. http://news.bbc.co.uk/1/hi/sci/tech/850358.stm (20 August 2002).

Insurance

15.27 The implications of the use of genetic information by insurers have been considered in detail by various bodies in recent years.[26] Many concerns have been raised, including the risk of basing decisions on unreliable tests and the possibility of excluding vulnerable groups from obtaining insurance. The Nuffield Council on Bioethics recommended a moratorium on the use of genetic information by insurers in most situations in 1993, and many other groups subsequently endorsed this suggestion, most recently the HGC.[27]

15.28 In the late 1990s, most British insurance industry, acting through the Association of British Insurers (ABI)[28] agreed on a self-regulatory Code of Practice[29] on use of genetic tests in insurance.[30] In April 1999, the UK Government established the Genetics and Insurance Committee (GAIC) to evaluate genetic tests, to recommend to insurers and the Government whether particular tests are appropriate for use by insurers and to oversee the use of genetic tests by insurers. In 2001, a moratorium, which exceeds in length and financial limits that recommended by the HGC, was announced by the insurance industry on the use of DNA test results in insurance. This remains a voluntary agreement and the Government has not yet considered it necessary to make any legislative interventions in this area.

15.29 The existing debate has not addressed the regulatory issues which arise from the possibility of using genetic information about behaviour. Indeed, the ABI Code of Practice itself defines a 'Genetic Test' in a manner which is limited to tests which indicate the risk of a disease developing in the future.[31] This is principally because, as the ABI has stated, 'behavioural genetics is unlikely to be of relevance to insurers, because [the ABI] cannot see that it would be possible to robustly demonstrate a clear link between genetic information regarding susceptibilities to particular behavioural traits and a change in the risk of an individual claiming on an insurance policy'.[32]

15.30 If research in behavioural genetics were to provide such evidence, there are clearly important social and regulatory issues which arise. The ABI has asserted that the suggestion that genetic information indicating susceptibility to particular types of behaviour (such as aggression or novelty-seeking) would be used displays a misunderstanding of the manner

---

26 Nuffield Council on Bioethics. (1993). *Genetic screening: ethical issues*; Human Genetics Advisory Commission. (December 1997). *The Implications of Genetic Testing for Insurance*; House of Commons Select Committee on Science and Technology. (April 2001). *Genetics and Insurance*, Fifth Report; Human Genetics Commission. (May 2001). *The Use of Genetic Information in Insurance: Interim Recommendations of the Human Genetics Commission*. The HGC convened various meetings to discuss insurance and genetics and the relevant minutes are collected at http://www.hgc.gov.uk/topics.htm#ins (19 July 2002).

27 Human Genetics Commission. (May 2001). *The Use of Genetic Information in Insurance: Interim Recommendations of the Human Genetics Commission*.

28 The ABI comprises over 400 insurance companies which between them account for over 96% of the business of insurance companies in Britain.

29 Association of British Insurers. (December 1997 and revised August 1999). *Genetic Testing: ABI Code of Practice*. The principal feature of this code is that applicants for insurance may not be asked to undertake a genetic test to obtain insurance and only tests approved by, or currently under consideration by, the GAIC may be taken into account. People with negative test results may benefit where the test result counteracts a family history of a condition.

30 Both the House of Commons Select Committee and the HGAC have been critical of the system of self-regulation, and particularly the lack of uniformity of application of the Code of Practice amongst insurance companies. The House of Commons Select Committee noted in particular as one of its conclusions (paragraph 23) that 'There must be doubts whether the ABI, a trade organisation funded by insurers to represent their own interests, is the right body to regulate the use of genetic test results'.

31 A Genetic Test is defined as 'an examination of the chromosome, DNA or RNA to find out if there is an otherwise undetectable disease related genotype, which may indicate an increased chance of developing a specific disease in the future'.

32 Association of British Insurers. (August 2001). *ABI Response to Public Consultation*, paragraph 2.2.

in which the risk profile of an individual is established.[33] However, in its response to the Working Party's consultation with the public, the Genetics Group of the Faculty and Institute of Actuaries observed that while 'at this stage, no-one knows whether information on behavioural traits which is useful for predicting abnormal levels of insurance risk will ever be obtained from Genetic Tests ... it cannot be ruled out. Further, the distinction between behavioural and medical conditions could well be blurred.' When one considers the manner in which information as to past behaviour is currently required by insurers in proposals for policies and then used as an actuarial predictor of future risks, the view of the ABI seems less convincing than that of the Faculty and Institute of Actuaries. This matter is considered further in paragraph 15.33.

15.31 There are various types of relevant insurance in this context: life insurance, critical illness insurance, income protection and medical insurance. As noted by the Consumers' Association, with the contraction of the welfare state and prominence being given by both major political parties to private sector provision, insurance-based and insurance-related products and services are likely to play an increasing role in the lives of citizens.[34] Society is moving towards a position where access to insurance can no longer be seen as a mere commercial decision by an individual to purchase an extra benefit which he or she will enjoy in addition to a guaranteed safety-net of state provision. This change in the role of insurance strongly suggests that access to insurance should more properly be viewed in terms of an essential social right rather than an option for the few with appropriate financial resources. This change requires one to ensure that unreasonable discrimination on the basis of genetic information as to behaviour is prevented by strict regulation. Without such regulation, there is a real risk that scientific developments in the future will lead to the creation of a group of individuals whose genetic characteristics make them either uninsurable in the commercial judgement of the insurance industry, or insurable only at a level of prohibitively high premiums. The HGC has emphasised the wider moral and social consequences of allowing use of genetic information (albeit in the context of disease prediction) in decision-making in insurance.[35] We concur with the HGC that where insurance is linked to important public goods such as house ownership or life insurance and persons are restricted from obtaining these goods because of personal genetic qualities, it is not unreasonable to balance the costs to these individuals and to society against the costs to the insurance industry.

15.32 Against this one must, however, balance another aspect of the public interest, namely the need to ensure that the cost of obtaining insurance is not rendered prohibitive to society as a whole because premiums are calculated without access to important predictive genetic information which would allow those without genetic predispositions to certain behaviour to benefit from lower premiums. An argument can be made that the greater transparency provided by accurate genetic information in assessing individual risk will be of benefit in setting appropriate premiums for particular individuals. In addition, the insurance industry contends that the problem of so-called 'adverse selection' might arise if there were a prohibition on use of genetic tests. 'Adverse selection' can occur if applicants for insurance need not disclose relevant risk factors and consequently individuals at high-risk apply more

33 Association of British Insurers. (August 2001). *ABI Response to Public Consultation,* paragraph 2.3.

34 Consumers' Association, Consumer Briefing, *Genetics and Insurance: Unravelling the Code for Consumers.*

35 Human Genetics Commission. The use of genetic information in insurance: Interim recommendations of the Human Genetics Commission. 1 May 2002. http://www.hgc.gov.uk/business_publications_statement_01may.htm (20 August 2002).

for insurance, or persons at low-risk apply less, thereby skewing the pool of individuals requesting insurance.

15.33 Although science has not yet developed to a stage where genetic information can be used to indicate susceptibility to specific behavioural patterns, it is not difficult to foresee how insurers could use such information in the future to decide which individuals will be offered insurance, and on which terms. This is because the decision to underwrite and the terms of insurance are based essentially on personal information concerning a proposed person. In the example of driving insurance, this will include data such as age, sex, occupation, past driving record and so on. Such information determines premiums. If one were able to classify a person as being more likely than others to be aggressive or exhibit novelty-seeking behaviour using genetic tests, this is just a further layer of information which an insurance company could use to inform its decisions. Just as an individual's past record of driving is an indicator of the likelihood of future accidents, it could be said that an aggressive personality equally bears on the future risks of an accident. Conversely, an insurer may consider that a person with a passive personality is a much better risk to insure.

15.34 The essential issue for regulation and policy is whether, if such information can in future be obtained, an insurance company should be able to demand an appropriate test and use the results, and to refuse to offer insurance to those who refuse to take the test or offer higher premiums. This is a difficult question and the answer depends on the social and ethical perspective from which it is approached.

15.35 From a purely commercial perspective, one could view such information as being merely another fact which an insurer should be permitted to act upon in making a commercial decision as to whether he will contract with a person and the terms upon which he will contract. As observed above, there is a cogent case to be made for permitting the use of such information in the public interest. However, when one considers the fact that a genetic predisposition to certain patterns of behaviour is not a matter within one's control, and that use of such information could lead to denial of access to an essential social benefit (the ability to contract for insurance), the right of the insurer to demand and use a test is much less clear. It could be said against this that using such information regarding susceptibility to certain future behaviour patterns is no different from the current use of family history of illness by insurers in determining access to, for example, life insurance and critical illness policies and in the setting of premiums.[36] This presupposes that the use of family history, an equally unchangeable fact about an individual, is a legitimate factor in decisions about the provision of insurance. It can be argued that if one views access to insurance as being a social right, family history should not be permitted to weigh against an applicant for insurance.

15.36 Given that even in the case of predicting genetic diseases, scientific developments have not yet caused the UK Government to intervene with a system of regulation for the insurance industry, it is premature to arrive at any conclusions on the use of genetic information

---

[36] In the context of genetic tests which predict disease, this very argument appears to have already been deployed by the insurers: see Minutes of Plenary Meeting of HGC, 2 March 2001, paragraph 5.5 where the consultation responses to *Whose Hands on Your Genes?* were considered (www.hgc.gov.uk/business_meetings_02march.htm). The HGC has expressed particular concern that the existing use of family history, especially where this clearly has a large genetic (inherited) component, should be given further consideration (Human Genetics Commission. (May 2001). *The Use of Genetic Information in Insurance: Interim Recommendations of the Human Genetics Commission.*)

about behavioural traits in the normal range. It is clear, however, that one cannot continue to view insurance provision and the terms of such provision as purely commercial decisions. The commercial imperative of insurers is clearly to set premiums and offer insurance based on the best possible information as to risk. Genetic information may be valuable in this regard and safeguards as to its use must be developed to ensure that an uninsurable group of individuals is not created.

15.37 **We recommend that the use of genetic information about behavioural traits in the normal range should be interpreted as falling under the scope of the five-year moratorium agreed in the UK in 2001, and should therefore not be used by insurance companies in setting premiums. Future discussion of possible legislation should include specific consideration of genetic information regarding behavioural traits. If the use of such information were considered, a thorough examination of the accuracy and reliability of any genetic tests and their likely predictive power would be essential.**

Appendices

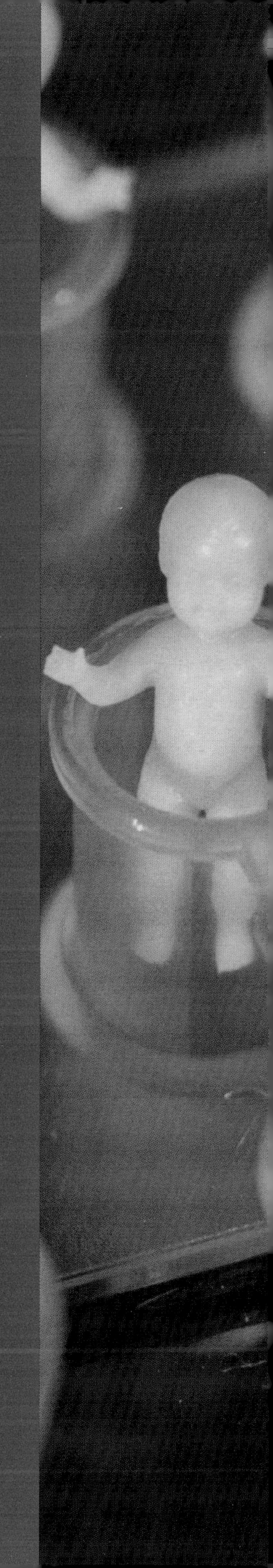

Appendix 1: Methods of working

In November 1999, the Council held a Workshop that addressed issues arising from the study of the genetics of variation within the normal range of behavioural characteristics. Subsequently, in November 2000, the Working Party on Genetics and Human Behaviour was established. The Working Party met eleven times between November 2000 and May 2002. As part of its work, the Working Party held six fact-finding meetings with experts in the field of behavioural genetics, philosophy and sociology in Britain. Three reviews were commissioned to assess critically the current scientific evidence in various fields of research in behavioural genetics. The Working Party also held a consultation with the public, the responses to which are summarised in Appendix 2.

Fact-finding meetings

The Working Party is very grateful to the following individuals for taking the time to meet with members of the Working Party and for providing insights into issues relating to research in behavioural genetics.[1]

12 June 2001, London

Professor Sir Michael Rutter, Senior Researcher, Department of Social, Genetic and Developmental Psychiatric Research, Institute of Psychiatry, London

Professor Steven Rose, Professor of Biology and Director, Brain and Behaviour Research Group, Open University and Joint Professor of Physic, Gresham College

Dr Jonathan Flint, Wellcome Trust Senior Clinical Fellow, Wellcome Trust Centre for Human Genetics, Oxford

4 July 2001, London

Professor Andrew Heath, Professor of Psychology in Psychiatry and Associate Professor of Genetics, University of Washington St Louis and Director, Missouri Alcohol Research Center, US

9 July 2001, Cambridge

Professor Dorret Boomsma, Professor of Biological Psychology, Vrije Universiteit, Amsterdam, The Netherlands

Professor John DeFries, Professor, Department of Psychology, and Director, Institute for Behavioral Genetics, University of Colorado at Boulder, US

Professor Nick Martin, Senior Principal Research Fellow, Queensland Institute of Medical Research and Adjunct Professor, Department of Pathology, University of Queensland, Australia

Associate Professor Irwin D Waldman, Associate Professor of Psychology, Emory University, US

Professor Thomas Bouchard, Professor of Psychology, University of Minnesota, Director of the Minnesota Center for Twin and Adoption Research and Principal Investigator on the Minnesota Twin Registry, US

Professor Richard Rose, Professor of Psychology and Medical Genetics, Indiana University, US

Professor Matthew McGue, Associate Chair, and Director, Graduate Program in Individual

[1] Institutional affiliations at the time of the meeting are listed.

Differences and Behavioural Genetics, Department of Psychology, University of Minnesota and Principal Invesigator, Minnesota Twin Family Study, US

Professor Lindon Eaves, Professor of Psychiatry and Distinguished Professor of Human Genetics, Medical College of Virginia, Richmond and Director, Virginia Institute for Psychiatric and Behavioral Genetics, US

26 September 2001, London

Professor Nick Craddock, Wellcome Trust Senior Research Fellow in Clinical Sciences and Professor of Molecular Psychiatry, and Honorary Consultant Psychiatrist, University of Birmingham

Professor Robert Plomin, Deputy Director, Social, Genetic and Developmental Psychiatric Research Centre, Institute of Psychiatry, London

3 October 2001, London

Professor Jonathan Glover, Director, Centre of Medical Law and Ethics, King's College, London

Professor Søren Holm, Reader in Bioethics, Institute of Medicine Law and Bioethics, University of Manchester

Professor Nikolas Rose, Professor of Sociology, Goldsmiths College, University of London

14-16 November 2001, Washington DC, US

Members of the Hastings Center/American Association for the Advancement of Science Group on Crafting Tools for Public Conversation about Behavioral Genetics:

Dr V. Elving Anderson, Professor Emeritus, Genetics and Cell Biology, University of Minnesota, US

Cathy Baker, Plain Language Communications, Bethesda, US

Professor Jonathan Beckwith, American Cancer Society Professor of Microbiology & Molecular Genetics, Department of Microbiology & Molecular Genetics, Harvard Medical School, US

Dr Audrey Chapman, Director, Dialogue on Science, Ethics, and Religion, American Association for the Advancement of Science, US

Professor Troy Duster, Director, Institute for the Study of Social Change, University of California, Berkeley, US

Professor Lee Ehrman, Distinguished Professor of Biology, Division of Natural Sciences, Biology Program, SUNY Purchase, US

Professor Leonard Fleck, Center for Ethics & Humanities, Michigan State University, US

Dr Mark Frankel, Director, Scientific Freedom, Responsibility and Law Program, American Association for the Advancement of Science, US

Professor Irving Gottesman, Sherrell J. Aston Professor of Psychology, Department of Psychology, University of Virginia, US

Professor Patricia King, Carmack Waterhouse Professor of Law, Medicine, Ethics and Public Policy, The Law Center, Georgetown University, US

Dr Yvette Miller, Medical Director, American Red Cross Great Lakes Region, US

Dr Erik Parens, Director, The Hastings Center, US

Professor Nancy Press, Associate Professor Genetic Anthropology, Department of Public Health and Preventive Medicine, Oregan Health Sciences University, US

Professor Kenneth F. Schaffner, University Professor, George Washington University, US

Dr Robert Wachbroit, Research Scholar, Institute for Philosophy & Public Policy, University of Maryland, US

Rick Weiss, Staff Writer, Washington Post, US

Professor Dan W. Brock, Director, Center for Biomedical Ethics, Department of Philosophy, Brown University, US

Professor Marcus Feldman, Professor of Population Biology, Stanford University, US

Reviews of the evidence

The Working Party commissioned papers from experts on three areas of research in behavioural genetics: research into intelligence, personality traits and addiction. A review of research into antisocial behaviour was written by a member of the Working Party Professor Terrie Moffitt, and a review of research into sexual orientation was compiled by the Secretariat. These papers were used to inform the Working Party.

Chapter 7 - Intelligence

Professor Nicholas J. Mackintosh, Department of Experimental Psychology, University of Cambridge.

Chapter 8 - Personality Traits

Professor Jeffrey Gray, Emeritus Professor at the Institute of Psychiatry, Kings College London

The paper commissioned on research in behavioural genetics in the field of addiction was used to inform the deliberations of the Working Party but was not included as a separate chapter. This paper was commissioned from Professor John C. Crabbe, Director, Portland Alcohol Research Center, and Department of Behavioral Neuroscience, Oregon, US.

The papers can be viewed on the Council's website www.nuffieldbioethics.org.

Appendix 2: Consultation with the public

A consultation with the public was held between March and July 2001. Approximately 1,500 consultation documents were disseminated and 111 responses were received from individuals and organisations. 37 were from individuals affiliated to academic institutions, 27 were from individuals who did not indicate any affiliation, and 44 were representatives of organisations. The responses came not only from the UK, but also the US, Israel, Australia and New Zealand. Those who responded are listed below and the Working Party is grateful to them all. Some of the main themes to emerge from the consultation responses included:

- an emphasis on the lack of information or evidence to date;
- the complexity of the topic and the importance of environmental factors as well as genetic factors;
- the difficulties in determining the 'normal' range, and questions about who should define 'normal' and 'abnormal';
- the importance of seeing behaviour in terms of its social and cultural context.

A summary of the responses to specific questions posed by the consultation is set out below. It is not intended to constitute a statistical analysis of the answers, but to reflect the issues and concerns that were raised.

Why study behavioural genetics?

What do you think are the likely advantages and disadvantages of research in behavioural genetics?

Possible advantages of the research in behavioural genetics were identified by a number of respondents. They included:

- contribution to a better understanding of human behaviour;
- possible clinical applications;
- better information about normal variation;
- an improved understanding of the full range of factors that influence behaviour, including environmental factors.

Possible disadvantages of the research were also submitted, including:

- fear of eugenics;
- misuse of genetic information for commercial interests or exploitation;
- increased discrimination;
- erosion of individual moral responsibility;
- medicalisation of non-medical, or social, 'problems' especially those characteristics that should be seen as part of normal human variation or that are currently tolerated by society, for example homosexuality;
- neglect of social and environmental factors that influence behaviour and a temptation to overstate the role of genetic factors;
- misinterpretation or oversimplification of the results;
- risk of cultivating a reductionist view of humanity.

Do you think that behavioural genetics has special features?

There was a general feeling that behavioural genetics does have special features because behaviour is integral to our identity. The research raises questions about consciousness and what it means to be human, and is therefore likely to arouse strong feelings.

Should there be limits to scientific inquiry in this field?

The most common response to this question was that there should not be limits to scientific inquiry in this field, providing that research is carried out within defined ethical boundaries. The central problem was seen to be not the research itself, but the potential applications of the research. Public debate about the value and uses of the research, and potential constraints on the uses of information were therefore seen to be important. It was felt to be undesirable to censor research and several respondents suggested that it was better to carry out the research in the UK, where it could be regulated, rather than elsewhere.

In your view, will research in behavioural genetics have a negative or positive impact on research into social and environmental issues?

Opinion was evenly divided on this question. Those concerned about research in behavioural genetics felt that 'geneticisation' or 'medicalisation' could mean that less attention would be paid to educational and social influences. There was concern that a focus on a simple deterministic model would be seen as an easy solution that governments would grasp. However, others believed that it might have a more positive impact. One suggestion was that, in the long term, there might be greater concentration on environmental factors as a result of the improved understanding of genetic influences on behaviour. It was also suggested that there was a need to counter the risk of adverse consequences actively, for example by giving parallel funding for genetic and environmental research of the same topic to ensure a balanced approach.

How will findings in research in behavioural genetics be translated into practice?

Should genetic tests for behavioural traits and personality characteristics be developed? Why, or why not? Does this apply to all types of behavioural trait?

For genetic tests for behavioural traits to be accepted, it was suggested that several conditions needed to be fulfilled. These included the requirement that the behavioural trait or characteristic in question must be likely to present a serious danger to others or to the individual; that the gene must have a major effect on the trait; that effective therapy must be available; and, most importantly, that the test must be accurate and reliable. There was some debate whether genetic testing would give added advantages over behavioural tests that are in use already, for example psychometric tests. Some felt that genetic testing would not be any more detrimental than such evidence-based clinical assessment, while others felt that genetic tests would not be any more useful and would be unnecessary. There was consensus that no one should be forced to take a test against their will.

Would the prenatal selection of behavioural and personality traits within the normal range be morally acceptable?

The vast majority felt that the prenatal selection of behavioural traits within the normal range would never be morally acceptable. Reasons cited included that the factors that influence behaviour are not just genetic but social and environmental, and the related point, that predispositions to a certain type of behaviour do not mean that the behaviour will necessarily develop later in life. It was suggested that prenatal selection for behavioural traits could lead to children being treated as commodities. There was also concern about reducing variation in the gene pool, and the difficulty of defining the normal range. Only three out of 100 people who responded to this question were in favour of such prenatal selection. However, pre natal selection for the avoidance of serious or life-threatening conditions was thought to be more acceptable.

What are the ethical, legal, practical and social implications of these applications of research in behavioural genetics?

What, in your view, might be the effect of research in behavioural genetics on our understanding of health, illness, disability and abnormality?

Some respondents suggested that research in behavioural genetics should give a better understanding of health and illness, leading to important therapies and improved social and practical support. Others were concerned that the research could also help reduce prejudice. However, there were concerns about the possibility of the medicalisation of traits which are not currently thought of as medical problems. In addition, it was suggested that behavioural genetics could lead to an erosion of moral responsibility. Many respondents questioned what was meant by 'health' and 'normality', and who should decide on these definitions. It was observed that fashions, cultures and perceptions can all affect how normal behaviour is defined.

Is there a moral difference between the correction of a trait thought to be the result of a genetic abnormality or defect, and the enhancement of that same trait for a 'normal' individual? If so, why?

Questions about correction and enhancement were felt to raise some of the most difficult issues of all, and opinions were divided.

Those who said there was a moral difference, felt that correction was about restoring function and treating illness and suffering, and was therefore acceptable. However, enhancement was seen to be interference, or an attempt to render some people superior and was therefore viewed in a different light. The main concern was that enhancement would lead to the elimination of human diversity. Some respondents felt there was no moral difference between correction and enhancement.

Many respondents referred again to the difficulty of defining the normal range. The boundaries between normal and abnormal were seen to be blurred, and changing. Cosmetic surgery, for example, could be for correction or enhancement, and was now increasingly accepted. Other issues raised included the motive for making use of an enhancement; the question of whose choice it was; and issues of the allocation of resources. It was felt that enhancement could exacerbate already existing social inequalities and lead to greater discrimination.

Is the genetic enhancement of behavioural or personality traits morally different from enhancement by non-genetic means such as education or medical intervention?

The most common response was that the means of enhancement does have a moral difference. Non-genetic means, it was suggested, can be withdrawn, terminated, ignored or forgotten. Genetic interventions were thought to be irreversible and to have a permanent effect. They were thus seen to be less acceptable. Concerns were raised about the safety and effectiveness of germline therapy. One of the most important moral issues was felt to be the possibility that genetic enhancement may remove or reduce the freedom of individuals to consent. One respondent suggested that whereas education allows greater freedom of action, genetic modification could do the opposite, enslaving an individual to our idea of what they should be.

However, some felt there was no moral difference if the end result was the same. If it was acceptable to enhance a trait by changing the environment, it should be equally acceptable to change it genetically. However, genetic enhancement was seen to be less predictable. Only one respondent expressed the view that genetic enhancement of behavioural traits is ethically superior to non-genetic enhancement, through education, since the former makes learning a pleasure rather than a pain.

Are there implications of research in behavioural genetics for our general responsibility for our own behavioural and personality traits?

Although it was felt to be difficult to predict the likely effect of the research on our concept of responsibility, many respondents felt that individuals might feel less responsible for their actions if it were shown that genes have a substantial influence on behaviour. Others felt that although research might change the way we view personal responsibility, it would not necessarily be for the worse.

What are the implications for criminal justice, and the legal process generally, of research in behavioural genetics in the areas of aggression and antisocial behaviour?

For research to be admissible as evidence, and thus to have an impact on the justice system, results would need to be conclusive and reliable. This was seen to be unlikely in the short term. However, if a genetic basis for aggression and antisocial behaviour was established, it was suggested that the increase in expert witnesses and evidence would need careful handling. Lawyers would also need instruction in behavioural genetics, to ensure they did not misrepresent genetic evidence.

A core concern was that the criminal system would break down if a genetic defence allowed pleas of no free will. It would be difficult to assign responsibility for acts. Respondents asked whether a person who has a predisposition to aggression deserves credit for not responding to provocation, and conversely, whether a person who has a predisposition to placid behaviour be punished more severely for a violent act?

On the positive side however, it was suggested that research in behavioural genetics could influence the methods used to punish, treat or education offenders, with a system based on treatment where possible.

In your view, might research in behavioural genetics heighten or reduce discrimination, stereotyping and social discrimination between groups?

The majority of respondents felt that research in behavioural genetics would heighten discrimination, by making stereotyping easier and leading to the creation of a genetic underclass. However, a few people felt that discrimination could be reduced, if better knowledge helped reduce fear and encourage understanding and sympathy. The Institute of Alcohol Studies, for example, suggested that the discovery of a strong genetic contribution to problem drinking could possibly reduce stigma. By giving additional credence to the concept of alcoholism or addiction more generally as a disease, the condition would become less likely to be regarded as self-inflicted and caused by weakness of will or irresponsibility. Several respondents felt that in the short-term discrimination would be heightened, but in the long-term it could be reduced. If differences were shown to be normal and unavoidable, there might be increased tolerance. Social discrimination between groups might also be reduced if research showed how much greater genetic variation is among individuals than among groups. It was also pointed out that it was not the research itself, but the uses to which it was put that would lead to discrimination.

What do you think will be the impact of genetic knowledge about behavioural traits on the individual, on families and on communities?

There was concern that genetic knowledge about behavioural traits could be divisive and cause discrimination. The impact on an individual would depend whether there was a therapy. If there was not a possible treatment, knowledge could lead to individual despondence and hopelessness. Families may be put under pressure to take action and seek a 'cure'. Communities may be less willing to help those with challenging behaviour that could have been avoided, although there may also be increased sympathy. The importance of genetic counselling and education of the public was emphasised.

How might health professionals, governments, employers, insurers, education authorities and others use genetic information concerning human behaviour?

The hope was expressed that health professionals and others could use genetic information to improve treatment and welfare provision. Educational authorities could use the information either positively or negatively. There could be streaming of children according to their IQ score, discrimination against those disposed towards aggressiveness or low intelligence, or education programmes targeted according to an individual's genetic potential. The use of genetic information by governments was felt to be a matter of concern, particularly if poor or inconclusive evidence was used. Several respondents were worried that those in a position to misuse information would invade a person's privacy and discriminate against them. Discrimination by employers was thought to be a particular problem. However, a potential benefit, from the perspective of health and safety, was that some people may be helped by ensuring they would not be placed in environments which would be especially hazardous to them.

There was also concern that insurers would use genetic information to increase discrimination. Respondents from within the insurance industry offered different views as to whether such information would be of use.

Are there any circumstances when such information should be available to third parties either with or without the consent of the individual?

Respondents felt that the only circumstances when such information should be available to third parties would be if it were in the public interest, that is, if it were the case that not to do so could put the individual or other people in danger. It was also felt the information should be available in some criminal cases. However, several respondents added that the information should only be made available to qualified people, and that it must be with the consent of the individual.

How can we ensure that consent to the disclosure of such information is properly informed and freely given?

The use of genetic information was seen to be one of the core issues, and the importance of consent, confidentiality and appropriate use of information were emphasised. Some respondents suggested that stringent new regulation would be necessary while others felt that an extension of the current system for disclosure of medical records could be appropriate. Information should only be disclosed to a third party following proper informed consent from the individual concerned. In any event, there was seen to be a need for high quality behavioural genetic counselling.

Given the complex and sensitive nature of research in behavioural genetics, how can members of the public best be informed about it?

It was felt to be extremely important that the public should be informed as fully as possible, with open and transparent debate. Suggestions as to strategies for achieving this aim included sensitive and intelligent media coverage, responsible television documentaries, a soap opera story line, public posters, citizenship classes in schools, and public debates and discussion meetings. One respondent suggested an official body should be established to ensure media reports are not simplistic and misleading.

Do you think that research in behavioural genetics and genetic tests for behavioural traits might require new codes of practice or new regulatory controls? What in your view should be the nature of such codes of practice or controls?

Most respondents felt that new codes of practice and regulatory controls would be necessary. Several people suggested that a statutory regulatory body, similar to the Human Fertilisation and Embryology Authority, should be established. An alternative was a national ethics committee that would focus specifically on research in behavioural genetics. Others felt that international regulation would also be important, for example through the United Nations. Regulation in this area should be kept under continuous review. Some respondents took the view that current codes might be sufficient.

How much priority would you accord research in behavioural genetics in the competition for necessarily limited research funds?

The majority of respondents felt that research in behavioural genetics should be given low priority. Some specified that research should remain within the public domain, or that environmental factors should be given more priority. Six respondents expressed the view that such research should be given no priority at all, while only one suggested it should be given the highest priority possible. The difficulty of separating out genetic research into normal traits from that into diseases, and the difficulty in separating research into genetic influences from that into environmental influences on behaviour, were highlighted.

Responses to the public consultation

The Working Party wishes to thank the following individuals and their organisations for their interesting and helpful responses:

Organisations

Academy of Learned Societies for the Social Sciences

Association of Medical Research Charities

Association of British Insurers

Association of British Pharmaceutical Industry

The Bioethics Advisory Committee of the Israel Academy of Sciences and Humanities and the Israel Helsinki Committee for Human Genetic Research

British Medical Association

British Psychological Society

Christian Action Research and Education

Church of Scotland Board of Social Responsibility

Centre for Bioethics and Public Policy

Christian Medical Fellowship

Consumers' Association

Cumbria-Westmorland Federation of Women's Institutes

Derbyshire Federation of Women's Institutes

East Berkshire Research Ethics Committee

East Kent Federation of Women's Institutes

East Suffolk Local Research Ethics Committee (LREC)

East Yorkshire Federation of Women's Institutes

GeneWatch UK

Genetic Interest Group

Genetics Group of the Faculty and Institute of Actuaries

GlaxoSmithKline

Gloucestershire Federation of Women's Institutes

Human Fertilisation and Embryology Authority

Human Genetics Alert

Human Genetics Commission

Institute of Alcohol Studies

Institute of Psychiatry, King's College London: Department of Forensic Psychiatry

Isle of Man Freethinkers

Lothian Research Ethics Committee

Medical Research Council

Mind

The National Council of Women of Great Britain

National Federation of Women's Institutes

National Foundation for Gifted and Creative Children

National Schizophrenia Felloship

Northallerton LREC

North Nottinghamshire LREC

One-in-a-Thousand Society

Alzheimer's Society Carers National Association

Public Health Genetics Network

Royal College of Nursing

Royal College of Paediatrics and Child Health

Royal College of Psychiatrists: Ethics Sub-committee

The Wellcome Trust

Individuals

Dr Bill Albert

Dr Michael Antoniou and Janey Antoniou

Dr Mark Bailey

Chris Barchard

Rev Stephen Bellamy: Vicar of St. James', Birkdale

Lesley M Bosworth

Professor Robert Boyd: Principal, St. George's Hospital Medical School

Janet Bryden

Peter Bryden

Adam Buick

Professor C.C.H. Cook: Professor of the Psychiatry of Alcohol Misuse, University of Kent at Canterbury

A.B. Dunlop: Lothian Ethics of Medical Research

Merinda Fargher

Stephen Finlan

Dr David S. Gordon

Mr and Mrs SH Hexter

David Hill

C.A. Hobby

Samantha Hodge

Mark Howitt

Dr G Royden Hunt: Centre for Lifelong Learning, Cardiff University

James B Jack

Marjorie Katjire

Dr Anthony Kessel: London School of Hygiene and Tropical Medicine

Dr Jenny Lewis

Alistair C MacDonald

Dr Calum MacKellar

Sandra MacPhee

Fiona McCandless: School of Nursing, University of Nottingham

Gail Mannion: Genetic Associate, Member of Liverpool Health Authority Paediatric Ethics Committee

Professor Theresa Marteau: King's College London

James Miles

Stephen Milton

Gaynor Mitchell

Gemma Monks

Hilary Murray: President, Manchester Medical Ethics Group

Emilio Mordini; Psychoanalytic Institute for Social Research, Italy

Ainsley Newson: Ethics Unit, Murdoch Children's Research Institute, Australia

Dr Ian K. Pople

Betty Rathbone: Clinical Psychologist

Dr Ann Richardson: Independent Research Consultant

Mervyn Richardson

Matt Ridley

Robin Rootes

Professor Hilary Rose: Visiting Research Professor in Sociology, City University; Joint Professor of Physic (with reference to genetics and society), Gresham College and Professor Emeritus of Social Policy, University of Bradford

Professor Steven Rose: Professor of Biology and Director, Brain and Behaviour Research Group, Open University and Joint Professor of Physic, Gresham College

Roy G. Silson

Jonathan Sussex

Professor R. Tallis: Department of Geriatric Medicine, University of Manchester

Mark Taylor: Law Faculty, University of Sheffield

Grant D Vallance: Department of Philosophy, Open University

Rev. FCM Van Den Broeder

Professor Veronica van Heyningen

Attam Vetta

David Vile: Research Psychologist, St James' Hospital, Dublin

Professor Dorothy C. Wertz, University of Massachusetts Medical School, Shriver Division, US

Ian Whittaker

Peter Windle

Glossary

Additive genetic variance: Variation due to the effects of numerous *genes* which combine in a linear fashion, each gene contributing a relatively small effect to a phenotypic feature. See also *non-additive genetic variance*.

Allele: A variant form of a gene, which differs in *DNA* sequence from alternative alleles of the same *gene*.

Amino acid: A molecule which serves as the building block of *proteins*. *Proteins* have different characteristics as determined by the sequence of *amino acids*. *Genes* specify this sequence.

Association studies: An association study compares the frequency of a particular *genetic variant* in a group of people with a particular trait with a matched set of controls (a similar group of people not displaying the characteristic).

Balanced polymorphism: The maintenance of two or more different *alleles* in a population because each is advantageous over the other under particular circumstances.

Behavioural genetics: The field of research that attempts to quantify the genetic contribution to behaviour and locate specific *genes*, or groups of *genes* associated with behavioural traits, and to understand the complex relationship between these genes and the environment.

Candidate gene: A *gene* suspected to contribute to a disease or behavioural trait by virtue of knowledge of its function and/or chromosomal position.

Chromosome: The thread-like *DNA* in a cell is divided into several separate lengths. Each length forms a structure called a chromosome. Most mammalian cells contain two copies of every chromosome, with the exception of sex chromosomes in males. Human cells contain 23 pairs of chromosomes.

Concordance: The rate of co-occurence of a *phenotype* between individuals (for example, pairs of twins).

Dizygotic (DZ) twins: Dizygotic twins arise when two eggs are released and fertilised separately. They are also known as fraternal or non-identical twins.

DNA (deoxyribonucleic acid): The chemical substance of which a *gene* is made and which encodes genetic information.

Dominant/dominance: The form of inheritance in which a genetic variant has an effect when it is present in only one of a pair of *chromosomes*. See also *recessive*.

Effect size: The proportion of individual differences for a trait in the population accounted for by a particular factor. For example, in *molecular genetics* studies, the effect size of a *gene* is the proportion of variance that the *gene* is thought to explain.

Egalitarian: A type of ethical or political position that seeks to minimize unjustifiable inequalities between people, especially inequalities in the opportunities open to them.

Embryogenesis: The phase of prenatal development wherein an embryo develops.

Environment: The environment is taken to include everything that influences a person's *phenotype*, apart from their *genotype*. It is understood very broadly in research in *behavioural genetics*.

Epidemiological research: Research relating to the distribution and determinants of health-related states or events in specified populations, and the application of this study to the control of health problems.

Epistasis: The masking or unmasking of the effects of one *gene* by the action of another. For instance, a *gene* that causes complete baldness would be epistatic with a *gene* that determines hair colour. Epistatic effects contribute to *non-additive genetic variance*.

Eugenics: The literal meaning of the term eugenics is 'well born'. It refers to the doctrine that humanity can be improved by selective breeding, that is, by encouraging those with desirable traits to reproduce or discouraging those with undesirable traits from doing so.

Founder effect: The principle that when a small sample of a larger population establishes a colony in a new location, its gene pool carries only a fraction of the genetic diversity represented in the original population. Changes in the frequency of *alleles* are likely to occur as a result of different evolutionary pressures operating on different *gene* pools.

***g* (general cognitive ability):** A concept derived from statistical analysis that refers to the common factor measured by different intelligence tests.

Gametes: A gamete is a cell involved in sexual reproduction (egg or sperm) and contains only one copy of each *chromosome*.

Gene: The fundamental physical and functional unit of heredity consisting of a sequence of *DNA*, occupying a specific position within the *genome*.

Gene-environment correlation: The genetic influence on exposure to *environment*. Children not only inherit *genes* from their parents but are also exposed to *environments* that are shaped by their own and their parent's genetic makeup.

Gene-environment interaction: Genetic susceptibility to *environments*. The impact of environmental factors may differ depending on a person's genetic makeup.

Gene expression: The process by which information contained in a *gene* is transcribed to produce functional *RNA* molecules which are then translated to produce *proteins*.

Genetic determinism: The view that a person's genes determine by themselves important characteristics of a person, such as their character or intelligence.

Genetic drift: The random fluctuations of *gene* frequencies due to sampling errors. While drift occurs in all populations, its effects are most evident in very small populations.

Genetic marker: Any *locus* that, by virtue of allelic variation between individuals, serves to distinguish one group of *chromosomes* from another at a particular location. Depending on the context, *microsatellites, SNPs* and *polymorphisms* in *proteins* may all serve as genetic markers.

Genetic variation: The presence of different combinations of *alleles* in different individuals in a population.

Genome: The total genetic complement of an individual or of a species.

Genotype: An individual's genotype is their entire genetic constitution, as distinguished from their physical characteristics. See also *phenotype*.

Germline gene therapy: An experimental process of inserting *genes* into germ cells or fertilised eggs in order to correct a hereditary disease. The new genetic material can be passed on to offspring. See also *somatic gene therapy*.

Haploinsufficiency: A situation in which the *protein* produced by a single (normal) copy of a *gene* pair is not sufficient to assure normal function.

Heritability: A statistical estimate of how much of the total variation in a population can be explained by genetic differences. Broad-sense heritability includes both *additive genetic variance* and *non-additive genetic variance*. Narrow-sense heritability refers only to *additive genetic variance*.

Heterozygote: An individual is said to be a heterozygote when the two *alleles* at a particular *locus* are different.

Homozygote: An individual is said to be a homozygote when the two *alleles* at a particular *locus* are identical.

Knockout models: Animal models in which a specific *gene* has been inactivated.

Lesion models: An animal model in which the function of an organ is studied by causing a specific injury or disease to occur.

Linkage disequilibrium: When *alleles* at two distinctive *loci* occur together in *gametes* more frequently than expected, the *alleles* are said to be in linkage disequilibrium. Evidence for linkage disequilibrium can be helpful in mapping disease *genes* since it suggests that the two may be very close to one another.

Locus: The site of a specific *gene* on a *chromosome*.

Mendelian disease: A disease which follows the patterns of inheritance originally identified by Gregor Mendel.

Microsatellites: Microsatellites contain tandem repeats of a simple *DNA* sequence that vary in number and are usually of no functional significance. Because these repeat lengths are usually stably inherited from generation to generation, differences in the distribution of repeat lengths between two populations may indicate differences in their genetic origins.

Molecular genetics: Molecular genetic methods involve studying *genes* at the level of the *nucleotide* sequence.

Monozygotic (MZ) twins: Monozygotic twins arise from a single fertilised egg and are therefore assumed to be genetically identical. They are also known as identical twins.

Multifactorial: A term which denotes that many factors, both genetic and environmental, contribute to the development of a disease.

Mutagenesis: A process that results in modification of *DNA* sequence. See also *mutation*.

Mutation: The modification of a *DNA* sequence that can potentially result in a change in the function of a *gene*. Mutations may be caused by mistakes during cell division, or they may be caused by exposure to DNA-damaging agents in the *environment*. Mutations can be harmful, beneficial, or have no effect. If they occur in cells that make eggs or sperm, they can be inherited; if mutations occur in other types of cells, they are not inherited.

Non-additive genetic variance: Variation due to the effects of numerous *genes* which combine to have an effect in a non-linear or interactive fashion. See also *additive genetic variance*.

Non-shared environment: Environmental influences that make family members different from each other. See also *shared environment*.

Nucleotide: Nucleotides are the subunits from which *DNA* and *RNA* molecules are assembled. A nucleotide is a base molecule (adenine, cytosine, guanine or thymine in DNA; adenine, cytosine, guanine or uracil in RNA), linked to a sugar molecule and phosphate groups. Nucleotides combine in groups of three to code for *amino acids*.

Ontogeny: The development of an individual from fertilisation to maturity.

Over-expression: Greater than normal production of a gene product, for example a *protein* or *RNA* molecule, from a *gene*. Many animal studies involve the over-expression of a *gene* in order to determine the function of its product. See also *under-expression*.

Phenotype: The observable or measurable traits of an individual as produced by its *genotype* and the *environment*.

Phylogeny: The relationship of groups of organisms as reflected by their evolutionary history.

Pleiotropy: The phenomenon in which a single *gene* gives rise to a number of seemingly unrelated characteristics.

Polygenic: A disease or trait is said to be polygenic when it is influenced by more than one *gene*.

Polymorphism: Where two or more *alleles* exist for a *gene*, such that at least two of the *alleles* are present in more than 1% of the *chromosomes* in a population.

Population variation: The range of differences between individuals in a population.

Preimplantation genetic diagnosis: A technique used to determine whether an embryo created by *in vitro* fertilisation carries a genetic disease or trait, prior to it being implanted in the uterus.

Prenatal diagnosis: Determining whether a fetus has a disease or trait.

Protein: Proteins are biological molecules that are essential for all life processes and are encoded by an organism's *genome*. A protein consists of chains of *amino acid* subunits and its function depends on its three-dimensional structure, which is determined by its *amino acid* sequence.

Quantitative genetics: Quantitative genetic methods are used to estimate the effect of genetic and environmental influences on variation of a trait within a population. Research into quantitative genetics uses statistical methods to examine and compare groups of people without focusing on particular *genes*.

Quantitative Trait Locus (QTL) analysis: A technique for identifying *genes* that influence *polygenic* traits varying between individuals in a continuous fashion.

Recessive: The form of inheritance where a genetic variant causes little or no outward effect unless it is present in both of a pair of *chromosomes* and therefore has been inherited from both parents. See also *dominant*.

RNA (ribonucleic acid): A single stranded nucleic acid molecule comprising a linear chain made from four *nucleotides*, whose sequence determines the informational content of the molecule. RNA is produced by *transcription* from *DNA* and may either be translated into *protein* or may itself play a functional role.

Shared environment: Environmental influences that make family members more similar are said to be part of the shared environment. See also *non-shared environment*.

Single nucleotide polymorphism (SNP): SNPs are single DNA base pair variations. In the human genome project they are being used as *genetic markers* to locate *genes* that cause disease or influence behaviour or other traits. Most SNPs fall within the non-coding regions of human *DNA* and make no difference to the individual.

Somatic gene therapy: An experimental process of inserting *genes* into any cell other than a germ cell for therapeutic purposes. The new genetic material cannot be inherited by offspring. See also *germ-line gene therapy*.

Stratification: This refers to a problem with association studies where there are subtle, but undetected differences in the populations from which the cases and matched controls were sampled. In this situation, differences in *allele* frequency might simply reflect the background evolutionary differences between the two samples, rather than reflecting true trait-specific differences.

Susceptibility allele: An *allele* which is associated with a predisposition to a trait.

Transcription: The process by which a *gene's DNA* sequence is copied into *RNA*.

Translation: The process by which RNA directs the synthesis of a protein.

Transgenic: An organism into which foreign *DNA* has been experimentally transferred.

Under-expression: Lower than normal production of a *gene* product from a *gene*. See also *over-expression*.

Zygosity: Twins are referred to as *monozygotic* or *dizygotic* based on whether they were derived from a single *zygote* (and thus are considered to be genetically identical) or not.

Zygote: A cell with two sets of *chromosomes* produced by the fusion of male and female *gametes*. A fertilised egg.

Glossary of Abbreviations and Acronyms

ABI	Association of British Insurers
ACGT	Advisory Committee on Genetic Testing
ADA	Americans with Disabilities Act 1990
ADHD	Attention Deficit Hyperactivity Disorder
AID	Artificial insemination by donor
CARE	Christian Action Research & Education
CBCL	Child Behaviour Check List
CIPD	Chartered Institute for Personnel and Development
CPI	California Psychological Inventory
DDA	Disability Discrimination Act 1995
DNA	Deoxyribonucleic acid
DPA	Data Protection Act 1998
DRC	Disability Rights Commission
DRD4	Dopamine receptor D4 gene
DSM-IV	Diagnostic and Statistical Manual of Mental Disorders, fourth edition
DZ	Dizygotic
EC	European Community
ECHR	European Convention on Human Rights and Fundamental Freedoms
ERA	Employment Rights Act 1996
EST	Expressed sequence tag
EU	European Union
FDA	Food and Drug Administration (US)
g	General cognitive ability
GAD	Generalised anxiety disorder
GAIC	Genetics and Insurance Committee
GTAC	Gene Therapy Advisory Committee
HFEA	Human Fertilisation and Embryology Authority
HGAC	Human Genetics Advisory Commission
HGC	Human Genetics Commission
IGF2R	Insulin-like growth factor 2 receptor
INAH	Intersticial nuclei of the anterior hypothalamus
IQ	Intelligence quotient
IVF	*In vitro* fertilisation
MAOA	Monoamine oxidase A
MMPI	Minnesota Multiphasic Personality Inventory
MPQ	Multidimensional Personality Questionnaire
MRC	Medical Research Council
MZ	Monozygotic
NHS	National Health Service
PAH	Phenylalaninehydroxylase gene
PGD	Pre-implantation genetic diagnosis
PKU	Phenylketonuria
PND	Prenatal diagnosis
QTL	Quantitative trait locus
SAD	Social anxiety disorder
SNP	Single nucleotide polymorphism
UNESCO	United Nations Educational, Scientific and Cultural Organization

Index